Gat Snyder

Themes familiar to our own literary heritage—th[e]
loss of paradise, the cause of death and diseas[e,]
the origin of fire—can be found in many of the[se]
myths and tales from Africa. There are stori[es]
about animals: how they got their tails and colo[rs,]
why they pursue other animals. There are adve[n-]
tures with ogres, giants and cannibals, and the[re]
are even analogues to Cinderella and The Goo[se]
That Laid the Golden Egg. There are myths abou[t]
the relations between men and gods, and between
men and animals.

The stories are grouped to emphasize the ways
various tribes handle a particular theme, to illustrate how the same story may be used by several
tribes to explain different facts, and to invite com-
parison with myths of other cultures. The details
about everyday African life bring the reader closer
to the people gathered around the storyteller for
entertainment and edification.

Educated at Bryn Mawr, Radcliffe, the University
of Geneva, and the Sorbonne, Susan Feldmann has
taught comparative mythology and related subjects
at Columbia University, where she is also curator
of the Bush Collection of Religion and Culture.
Under the name Susan Taubes she has published a
number of articles on the theater and the history
of ideas. She is preparing a companion volume to
this on the myths and tales of the American Indian.

GAMBIA
SENEGAL
Senegal R.
FRENCH SUDAN
• Bandiagara
PORT. GUINEA
BAMBARA
UPPER VOLTA
Niger R.
Nok
BAGA
FRENCH GUINEA
MANDINGO
BOBO
BRON
Owo•
SIERRA LEONE
TOMA
SENUFO
AGNI
GOLD COAST
TOGO
DAHOMEY
Ife•
MENDE
LIBERIA
IVORY
COAST
KRACHI
BR.
Benin
DAN
LOBI
EWE
R.F.
YORUBA
BAULE
ASHANTI
Abomey

GULF OF GUINEA

AFRICAN MYTHS AND TALES

edited with an introduction by
SUSAN FELDMANN

A LAUREL ORIGINAL

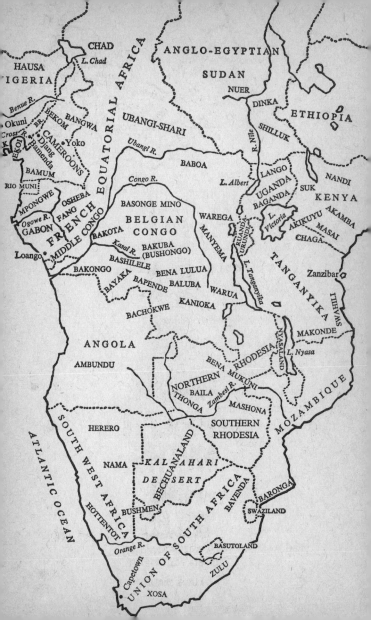

Published by
Dell Publishing Co., Inc.
750 Third Avenue, New York 17, N.Y.

© Copyright, 1963, by Dell Publishing Co., Inc.

Laurel ® TM 674623, Dell Publishing Co., Inc.

First printing—November, 1963

Printed in U.S.A.

Grateful acknowledgment is made to the
publishers, authors, and translators whose
specific contributions are listed on pp. 314-316
of the Bibliography. "A Tug of War,"
"The Hunter and His son," "The Son-in-Law,"
"The Leftover Eye," and "The Two Strangers"
are reprinted by permission of Horizon
Press, Inc., from YES AND NO, The
Intimate Folklore of Africa, by
Alta Jablow, copyright 1961
by Alta Jablow.

CONTENTS

INTRODUCTION

The Ekoi relate how in former times Mouse wove story children from what she saw in men's houses:

> Mouse goes everywhere. Through rich men's houses she creeps, and visits even the poorest. At night her little bright eyes watch the doing of secret things and no treasure chamber is so safe but she can tunnel through and see what is hidden there.
>
> In the old days she wove a story child from all that she saw, and to each of these she gave a gown of different colors—white, red, blue, and black. The stories became her children and lived in her house and served her, because she had no children of her own.

The choice of Mouse, this tiny, drab, inconspicuous yet uncanny creature of the night and hidden corners, tells much about the spirit of African folklore. The continuation of the story, the oddly irrelevant tale about the sheep and leopard which account for how these story children came down to man, is likewise revealing. A series of episodes relate how the sheep outwits the leopard, obtains "medicine" by trickery, and, while fleeing the wrathful medicine woman, runs against the door of the house where Mouse lives.

The door was old and it broke and all the stories on earth and all the histories ran out. After that they never went back to dwell with Mouse any more, but remained running up and down over all the earth. (See story 60.)

The connection between sheep's adventures and the fate of Mouse's story children could not be more accidental.

African traditions reach us through the publications of fieldworkers, folklorists, and anthropologists who have collected and studied them over the last century. To the folklorist belongs the task of tracking down these errant children of Mouse, as they pass from mouth to mouth, to study their transformations and persistence, their ways of adapting to different environments, their readiness to serve as vehicles for different meanings and purposes. While the original form of any story is necessarily a matter of conjecture, folklore studies have shown that the same story may be told about a god in one area, a trickster figure in another, and the hero of a fairy tale in a third; that it will be told for entertainment by one tribe and held sacred by another. The same story, finally, will serve to explain different facts.

Some myths appear to be universal. Tales of witches and ogres, such themes as the slaying of monsters, the theft of fire, the testing of the son-in-law, or how man was cheated out of immortality, can be found in the folk tradition of almost every people. In many instances the same tale is told with minor variations on different continents. The unity of folk tradition suggests that certain human situations, roles, conflicts, and questions are universal. It would be difficult to imagine how stories would travel otherwise, even if we assume that they have spread from one or a few centers. The particular form of a given tale, however, seems to be the result of elaborations and losses and permutations of themes which it undergoes in the course of its journey. Folklorists tend to stress the mobility of oral tradition, the tendency of tales to travel both from tribe to tribe and across the boundary dividing the sacred from the profane. Given that myths and tales will have different meanings and functions in different contexts, the folklorist concentrates on what remains the permanent element, namely the story, or plot.

Anthropologists, by contrast, have been mainly interested in understanding a tale in its cultural context, to study its social function, its relation to cult, and the ways in which it both reflects and informs tribal values and modes of behavior.[1] They have stressed the natives' own attitude to their traditions, and specifically, the almost universal distinction made by native cultures between sacred narratives which are regarded as true and tales told for entertainment. Myth for the native is a true story; it relates events which are believed to have actually happened in primeval times. We must beware of reading into native categories of sacred and profane, our distinctions between truth and fiction, or history and poetry.[2] However, tales of a nonsacred character afford more than recreation to the natives, and play as vital a role, educational and opinion-molding, as the myths. Not infrequently they are invoked in cases of legal dispute. Captain R. S. Rattray who lived among the Ashanti for many years comments on the social use of the tales in day-to-day situations that men must meet and resolve:

> The names of animals, and even that of the sky god himself, were substituted for the names of real individuals whom it would have been very impolitic to mention. Later, no doubt, such a mild exposé in the guise of a story often came to be related qua story. The original practice is still resorted to, however, to expose someone whom the offended party fears to accuse more openly.[3]

[1] S. Thompson's *The Folktale*, and B. Malinowski's *Myth in Primitive Psychology* are representative of folklorist and anthropological approaches to myth respectively. Cited in Bibliography.

[2] The Dahomeans, for example, recognize two broad categories of stories: *heho*, or tale, and *hwenoho* (literally: time-old story) or history, tradition, myth. Cf. M. Herskovits, *Dahomean Narrative*. For analogous classification of their oral tradition of other tribes, see R. Pettazzoni "The Truth of Myth" in *Essays on the History of Religions*.

[3] *Akan Ashanti Folktales*, Leyden Brill, 1954.

Often the audience is questioned by the storyteller when a character must justify his act. Interpolations from the audience as the tale unfolds are regularly heard.

The Africans' attitude to their tradition is more flexible and complex than we would suppose. "We do not really mean, we do not really mean, that what we are going to say is true" is the traditional beginning of every Ashanti tale. The Sudanese regard their tales as lies in which not everything is false—lies containing a grain of truth, a form of wisdom, common sense, and a moral. Storytelling sessions usually begin with the following formula:

"I'm going to tell a story," the narrator begins.

"Right!" the audience rejoins.

"It's a lie."

"Right!"

"But not everything in it is false."

"Right!"

It ends with the formula: "I put the tale back where I found it."[1]

The oral tale lives in the telling. We are aware of standing outside of the vital circulation of an oral tradition, for the stories in this volume do not reach us in the course of their running up and down on earth. A tale that travels from some tribal elder via the anthropologist to the paperback rack has, like many contemporary voyagers, suffered a too abrupt and artificial transplantation.

These tales come to us from a world in which the word has not yet been divorced from the act of personal communication. A book can be read anywhere, at any time, by any literate person. It is addressed to everyone and no one in particular. By contrast, the oral tale draws its vitality from the context of its telling. In most instances this is quite strictly defined. There are stories told by parents to children, by elders to young men about to be initiated, stories told in cases of legal disputes, stories told to entertain the dead or on other ritual occasions. A book is usually read in private. The tale is always a public occasion. African storytelling, it

[1] B. Cendras, *Anthologie Nègre*.

should be added, is a highly dramatic art, interspersed with songs and dances and involving a great deal of audience participation.[1]

Finally, in a living oral tradition a given story will have many variants. No single version is privileged as the "true" one. The life of the story consists in the manifold variations of its telling, variations not only in delivery and style, but the development of the plot, incidents, characters, and ending. The printed story thus reproduces the tale in one of its many possibilities. The collector's prize is a butterfly on a pin.

The penetration of Western modes of life and thought is rapidly eroding Africa's traditional cultures. With growing literacy the oral tale falls into decline. We behold our impact on native life not without a certain uneasiness and salvage what we can from a vanishing part of our human heritage. It is not without a certain tragic irony that ancient traditions should claim our growing interest at a time when among the youth of the continent they tend to fall into oblivion in favor of Western modes of thinking.

2

African folklore displays a remarkable abundance and unity over an area comprising the continent south of the Sahara; an area in which we find communities living at the most different levels of culture, ranging from primitive hunting tribes to hieratic states of Byzantine splendor. The number of stories circulating has been estimated at a quarter of a million, and according to a survey made in 1938 some five thousand different tales have been recorded. African folklore tradition is further distinguished for the sophistication and high literary quality of its stories. Stories featuring feats of strength or magic, so common in the mythology of almost every other people, whether the ancient Greeks or American Indian tribes, are surprisingly rare. Instead, the pervasive theme of African folktales is the victory of cunning

---

[1] See Story 72, where two tales are recorded with audience response as well as a description of the storytelling session.

over force. The high god himself is outwitted by the trickster
hero. The sense of realism and ironic reflection on life which
informs both myths and tales may very well be the fruit of
centuries of political upheaval and slavery. For all the distance between the milieu in which these tales took root and
our own, their tone of disenchantment and not infrequently
of cynicism, as well as their preoccupation with such themes
as the distance between god and man, bring them close to
our modern sensibility.

The sophistication of African folklore is evident in its
central figure, the highly humanized animal trickster, a
variety of and precursor of the picaresque hero. *Anansi the
Spider* figures as the hero of an enormous body of West
African folktales and is known under various names in the
folklore of the Gold Coast, Ivory Coast, Sierra Leone,
Liberia, Togoland, Dahomey, Hausa, Yoruba, Warry Fiort,
Cameroons, Congo, and Angola. *Hare* is best known in East
Africa and among the Jukun and Angan of Nigeria. *Tortoise*
plays a primary role in the tales of the Yoruba, the Edo, and
the Ibo of Nigeria and in a place of less importance is found
also in East Africa. Since, moreover, cunning is the prime
virtue of the African hero, typical trickster incidents occur
in myths, fairy tales, realistic stories as well as in animal
tales. Even the divine Kintu passes the impossible test imposed by the Sun through cunning and proves himself by the
fact that "no one could fool him." (See 21.)

The comic tone of these tales would lead us to suppose
that they were told exclusively for entertainment. Actually,
however, in the category of animal tales we find sacred
stories, or myths, as well as moral and explanatory tales. In
Gold Coast mythology Anansi was originally regarded as
the creator of the world and still plays the role of the culture
hero in certain tales, notably the story where he steals the
sun. Not infrequently we find animal trickster stories associ-
ated with cult. Among the Saramacca, for example, Spider
stories play a central role in funerary rites and are told to
entertain the dead. Similarly, among the Bush Negroes,
Spider stories are told to the dead during the seven days the

body lies in the village death house awaiting burial. Moreover, the secular animal tales of one tribe often appear in narratives of other tribes having the same plot but with the gods as characters. Thus in many Yoruba tales the god Eshu appears in a role similar to that other tribes assign to the trickster Tortoise. The transformation of animals into men or gods and vice versa, present no difficulty to the native mind. Tradition often relates that an animal trickster was formerly a god or a man, and in the tales his person emerges as unmistakably human. It is not surprising, therefore, to find cycles of stories around human or divine tricksters, such as the tales about Hlakanyana among the Zulu, or the god Legba among the Dahomey.

Trickster is an animal of inferior size and strength and superior cleverness. By no means an exemplary moral figure, he displays cupidity, gross appetite, and ruthlessness and often gains the advantage over his dull-witted and earnest opponent by sheer lack of scruple. The African trickster differs in many important respects from his American Indian counterpart.[1] Unlike the New World trickster he is represented as the underdog rather than as a chief. His amorality is not that of the anomic, presocialized individual, who has not yet matured to a sense of responsibility. Suave, urbane and calculating, the African trickster acts with premeditation, always in control of the situation; though self-seeking, his social sense is sufficiently developed to enable him to manipulate others to his advantage. He is mercenary rather than promiscuous. Hare will marry Antelope for the value of her horns and eat her, but he would not, like so many American Indian tricksters, violate his grandmother. On the whole he shows a singular indifference to sex in favor of food or the sheer enjoyment of making a dupe of another.

Though in a given cycle trickster will victimize any of his fellow creatures, he usually concentrates on a particular prey. Trickster's favorite foils and dupes are Lion, Elephant,

[1] For a comparative study of the trickster, cf. C. G. Jung, C. Kereny, P. Radin, *The Trickster;* and N. O. Brown, *Hermes, the Thief.* Madison, Wisc., 1947.

and Hyena. The victim is always larger and therefore stronger, inevitably slow and dull-witted, often hard-working and honest. Despite the many times they have been tricked, they eventually yield to the trickster's suave arguments and alluring promises to afford him yet another triumph. Trickster is not always depicted as besting his intended victim; sometimes the trick backfires and in stories like the Tar Baby incident, he appears anything but clever. (See 57 and 58.)

While trickster sometimes figures as a culture hero, a kind of primitive Prometheus, it is interesting to note that in African, as well as in many American Indian tales, even when he benefits mankind he does so inadvertently. A popular West African tale recounts how Spider, having put all the wisdom of the world in a calabash with the intention of keeping it for himself, decides to hide the container atop a tree. He slings it about his neck to enable him to climb, but because the calabash is over his chest he cannot make any progress. After a while, his child calls to him to change the position of the gourd, whereupon Spider dashes the calabash to the ground and wisdom becomes disseminated throughout the world.

The following may be cited as the most typical incidents in the rich repertory of trickster's adventures: Trickster bests his faster opponent in a race by posting his relatives at regular intervals along the racecourse, so that he always appears ahead of his opponent. (Story 56.) Trickster challenges two powerful animals, usually the rhinoceros and the hippopotamus, to a tug of war which he arranges so that they pull against each other without knowing it. (77.) Trickster devours the children of a larger predatory animal by posing as their nurse or doctor. (58.) Trickster takes a loan from a series of animals who habitually prey on each other and arranges his payment so that each animal that comes to collect is devoured by a stronger creditor, the last creditor being tricked into canceling his debt! (55.) Trickster finds an object that yields food when the proper formula is pronounced and hides it so that no one else should benefit from it. When others discover his secret, he contrives to obtain a magic whip that punishes the thieves. (53.) Trickster humiliates a larger, dull-witted opponent by using him as a riding horse. Of particular interest are tales in which trickster escapes an impossible obligation by posing an equally impossible condition.

These tales illustrate the traditional right of the individual to contest irrational authority. A Kru tale offers a good example of the African attitude toward chiefs. When Noyomo receives the king's impossible command to weave a mat of rice grains, he meets the challenge by asking for an old mat of the same kind to use as a pattern. Similarly among the Bulu of the Cameroon, when Turtle's prospective father-in-law demands in the way of a test that he fetch water in a basket, Turtle asks him for a carrying strap of smoke. Story 78 gives a variant of this motif. Many of the plots of these trickster tales resemble those of familiar fairy tales. What is striking, however, is that unlike the fairy tale hero, trickster accomplishes the seemingly impossible by trickery rather than by supernatural aid. Trickster operates in a real world where the hero cannot count on supernatural helpers, and clever cheating replaces magic.

A popular theme, especially in West African folktales, is the rivalry between trickster and the high god. In stories like "How Spider Read the Sky God's Thoughts" (51) and "How Spider Obtained the Sky God's Stories" (52) Spider passes by sheer cunning a series of tests which seem to require superhuman strength or magic. In the end the Sky God must concede that he has met his equal in the battle of wits. (See 9.)

Besides trickster stories, African folklore abounds in animal tales of an explanatory character. (See Chapter IV.) Most of these explain why animals look and act as they do and why certain animals prey on others. Many stories account for the characteristics and habits of human beings. Whether the fact in question belongs in the domain of nature or society, it is invariably derived from a dramatic incident of the past, an event which set a precedent once and for all. Some explanatory tales (like 60, 67), we often find, are simply fairy tales and romances with an explanatory end tagged on.

The relation between men and animals is another favorite theme of animal tales. One widely spread story of this kind related how the speech of animals was revealed to a man on condition of secrecy. When the man vaunts his new endowment he is subjected to various penalties. This story may reflect the strict tabus surrounding the use of secret languages, which are also thought to be the language of the gods, of animals and of the dead. Another widely known tale treats of man's ingratitude—and occasionally his thankfulness—to beasts that rescue him from danger. Finally, there is a common tale in which a vegetable or animal agrees to become the child of a barren woman on condition that its origins will never be mentioned. (90.) The bargain broken, the generous plant or animal child returns to its former shape. This type of story may be an elaboration on primitive totemic beliefs that children come from plant and animal souls.

Besides the animal tale, African oral tradition offers a wide variety of story types ranging from primitive ogre tales to realistic novelettes. Of greatest interest among these are the dilemma stories which are at once typically African and most appealing to the Western imagination. A tale like "The Dog's Wisdom" (78) with its cynical logic and melancholy moral could easily find a place among the pages of Kafka's parables. Dilemma tales are usually unfinished stories where the audience is left to decide between two contending claims. Sometimes a startling solution is offered on which the listeners are invited to comment. In contrast to the moral fable and fairy tale, where right and wrong are clearly defined, the dilemma tale specializes in ambiguous cases where the questions continue to haunt us even after a decision has been reached. Take the instance of the boy who was raised by a kindly foster-father after fleeing from his own father's unjust cruelty. (76.) When it comes to a test, who deserves his greater loyalty? Can ties of blood be dismissed even when the parent is unworthy? Yet, what of the foster-father who in fact acted as a father should? In the story about the clever and the foolish son we meet again with the upright son whom an unjust father treats like an imbecile, robs of all rights and human dignity; shall he be blamed if when his father is in danger of death he behaves like an imbecile and breaks into a foolish song, instead of rushing to his aid? The verdict of the native audience in the version included here (72) is that the mistreated son was justified. A tale like "The Leftover Eye" (74) uses the most improbable situation to illustrate a most common conflict of loyalty: given a situation where a man cannot help but offend either his wife or his mother, which offense is the lesser sin? Another common type of dilemma tale (see 73) poses this problem: suppose A commits a mistake or misdeed which leads B (by way of covering up for A) to acts which bring unexpected benefits, should not A be credited for these benefits?

A survey of African tales discloses a large number of themes and motifs familiar from European fairy tales. There are analogues to "Cinderella," "The Spinning Woman by the Spring," "The Swallowing Monster," "The Magic Flight," "The Magic Whip," "The Goose that Laid the Golden Egg," "Frau Holle," "The Lucky Youngest Son," "The Dragon Slayer," and many others. The parallels between African tales and Old World themes together with the many resemblances between animal trickster tales and Aesop's fables, the medieval cycle of Reynard the Fox, the Panchatra tales of India, and the Jataka tales of China, point to a historical connection between Africa and other areas of the Old World.

In the fairy tales as in the trickster stories and myths, the cleverness of the hero rather than strength, magic, or luck drives the plot to a happy ending. "The Lucky Youngest Son" (101) would be more appropriately titled "The Clever Youngest Son" for he rises to fortune not by the grace of luck or supernatural aid but by means of crafty stratagems.

The type of ingenuous hero whose every blundering step leads him to some advantages and who is saved in spite of himself is practically unknown. In practically every African treatment of the test theme, the hero proves himself by his intelligence.

In Africa, the genre of the fairy tale is not as clearly defined as in the Old World; the lines of demarcation we are accustomed to draw between myth, cult legend, fairy tale, fable, and realistic tale are still fluid.

Of particular interest are the two extreme cases where the fairy tale is still embedded in actual tribal customs, or where it is on the verge of becoming a realistic tale. Stories 98 and 99 are good examples of a rough fairy tale plot on a concrete base of ritual practices, while Stories 95 and 106 are purely tales of magic. Stories with unhappy endings like "The Children of the Knee" (86) are not uncommon. Justice does not always triumph and often misfortune strikes the innocent. Even in tales of retribution the treatment often carries us beyond the simplicity of fairy tale or moral fable where everybody gets his just desert. In "The Jealous Wife" (96) a familiar fairy tale is transformed into a human story, leaving us not with the sense of the just punishment of the jealous wife, but rather her tragedy. The older wife plots to kill the child of the younger because it is brighter than hers; by mistake she kills her own. In the final episode of the story, we see her through the eyes of the husband who follows her through the fields while she is still hugging her dead child and singing wildly in the hope of bringing it back to life. The treatment of character in "The Wonder Worker of the Plains" (88) is nearer to tragedy than to moral allegory. Similarly, the story of M'wambi, who kills himself when his supernatural luck-bringing animal dies, is a tragic fairy tale. (94.) A parallel transformation may be noted in the case of romances elaborated from very primitive material involving human sacrifice and fertility magic. (See Stories 67 and 97.)

In tales like "Let the Big Drum Roll" (84) and "How an Unborn Child Avenged Its Mother's Death" (85) we leave the realm of fairy tale and fable and are on the threshold of the realistic tale, or novelette. These tales of sin and retribution do not move on the grandiose scale of Greek tragedy: hunger and want motivate the crime. Yet, the small but relentless voice of the helpless victim produces an effect of haunting horror. Before the crime can be avenged it must be revealed. Tales showing that every crime finds an unexpected revealer are particularly common in the Zambezi region. The revealer may be a child or a dog; usually it is a tiny bird which no amount of killing can prevent from rising from the dead and singing of the criminal deed until punishment is meted out to the guilty person.

In contrast to the wealth of recorded animal tales, moral and explanatory stories, fairy tales and romances, one is struck by the dearth of myths, or sacred tales recounting the activities of the gods and the primordial events of creation. While a considerable body of myths has been recorded for West Africa, no comparable collection exists for other regions. The gaps in the literature on myth are not surprising, for sacred stories, like sacred objects and persons, are highly potent, dangerous, and must therefore be guarded with secrecy. Only certain persons are authorized to recount myths and usually only under prescribed ritualistic conditions. Frequently atonement must be made before a myth can be told. Even in the case of recorded myths one is not on sure ground. Has the native told the white missionary, or colonial administrator, or the anthropologist only what is fit for his ears? We cannot help wonder, for example, if the Krachi "seriously" believe that god removed himself to the sky because people wiped their dirty hands on him.

In myths which play a vital role in cult, the story element tends to be weak. Sometimes the myth is quite unintelligible when read independently as story. The special interests the cult story serves tend to condition the details of the narrative so profoundly that it must be decoded by reference to a complex body of beliefs and practices. Here, the interpreter and his bias often stand between us and the material. Finally, in many instances native beliefs about the gods and primeval events are not articulated in narrative form. Then we can speak at best of a potential mythology, because myth is first and foremost a story.

A survey of the myths collected up to the present reveals that on the whole, the basic interest of native myths is moral rather than speculative. The human dilemma rather than the adventures of the gods dominates the scene. Rarely do we find grandiose mythic destinies projected on the gods. The Bakongo tales around the goddess Nzambi who wanders among men in the guise of a poor old woman and punishes those who refuse charity to the needy is almost Biblical in character.

There exists, however, an extraordinarily elaborate system of speculation about gods and the universe among the Dogon, the Bambara, the Yoruba of Nigeria and their neighbors, the Fon. It is significant that these are all strongly centralized hierarchic states with highly developed class prerogatives and functions. Here, as in other instances, a developed polytheism seems to go hand in hand with state organization. The divine pantheon is a reflection of the court on earth.

The cosmogonies of the Dogon and Bambara tend toward a degree of abstraction which places them beyond myth, strictly speaking. They involve an intricate system of correspondences between various scales of being: plant, vegetable, mineral, astral, and human. Since the cosmic order they describe is ultimately sustained by ritual acts, they cannot be regarded as pure speculative systems in our sense. They thus offer an instance of great intellectual ingenuity within a magical frame. Yoruba, also a kingdom, is perhaps richest in stories of the exploits of the gods of the type with which we are familiar in classical mythology.

Outside of these areas, there seems to be little interest in speculation about gods or the universe, although further research may change the picture. Most African myths assume the earth to be there more or less in its present shape. Sometimes a myth will recount how the "creator" pinched the surface of the earth to produce mountains and valleys. The greater bulk of myths of the beginning, however, are concerned with *tribal* origins.[1] Stories about the heavenly bodies do not describe their creation but mostly account for why they are up in the sky rather than down on earth. (See 17 and 18.) While myths of the origin of the world are extremely rare, we do meet with stories describing the creation of specific beings, animals, plants, and men in a universe already in existence. These are often steeped in magical practices, like the baffling Bushmen tale, "Mantis Creates Eland" (15), innocent of speculative or moral interest.

African traditions offer diverse accounts of the origin of man. At best, man descends from a family of gods or is quite literally lowered to earth from the sky. Among the Mano of Liberia the sky god sends down people, animals, medicine, laws and rules for living.[2] Similarly, in the Dahomean myth of the origin of man (11), the heavenly people establish worship, cult, bring ceremonial garments and ritual paraphernalia. Myths of this kind tend to validate sacred customs and abound in details of ritual observances. Man is sent down on earth to set up a sacred order. But this is not always the case. In the Ngombe myth where the first human family is lowered from the sky (4), we meet with the notion of the "Fall": man is evicted for making a nuisance of himself. There are instances of man being molded or kneaded into shape by a god (46), but for the most part man is not a "creation," but simply emerges from trees, rivers, caves, and holes in the ground together with his livestock. Or, even more disconcerting, he is simply found, a kind of anomaly, as in the Yao tale where the chameleon discovers the first human couple in his fish trap and both he and the supreme god are highly baffled. (1.) While the notion that man was created by a god occurs, it remains somewhat indistinct since the creator is never a clearly defined figure. The Zulu, for example, do not distinguish between the creator and the first

---

[1] Cf. The Masai "Beginner of the Earth," Story 14, where the interest is in accounting for the occupations of the tribes.

[2] G. Schwab, *Tribes of the Liberian Hinterland*. Cambridge, 1947.

ancestor, although there are references in their tradition to
the creation of man. The Yao term *Mulungu* is not a personal name but related to the concept of sacred power, or
mana; it applies equally to the supreme god, the ancestors,
the soul of the dead, and the aggregate of spirits of all the
dead.[1] According to one Zulu tradition, the first man
came out of a reed when the reed burst to liberate him.
According to another, the god Unkulunkulu broke off mankind from a reed. It is still customary among the Zulu to
stick a reed beside the door of a hut in which a child has
been born. The Herero relate how the ancestors emerged
from a certain tree called Omumborom Bonga. The tree is
still believed to exist in the Kakoko veld. Often the first men
and animals are thought to emerge from a hole or a cave;
the place is usually known and the natives will point to the
footprints of the first ancestors and the animals that emerged
with them.[2]

African mythology offers some analogues to both classical
and Biblical stories. Among the first we may note myths of
the origin of evil, death, disease, and work, myths of the
swallowing monster, and myths of the origin of fire. Story 42
is a variant of the Greek story of "Pandora's Box." Tales of
the swallowing monster are current all over Africa. Usually
a monster swallows up the population of a village, sometimes of the entire country. One woman escapes and gives
birth to a son. The boy, who is often miraculously preco-
cious, slays the monster, releases the peoples and their flocks,
and is appointed chief. Sometimes the story has a final episode, characteristically African in its pessimistic realism, in
which the people, grown envious of the prestige of their
savior, plan his destruction. (24.) The theme of the swallowing monster also occurs in the familiar tale of the testing
of the son-in-law. Here, the slaying of the monster is one of
the tasks of the hero before he can claim his bride.

The myth of the theft of fire is known in the folklore of

---

[1] Cf. H. Baumann, *Schöpfung und Urzeit des Menschen im Mythus der
Afrikanischen Völker.*
[2] Cf. A. Werner, *Myths and Legends of the Bantu.*

almost every people. Story 25 follows the myth in its classical form: a culture-hero-trickster figure steals fire from the sky or sun god who has guarded it jealously from mankind. The theft may, however, be accomplished by a simple man who steals it from a terrestrial being, as in the Bergdama tale (30) of the man who stole fire from the lions. The story may offer a realistic account of how fire, originally the jealous possession of one tribe, was stolen by a member of another tribe. (68.) Tales of this sort are common, and tribal memories of an actual theft of fire from another tribe may possibly lie at the origin of the theft motive. Africa abounds in diverse accounts of the origin of fire, among them such purely natural explanations as the discovery of fire by rubbing two sticks together. Other accounts describe how the first ancestors acquired fire from forest conflagrations caused by lightning. In some myths, fire is a gift rather than a theft. We meet with the generous creator in a Baluba tale. When the Great Spirit Kabezya Mpungu created First Man he put the seeds of all the edible plants in his hair, and placed wood in his hands and taught him to make fire and to cook. Similarly in the traditions about Unkulunkulu, the creator teaches man the use of fire. (See 13.)

We find interesting African analogues to Bible stories in stories like "The Tower to Heaven" (8), "The Forbidden Fruit" (10, 46, 47), and numerous accounts of the loss of paradise. Indeed, the loss of an original state of closeness and blissful harmony between god and man, free from death, disease, and work is perhaps the most persistent theme in African mythology. Stories of the loss of primeval harmony take the characteristically African form of the withdrawal of god. The supreme god does not play a major part in the mythology of most African tribes. He is usually depicted as passive and remote, having committed the government of the world to lesser gods. His one significant act is to remove himself from the earth. Even in myths where we find some reference to god's creative acts, the central interest of the story is to account for the fact that god has removed himself to the sky where men may no longer reach him. In

contrast to the Biblical story which recounts how god ex-
pelled man from the Garden of Eden, native stories without
exception relate how the people forced god to remove himself to the sky. It is interesting to note the active role as-
signed to man in disrupting the original harmony of things:
in most instances, god is literally and physically driven off
the face of the earth by human fires, poles and pestles. God
is not so much offended as personally mistreated by man;
he does not retaliate, but passively withdraws.

Variations on the theme of god's withdrawal can be
found all over the continent. Among the Songe the disobedience of the first human couple brings about the flight of
Fidi-Mukullu after he has cut out their tongues. The Loango
relate how god brought famine on disobedient mankind. The
survivors oppressed god with their pleadings until he withdrew to the sky, leaving behind the power of the earth which
renders the soil fertile. We meet with stories of god remov-
ing himself after man's first attempt to build a tower to
heaven or after death comes into the world. In a number of
tales the lack of communication between man and god is
presented as a matter of accident. The Dinka relate that
originally man lived on high with god. Consequent on their
sins, god sends mankind down to earth. The skyrope breaks,
making return impossible. In a Ndorobo variant there is
no reference to sin: mankind is sent down to earth and the
thread simply breaks.[1] In its most common form, however,
the story of the separation of god and man involves an act
of violence. A Luyi tale gives a singularly dramatic account:
the god Nyambe is forced to flee and climbs up the skyrope
when men attempt to kill him.

Most of these tales assume a closer affinity between god
and the animals than between man and god. In the Yao tale,
man is clearly an intruder in the peaceful household of
Mulungu and his people, the beasts. In several accounts of
the separation of god from man, god is forced to withdraw
because of man's aggression upon the animal world. In a
Tshwana tale, which accounts for mankind being scattered

[1] Cf. Baumann, *op. cit.*

over the face of the earth, we are told that in the beginning
men lived together with lions in caves. One day, when they
killed their favorite son, they were driven out by the lions.[1]

The loss of paradise is perhaps the most persistent theme
in African mythology. It comprises, besides the idea of the
separation of god from man, such familiar motifs as how
death, disease, and evil came into the world. The problem of
death occupies a central place of interest in native myths as
attested both by their number and variety. The most wide-
spread myth concerning the origin of death is the tale of
"The Perverted Message" or "The Two Messengers," motifs
familiar from classical mythology. In its most common form,
god sends the chameleon to mankind with the message that
they should have eternal life and the lizard with the message
that man must die. The chameleon loiters on the way and
the lizard reaches mankind first. By the time the chameleon
arrives, its message is no longer valid and death has entered
the world. (13.)

In the wide area of distribution of this myth, considerable
variations occur. A Zambezi tale would appear to answer the
disturbing question, Why does god send two messengers
with contrary orders? God hasn't made up his mind, according to the tale, and lets the issue depend on which messenger
reaches mankind first. The sending of two messengers is
sometimes justified by discord in the divine family, as in the
Barotse tale where Nyambi and his wife cannot agree on
whether men should have eternal life or die, and the out-
come of the race between the two messengers is to decide
the question. In an almost equal number of tales, however,
god wants man to live, dispatches an animal to mankind with
the message of life, but another animal, not sent by god,
hastens to get there first, and out of envy or spite delivers a
counter order. (See Stories 31 and 32.)

Another tale of wide distribution is one in which man is
offered two bundles, the one containing immortality and the
other death. Through ignorance or a misunderstanding, he
chooses the bundle containing death. (40.) Instances are not

[1] *Ibid.*

lacking, however, in which men knowingly choose death in exchange for children. (See 41.)

There is a large group of myths concerning the origin of death in which mortality is consequent upon the breaking of some tabu: eating, touching or looking at a forbidden thing. Of particular interest among these are tales where the transgression consists in beholding a forbidden act. One such tale (48) relates how in the beginning men rejuvenated themselves like snakes by sloughing their skin. They lost this power the moment a child caught its parents in the act of changing. In another tale, the son explicitly desires his father's death when he beholds him undressing. These and similar tales touch upon the connection between sexuality and death with a directness which makes both classical and Biblical accounts appear circumspect.

Africa also offers several versions of a story analogous to the familiar Sleep-Test motif. (See 37, 38, 39.) According to this story, man lost immortality when, subjected to the test of vigilance, he yielded to the power of sleep. How can he expect to have eternal life when he cannot even stay awake for seven days!

What is most striking, perhaps, in the African accounts of the origin of death is the decisive role allotted to accident, misunderstanding, ignorance, and man's unworthiness to receive immortality. The tale "The Perverted Message," in particular, strikes the tragic note of some of Kafka's parables. God wants man to live and so dispatches to mankind the message of life, but due to the distance between man and god, the necessity for intermediaries, the contingencies attending the transmission of the message, man is cheated out of immortality. Once the wrong message is delivered, it stands; god himself is powerless to revoke it. In several versions of the story, however, it says that god endorsed the false message because *men believed it.*

3

The present volume hopes to make accessible to the general reader, as well as to the student of myth, representative

African tales. The study of myth has been revolutionized in the past century through the discovery of the still vital and abundant oral tradition of preliterate peoples. But even though the problem of myth is in the forefront of contemporary discussions of psychology, literature, and the social sciences, the myths themselves—and this holds particularly true for primitive material—are not easily accessible. The bulk of published tales is scattered in special periodicals, ethnographic and anthropological studies, mostly out of print. The majority of existing works on primitive mythology offers a survey of the material rather than the narratives themselves. Yet contact with the native texts would appear to be essential for an understanding of myth.

In my choice of tales I have been guided by several considerations: to give a sense of the wide range as well as of the unity of the material, and to show both its affinities to and differences from the classical and Biblical traditions. While I have tried to draw material from the most important areas and cultures, my aim has not been to include specimens from all existing tribal traditions. I have sought rather to give instances of what appear to be the most persistent themes and types of story on the continent. I have included a minimal sample of what, to the nonspecialist at least, will be boring, rude, incomprehensible. We tend on the basis of the highly literate narratives of the Bible and Greek antiquity to think of myth as a story which is par excellence universal, transparent, and profound. But a considerable bulk of sacred traditions and particularly those which play a vital role in tribal ritual are provincial, obscure, and lacking in human depth. The restrictions of an anthology forbid giving each story in its several variants. Yet this is where we learn most concretely about the formation of myth. To compensate in part for this defect, I have included in the case of one theme, "The Origin of Death," some ten stories with their most important variants.

The tales are grouped according to types and thematic affiliations rather than by region. While the organization of the volume does not adhere to any strict classification, it is intended to aid the reader in drawing comparisons between African folktales and the traditions of other peoples.

The division of the material into myths and tales corresponds roughly to the native divisions between sacred and secular traditions. Part One comprises traditions concerning primeval times. Part Two includes for the most part tales of a nonsacred character grouped under four chapter headings: Trickster Tales, Explanatory Tales, Dilemma Stories and Moral Fables, and Tales of Human Adventure.

LEGEND

Before the arrival of the missionaries, if we asked, "By what were these stones made?" it was said, "They were made by Umvelinqangi." For we used to ask when we were little, thinking that the old men knew all things which are on the earth; yet forsooth they do not know; but we do not contradict them, for neither do we know.

(AMAZULU)

PART ONE

MYTHS

1

MYTHS OF PRIMEVAL TIMES: THE BEGINNING OF THINGS

1 MULUNGU AND THE BEASTS

In the beginning man was not, only Mulungu and his people, the beasts. They lived happily on earth.

One day a chameleon found a human pair in his fish trap. He had never seen such creatures before and he was surprised. The Chameleon reported his discovery to Mulungu. Mulungu said, "Let us wait and see what the creatures will do."

The men started making fires. They set fire to the bush so that the beasts fled into the forest. Then the men set traps and killed Mulungu's people. At last Mulungu was compelled to leave the earth. Since he could not climb a tree he called for the spider.

The spider spun a thread up to the sky and down again. When he returned he said, "I have gone on high nicely, now you Mulungu go on high." And Mulungu ascended to the sky on the spider's thread to escape from the wickedness of men.

(YAO)

2 GOD RETREATS TO THE SKY

In the beginning Nyambi made all things. He made animals, fishes, birds. At that time he lived on earth with his wife, Nasilele. One of Nyambi's creatures was different from all the others. His name was Kamonu. Kamonu imitated Nyambi in everything Nyambi did. When Nyambi worked in wood, Kamonu worked in wood; when Nyambi forged iron Kamonu forged iron.

After a while Nyambi began to fear Kamonu.

Then one day Kamonu forged a spear and killed a male antelope, and he went on killing. Nyambi grew very angry at this.

"Man, you are acting badly," he said to Kamonu. "These are your brothers. Do not kill them."

Nyambi drove Kamonu out into another land. But after a while Kamonu returned. Nyambi allowed him to stay and gave him a garden to cultivate.

It happened that at night buffaloes wandered into Kamonu's garden and he speared them; after that, some elands, and he killed one. After some time Kamonu's dog died; then his pot broke; then his child died. When Kamonu went to Nyambi to tell him what had happened he found his dog and his pot and his child at Nyambi's.

Then Kamonu said to Nyambi, "Give me medicine so that I may keep my things." But Nyambi refused to give him medicine. After this, Nyambi met with his two counselors and said, "How shall we live since Kamonu knows too well the road hither?"

Nyambi tried various means to flee Kamonu. He removed himself and his court to an island across the river. But Kamonu made a raft of reeds and crossed over to Nyambi's island. Then Nyambi piled up a huge mountain and went to live on its peak. Still Nyambi could not get away from man. Kamonu found his way to him. In the meantime men were multiplying and spreading all over the earth.

Finally Nyambi sent birds to go look for a place for Litoma, god's town. But the birds failed to find a place. Nyambi sought council from a diviner. The diviner said, "Your life depends on Spider." And Spider went and found an abode for Nyambi and his court in the sky. Then Spider spun a thread from earth to the sky and Nyambi climbed up on the thread. Then the diviner advised Nyambi to put out Spider's eyes so that he could never see the way to heaven again and Nyambi did so.

After Nyambi disappeared into the sky Kamonu gathered some men around him and said, "Let us build a high tower and climb up to Nyambi." They cut down trees and put log on log, higher and higher toward the sky. But the weight was too great and the tower collapsed. So that Kamonu never found his way to Nyambi's home.

But every morning when the sun appeared, Kamonu greeted it, saying, "Here is our king. He has come." And all the other people greeted him shouting and clapping. At the time of the new moon men call on Nasilele, Nyambi's wife.

(BAROTSE, UPPER ZAMBEZI)

3 THE QUARRELSOMENESS OF MEN DRIVES GOD INTO THE FOREST

Akongo was not always as he is now. In the beginning the creator lived among men; but men were quarrelsome. One day they had a big quarrel and Akongo left them to themselves. He went and hid in the forest and nobody has seen him since. People today can't tell what he is like.

(NGOMBE, BELGIAN CONGO)

4 HOW THE EARTH WAS PEOPLED

In the beginning there were no men on earth. The people lived in the sky with Akongo and they were happy. But there was a woman named Mbokomu who bothered everybody.

One day Akongo put the woman in a basket with her son and her daughter, some cassava, maize, and sugarcane and lowered the basket down to the earth.

The family planted a garden on earth and the garden flourished through their care.

One day the mother said to her son: "When we die there will be no one left to tend the garden."

"That can't be helped," the son replied.

"You must have children," the mother said.

"How?" asked the son. "We are the only people here. Where shall I find a wife?"

"Your sister is a woman," his mother replied. "Take her and have children by her." But the son recoiled from his mother's suggestion. The mother insisted, however. "That, or die childless, with nobody to continue our work. You can only get children by your sister so go and take her."

In the end the son gave in and went to his sister. The sister yielded to him quite willingly and became pregnant.

One day the sister met a creature who looked like a man except that he was completely covered by hair. She was afraid but the creature spoke so kindly to her that after a while they became friends. One day the sister took her husband's razor and went out to look for the hairy man. When she found him she made him lie down and shaved him. Now he looked like a man.[1] His name was Ebenga, meaning the beginner.

[1] A hairy body is an abomination to the Ngombe; it is the wife's duty to keep her husband's body shaved.

Ebenga bewitched the woman, so that when her child was born it brought witchcraft into the world. The child grew up under the spell of Ebenga. He practiced witchcraft and brought evil and sorrow to men.

In the course of time the brother and sister had other children. So the earth was peopled. But evil and witchcraft continued to the present.

The sky is supported by two creatures, Libanja and Songo. Libanja holds up the sky in the east by an enormous pole, and Songo in the west. When they grow tired the sky will fall down and men will turn into lizards.

(NGOMBE)

5 WHEN THE SKY WAS CLOSE

The Nyimang of the Nuba Mountains relate that long ago the sky was so near the earth that it pressed down on the people. The women couldn't stir the millet porridge properly with their long stirrers; they had to keep their hands so low over the pot that they burned them. Finally, one woman got angry and lifting the stirrer pierced the sky with its upper end. The clouds scattered in anger and went away from the earth.

In another version told by the Kadaru of the same area, long ago the rocks were soft and the sky was so near the earth that people cut pieces off the clouds and ate them. One day an angry woman stabbed the sky with her stirrer, and scattered the clouds. Ever since then the clouds give rain only during the rainy season.

(NYIMANG)

6 HOW HUVEANE CLIMBED UP TO THE SKY

In the beginning Huveane made the sky and the earth. When he had finished he climbed up into the sky. He drove in pegs on which he set his feet, but took out each one as soon as he had stepped on the next till he had drawn out the last peg and disappeared in the sky. Huveane took out the pegs by which he climbed up to the sky so that people should not be able to follow him.[1]

(BASUTO, TRANSVAAL)

7 THE NAMES OF GOD

Long ago—it is said—Ngewo made the earth and all things, and ended by making a man and a woman. They did not know Ngewo's name and referred to him as Maanda-lo ("He is grandfather").

One day Ngewo said to them: "You shall have everything you ask me for, if you want it." When they wanted anything they went to him and said: "Maanda, give us this . . . give us that"; and in giving it Ngewo always said: "Iy ngee: Yes, take it." So they thought his name was Mangee, "Grandfather take it." They came to him so frequently that he said

---

[1] Many primitive peoples think of the sky as a solid vault which joins the earth at the horizon. According to the Thonga, it is the place where women can hit the sky with their pestles. No one living today, however, has been able to reach that place.

to himself: "If I stay near these people they will wear me out with their requests; I will make another living place for myself far, far above them."

The people slept. In the morning they woke up, they looked about, but could not see him. They lifted up their heads and saw him *ngawongo wa* ("spread out very big"). For that they said: *Ngee-wolo-nga-wa-le* ("Take-it-wide-spread-great-is"). From this we say: *Ngewo wa* ("God great").

From that place where he stayed he made two living things, one for man and one for woman. He named them "fowl" and said: "Whenever one of you does wrong to his companion you must call me and when I come you must give me back my fowl." They agreed. He then returned to his own town. When one did wrong to his companion he said: *Ngewo ye-o, ngi bi le ve* ("God come down, I give you your fowl"). This has now become a "swear." The person who does wrong, when he hears this word, instead of allowing God to come down for the fowl to kill it, will at once apologize.

One day Ngewo came down to them and said: "Good-bye!" He warned them, saying: "I have made an arrangement with you concerning one another, therefore do not have a bad heart one to the other." Then he went to his own place. From that time they call him Leve ("Up high").

(MENDE)

8 THE TOWER TO HEAVEN

Long, long ago Onyankopon lived on earth, or at least was very near to us. Now there was a certain old woman who used to pound her mashed yams and the pestle kept knocking up against Onyankopon, who was not then high up in the sky. So Onyankopon said to the old woman: "Why do you keep doing this to me? Because of what you are doing I am going to take myself away up in the sky." And of a truth he did so.

Now the people could no longer approach Onyankopon. But the old woman thought of a way to reach him and bring him back. She instructed her children to go and search for all the mortars they could find and bring them to her. Then she told them to pile one mortar on top of another till they reached to where Onyankopon was. And her children did so, they piled up many mortars, one on top of another, till they needed only one more mortar to reach Onyankopon.

Now, since they could not find another mortar anywhere, their grandmother the old woman said to them: "Take one out from the bottom and put it on top to make them reach." So her children removed a mortar from the bottom and all the mortars rolled and fell to the ground, causing the death of many people.

(ASHANTI)

9 THE SEPARATION OF GOD FROM MAN

In the beginning of days Wulbari and man lived close together and Wulbari lay on top of Mother Earth, Asase Ya. Thus it happened that, as there was so little space to move about in, man annoyed the divinity, who in disgust went away and rose up to the present place where one can admire him but not reach him.

He was annoyed for a number of reasons. An old woman, while making her *fufu* outside her hut, kept on knocking Wulbari with her pestle. This hurt him and, as she persisted, he was forced to go higher out of her reach. Besides, the smoke of the cooking fires got into his eyes so that he had to go farther away.

According to others, however, Wulbari, being so close to men, made a convenient sort of towel, and the people used to wipe their dirty fingers on him. This naturally annoyed him. Yet this was not so bad a grievance as that which caused We, the Wulbari of the Kassena people, to remove himself out of the reach of man. He did so because an old woman, anxious to make a good soup, used to cut off a bit of him at each mealtime, and We, being pained at this treatment, went higher.

Established in his new setting, Wulbari formed a court in which the animals were his chief attendants. Everything seemed to run smoothly for a time until one day Ananse, the spider, who was Captain of the Guard, asked Wulbari if he would give him one corncob. "Certainly," Wulbari said, but he wanted to know what Ananse wished to do with only one corncob.

And Ananse said, "Master, I will bring you a hundred slaves in exchange for one corncob."

At this, Wulbari laughed.

But Ananse meant what he said, and he straightway took the road from the sky down to the earth, and there he asked the way from Krachi to Yendi. Some men showed him the road and Ananse set out. That evening he had gone as far as Tariasu. There he asked the chief for a lodging, and a house was shown him. And when it was time to go to bed, he took the corncob and asked the chief where he could put it for safekeeping. "It is the corn of Wulbari; he has sent me on a message to Yendi, and this corncob I must not lose."

So the people showed him a good place in the roof, and everyone went to sleep. But Ananse arose in the night and gave the corn to the fowls and, when day broke, he asked for the cob and lo! it was all eaten and destroyed. So Ananse made a great fuss and was not content till the people of Tariasu had given him a great basket of corn. Then he continued on his way and shortly sat down by the roadside, as he was weary from carrying so great a load.

Presently there came along a man with a live fowl in his

hand which he was bringing back from his field. Ananse greeted him and they soon became friends. Ananse said that he liked the fowl—in fact, he liked it so much that he would give the whole load of corn in exchange if the man would agree. Such a proposal was not to be met with every day; the fellow agreed, and Ananse went on his way carrying the fowl with him.

That night he reached Kpandae, and he went and saluted the chief from whom he begged a night's lodging. This was readily granted and Ananse, being tired, soon went to bed. First, however, he showed his fowl to the people and explained that it was the fowl of Wulbari and that he had to deliver it to Yendi. They were properly impressed with this information and showed Ananse a nice, quiet fowl house where it would be perfectly safe. Then all went to bed.

But Ananse did not sleep. As soon as he heard everyone snoring, he arose and took his fowl and went outside the village and there sacrificed the poor bird. Leaving the corpse in the bush and placing some of the blood and feathers on the chief's own doorpost, he went back to bed.

At cockcrow Ananse arose and began shouting and crying out that the fowl of Wulbari was gone, that he had lost his place as Captain of the Guard, and that the unfortunate village of Kpandae would most certainly be visited by misfortune. The hullabaloo brought everyone outside, and by this time it was daylight. Great indeed was the clamor when the people learned what the fuss was about, and then suddenly Ananse pointed to the feathers and blood on the chief's doorpost.

There was no use denying the fact—the feathers were undoubtedly those of the unfortunate fowl, and just then a small boy found its body. It was evident to all that their own chief had been guilty of a sacrilege too dreadful to think about. They, therefore, one and all, came and begged Ananse to forgive them and to do something or other to divert the approaching calamity, which everyone thought must be inevitable.

Ananse at last said that possibly Wulbari would forgive

them, if they gave him a sheep to take to Yendi.

"Sheep!" cried the people. "We will give you any number of sheep so long as you stop this trouble."

Ananse was satisfied with ten sheep and he went his way.

He had no further adventures until he reached the outskirts of Yendi with his sheep. He was a little tired, however, and sat down outside the village and allowed his sheep to graze. He was still resting when there came toward him a company of people, wailing and weeping. They bore with them a corpse, and when Ananse saluted them and asked what they were doing, they said that a young man had died and that they were now carrying him back to his village for burial.

Ananse asked if the village was far, and they said it was far. Then he said that it was more than likely that the body would rot on the road, and they agreed. He then suggested that they should give him the corpse and in exchange he would give them the ten sheep. This was a novel kind of business deal, but it sounded all right and, after a little while, the company of young men agreed and they went off with the sheep, leaving their dead brother with Ananse.

The latter waited until nightfall and then walked into the town, carrying with him the corpse. He came to the house of the chief of Yendi and saluted that mighty monarch, and begged for a small place where he could rest. He added:

"I have with me as companion the son of Wulbari. He is his favorite son, and, although you know me as the Captain of Wulbari's Host, yet I am only as a slave to this boy. He is asleep now, and as he is so tired I want to find a hut for him."

This was excellent news for the people of Yendi and a hut was soon ready for the favorite son of Wulbari.

Ananse placed the corpse inside and covered it with a cloth so that it seemed verily like a sleeping man. Ananse then came outside and was given food. He feasted himself well and asked for some food for Wulbari's son. This he took into the hut where, being greedy, he finished the meal and came out bearing with him the empty pots.

Now the people of Yendi asked if they might play and

dance, for it was not often that a son of Wulbari came to visit them. Ananse said that they might, for he pointed out to them that the boy was an extraordinarily hard sleeper and practically nothing could wake him—that he himself, each morning, had had to flog the boy until he woke, and that shaking was no use, nor was shouting. So they played and they danced.

As the dawn came, Ananse got up and said it was time for him and Wulbari's son to be up and about their business. So he asked some of the chief's own children who had been dancing to go in and wake the son of Wulbari. He said that, if the young man did not get up, they were to flog him, and then he would surely be aroused. The children did this, but Wulbari's son did not wake. "Hit harder, hit harder!" cried Ananse, and the children did so. But still Wulbari's son did not wake.

Then Ananse said that he would go inside and wake him himself. So he arose and went into the hut and called to Wulbari's son. He shook him, and then he made the startling discovery that the boy was dead. Ananse's cries drew everyone to the door of the compound, and there they learned the dreadful news that the sons of their chief had beaten Wulbari's favorite child to death.

Great was the consternation of the people. The chief himself came and saw and was convinced. He offered to have his children killed; he offered to kill himself; he offered everything imaginable. But Ananse refused and said that he could think of nothing that day, as his grief was too great. Let the people bury the unfortunate boy and perhaps he, Ananse, would devise some plan by which Wulbari might be appeased.

So the people took the dead body and buried it.

That day all Yendi was silent, as all men were stricken with fear.

But in the evening Ananse called the chief to him and said, "I will return to my father, Wulbari, and I will tell him how the young boy has died. But I will take all the blame on myself and I will hide you from his wrath. You must, how-

ever, give me a hundred young men to go back with me, so
that they can bear witness as to the boy's death."

Then the people were glad, and they chose a hundred of
the best young men and made them ready for the long journey to the abode of Wulbari.

Next morning Ananse arose and, finding the young men
ready for the road, he went with them back to Krachi and
from there he took them up to Wulbari.

The latter saw him coming with the crowd of youths and
came out to greet him. And Ananse told him all that he had
done and showed how from one single corncob Wulbari
had now got a hundred excellent young slaves. So pleased
was Wulbari that he confirmed Ananse in his appointment
as Chief of his Host and changed his name from Anyankon
to Ananse, which it has remained to the present day.

Now Ananse got very conceited over this deed and used
to boast greatly about his cleverness. One day he even went
so far as to say that he possessed more sense than Wulbari
himself. It happened that Wulbari overheard this, and he
was naturally annoyed at such presumption. So, next day, he
sent for his captain and told him that he must go and fetch
him *something*. No further information was forthcoming,
and Ananse was left to find out for himself what Wulbari
wanted.

All day Ananse thought and thought, and in the evening
Wulbari laughed at him and said, "You must bring me
something. You boast everywhere that you are my equal,
now prove it."

So next day Ananse arose and left the sky on his way to
find *something*. Presently he had an idea and, sitting down
by the wayside, he called all the birds together. From each
one he borrowed a fine feather and then dismissed them.
Rapidly he wove the feathers into a magnificent garment
and then returned to Wulbari's town. There he put on the
wonderful feather robe and climbed up the tree over against
Wulbari's house. Soon Wulbari came out and saw the garishly
colored bird. It was a new bird to him, so he called all the

people together and asked them the name of the wonderful bird. But none of them could tell, not even the elephant, who knows all that is in the far, far bush. Someone suggested that Ananse might know, but Wulbari said that, unfortunately, he had sent him away on an errand. Everyone wanted to know the errand and Wulbari laughed and said, "Ananse has been boasting too much and I heard him say that he has as much sense as I have. So I told him to go and get me *something*." Everyone wanted to know what this *something* was, and Wulbari explained that Ananse would never guess what he meant, for the *something* he wanted was nothing less than the sun, the moon, and darkness.

The meeting then broke up amid roars of laughter at Ananse's predicament and Wulbari's exceeding cleverness. But Ananse, in his fine plumes, had heard what was required of him and, as soon as the road was clear, descended from his tree and made off to the bush.

There he discarded his feathers and went far, far away. No man knows quite where he went, but, wherever he went, he managed to find the sun and the moon and the darkness. Some say that the python gave them to him, others are not sure. In any case, find them he did and, putting them into his bag, he hastened back to Wulbari.

He arrived at his master's house late one afternoon and was greeted by Wulbari who, after a while, asked Ananse if he had brought back *something*.

"Yes," said Ananse, and went to his bag and drew out darkness. Then all was black and no one could see. Thereupon he drew out the moon and all could see a little again. Then last he drew out the sun, and some who were looking at Ananse saw the sun and they became blind, and some who saw only a little of it were blinded in one eye. Others, who had their eyes shut at the moment, were luckier, so they lost nothing of their eyesight.

Thus it came about that blindness was brought into the world, because Wulbari wanted *something*.

(KRACHI)

Some women were busy planting in a country where water was scarce, so that they had brought their sangas, containing that precious fluid, with them. As they were working, a poor old woman, carrying a child on her back, passed by them, hesitated for a moment, and then walked back to them and asked them to give her child a cup of water.

The women said that they had carried the water from afar, and needed it for themselves, as there was no water just there.

The poor old woman passed on, but told them that they would one day regret their want of charity.

Noticing a man up a palm tree, she asked him if he would mind giving her baby a little palm wine, as the poor little thing, she was afraid, was dying of thirst.

"Why not, mother?" he replied, and straightway came down the tree and placed a calabash at her feet.

"But I have no cup," she said.

"Nay, mother, let me break this spare calabash, and give the child a drink."

She thanked him, and went her way, saying: "Be here, my son, at this time tomorrow."

He wondered what the old woman meant; but such was the impression her words had made upon him that he could not sleep at all that night and felt himself obliged, when the morrow came, to proceed to the place.

"Surely this cannot be the place," he said, as he came near to the palm tree where he had met the old woman. "There was no water where the women were at work yesterday, yet surely that is a great lake."

"Wonder not, my son," said the old woman, as she approached him, "for thus have I punished the women for their want of charity. See my son, this lake is full of fish, and you

and all men may fish here daily, and the abundance of fish
shall never grow less. But no woman shall eat the fish there-
of, for as sure as she eats the fish of this lake, so surely shall
she immediately die. Let the lake and its fish be tabu for
women. For I, Nzambi, have so ordered it." Nzambi then
loaded the young man with many gifts, and told him to depart in peace. The name of this lake is Bosi, and it is situated
a few miles inland behind a place called Futilla.

An old lady, after some days' journey, arrived at a town
called Sonanzenzi footsore and weary and covered with
terrible sores. The old lady asked for hospitality from each
householder as she passed through the town; but they all
refused to receive her, saying that she was unclean, until
she arrived at the very last house. Here the kind folk took
her in, nursed and cured her. When she was quite well and
about to depart, she told her kind friends to pack up their
traps and leave the town with her, as assuredly it was ac-
cursed and would be destroyed by Nzambi. And the night
after they had left it, heavy rains fell and the town was sub-
merged, and all the people drowned, for Sonanzenzi was in
a deep valley, quite surrounded by hills. And now as the
people of Tandu pass on their way to Mbuela and they look
down into the deep waters, they notice the sticks of the
houses at the bottom; and they remember that Nzambi
would have them take care of the sick, and not turn them
cruelly away from their doors.

Nzambi was in her town resting, when she was called to
settle a palaver in a town nearby. She and her followers
went, and after the usual preliminary formalities, commenced to talk the palaver. While they were yet talking,
Nzambi heard the drum beaten in her own town, and wondered greatly what the matter could be. She sent the pig to
see what the disturbance was, and to find out who had dared
to beat her Ndungu zilo, or great drum, during her absence.
But the pig returned, and said: "Princess, I did not see anyone in the town, and all was quiet and in order."

"Strange!" said Nzambi. "I distinctly heard the beating of my drum."

They continued the palaver until Nzambi again heard her drum beating.

"Go immediately, O antelope!" said Nzambi, "and find out who is beating my drum."

The antelope went and returned; but he had not seen or heard anything. They continued the palaver, and just as they drew it to a close, Nzambi heard the drum a third time.

"Let us all go and find out," said Nzambi, "who has thus dared to disturb us."

They went, but saw nothing.

"Hide yourselves in the grass round about the town, and watch for the intruder!"

Then they saw the crab coming out of the water. Breathlessly they all watched him. They saw the crab creep stealthily up to the drum and beat it. Then they heard him sing:

"Oh, Nzambi has gone up to the top of the mountain, and left me here all alone."

Then the people rushed out of the grass and caught the terrified crab and dragged him to Nzambi.

And Nzambi rebuked him saying: "Thou hast acted as one without a head, henceforth thou shall be headless, and shalt be eaten by all men."

According to another crab story, Nzambi had already given the crab a body and legs, and promised on the next day to give him a head. Then the crab sent invitations to all around to come and see Nzambi place his head on. And when they had all arrived, he was so proud that he could hardly walk straight. But Nzambi rebuked him for his great pride, and told those who were present that as a warning to them not to be self-glorious she would not give the crab a head. And thus it happens that when the crab wants to see where he is going, he has to lift his eyes out of his body.

Nzambi Mpungu made the world and all the people in it. But Nzambi had made no drum for her people, so that they could not dance. Nchonzo nkila, a little bird with a long tail, fashioned like a native drum that seems always to be beating the earth, lived in a small village near to the town that Nzambi had chosen as her place of residence. This Nchonzo nkila set to work, and was the first to make a drum. He then called his followers together, and they beat the drum and danced. And when Nzambi heard the beating of the drum she wanted it, so that her people might also dance. "What!" she said to her people. "I, a great princess, cannot dance because I have no drum, while that little wagtail dances to the beat of the drum he has made. Go now, O antelope, and tell the little wagtail that his Great Mother wants his drum."

And the antelope went to wagtail's town and asked him to send Nzambi his drum.

"Nay," answered the wagtail, "I cannot give Nzambi my drum, because I want it myself."

"But," said the antelope, "the great mother gave you your life; surely you owe her something in return."

"Yes, truly," answered wagtail, "but I cannot give her my drum."

"Lend it to me then," said the antelope, "that I may play it for you."

"Certainly," said the wagtail.

But after beating the drum for a short time, the antelope ran away with it. Then wagtail waxed exceeding wrath, and sent his people after him. And they caught the antelope and killed him, and gave him to their women to cook for them.

After a while Kivunga the hyena was sent by Nzambi to see why the antelope was so long away. And he asked Nchonzo nkila what had become of the antelope. And Nchonzo nkila told him.

"Give me then some of his blood, that I may take it to our mother, and show her."

Nchonzo nkila gave him some, and Kivunga took it to Nzambi, and told her all that had occurred. And Nzambi was grieved at not being able to secure the drum. Then she addressed the Mpacasa, or wild ox, and besought him to get her the drum. But Mpacasa tried the same game as the ante-

lope, and met with the same fate. Kivunga came again, and
was told by the wagtail that Mpacasa had been killed by his
people for trying to steal the drum. Kivunga returned to
Nzambi, and told her how Mpacasa had tried to run away
with the drum, and had been killed. Nzambi grieved sorely,
and would not be comforted, and cried out to her people,
praying them to get her Nchonzo nkila's drum.

Then Mfiti (the ant) stood out from among the people
and volunteered, saying: "Weep not, O Nzambi, I will get
the drum for you."

"But you are so small a creature, how will you secure the
drum?"

"From the fact of my being so small I shall escape detec-
tion."

And so the ant went out to wagtail's town, and waited
there until all were asleep. Then he entered the house where
the drum was kept, and carried it away unperceived, and
brought it to Nzambi. And Nzambi rewarded the ant and
then beat the drum and made all her people dance.

Then Nchonzo nkila heard the noise, and said: "Listen!
they are dancing in Nzambi's town. Surely they have stolen
my drum."

And when they looked in the house for the drum, they
found it not. So Nchonzo nkila became very angry and
called all the birds together; and they all came to hear what
he had to say, save the Mbemba, or pigeon. Then they discussed the matter and decided upon sending Nzambi a messenger, asking her to appoint a place of meeting where the
palaver between them might be talked. And Nzambi promised to be in Neamlau's town the next day to talk the palaver
over before that prince.

Then Nchonzo nkila and his followers went to Neamlau's
town and awaited Nzambi. Two days they waited, and on
the third Nzambi and her people arrived.

Then Nchonzo nkila said: "O prince! I made a drum and
Nzambi has taken it from me. It is for her to tell you why;
let her speak."

Nzambi arose and said: "O prince! My people wished to

dance, but we had no drum and therefore they could not.
Now I heard the sound of a drum being beaten in the village
over which I had set Nchonzo nkila to rule. I therefore first
sent the antelope as my ambassador to Nchonzo nkila, to
ask him for the drum; but his people killed the antelope.
I then sent Mpacasa for the drum; but they killed him also,
as Kivunga will bear witness. Finally I sent the ant; and he
brought me the drum, and my people danced and we were
happy. Surely, O prince, I who brought forth all the living
in this world have a right to this drum if I want it."

Then Kivunga told them all he knew of the palaver.

Neamlau and his old men, having heard all that was said,
retired to drink water. When he returned, Neamlau said:
"You have asked me to decide this question, and my judgment is this: It is true that Nzambi is the mother of us all,
but Nchonzo nkila certainly made the drum. Now when
Nzambi made us, she left us free to live as we choose, and
she did not give us drums at our birth. The drums we make
ourselves; and they are therefore ours, just as we may be
said to be Nzambi's. If she had made drums and sent them
into the world with us, then the drums would be hers. But
she did not. Therefore she was wrong to take the drum
from Nchonzo nkila."

Nzambi paid Nchonzo nkila for the drum, and was fined
for the mistake.

Then both Nzambi and Nchonzo nkila gave presents to
Neamlau and went their way.

(BAKONGO)

11   THE FIRST HUMAN FAMILY:
THE PEOPLE WHO DESCEND FROM THE SKY

Tradition tells that in very ancient times, a man and a
woman came down from the sky to the district of Somè in

Adja. This was the first family on earth. The man and woman brought with them a long wand and a calabash. They wore long shirts, much longer than those worn today.

It rained the day they came from the sky, and it rained for seventeen days more. All this time they did not speak. They only called out "Segbo, Segbo, Segbo!" This was the name of the one who had sent them on earth. After seven days, another man and woman came down from the sky. This man and woman wore the beads we know even today as *lisaje,* "Lisa's beads."

Then they began to teach the worship of Mawu and Lisa. We are told that the first temple they raised for Mawu-Lisa still exists in Adja. On the day they were to offer sacrifices to Mawu and to Lisa it rained once more. Many people came down from the sky with the rain to help them carry out the ceremony. But as soon as the ceremony was over, these went back to the sky.

This ceremony of giving offerings to Mawu and Lisa was carried out three or four times. Then the man and the woman who had brought the beads returned to the sky. They left their beads behind them. They also left a daughter on earth. Four shrines had by then been established, one for Mawu, one for Lisa, one for Gu and one for Agè. For Mawu they killed a sheep, for Lisa a white goat and a white chicken. For Gu they gave a white cock, and to Agè a dog was given. We make the same sacrifices today, because that is what these people had done who came from the sky to teach the worship of Mawu to man.

Then the woman gave birth to two children, the first a son and the second a daughter. Each child was born with a small wand in the hand, and the wand grew as the child grew. The children always had their wands with them. They were never lost. Then seven years later, the mother and father of the children returned to the sky. The children carried on the teaching of the worship of the Sky-gods. Since what they taught was good, the worship of these gods spread everywhere in Dahomey.

The first pair who came from the sky was accompanied by

a chameleon. The chameleon went everywhere the man and woman went, just as a dog goes with his master. The chameleon was sent by Lisa to protect them. Lisa knew that when they taught about Mawu and Lisa, there would be people who would refuse to receive their teaching, and who would conspire against them. But the chameleon, who was always in front, reflected on his smooth skin everything that happened behind their backs as they went about.

Any move by an enemy to strike them from behind was mirrored on the body of the chameleon. For the chameleon's body is like Lisa's, smooth as a mirror. This is why the chameleon is the animal sacred to the god Lisa.

(DAHOMEY)

12 MAWU'S WAYS ARE JUST

In ancient times Mawu sent a messenger to earth daily to travel from sunrise to sunset [from east to west]. He did this all the time; every year.

One day, while on his errands, he reached Adjala, and in Adjala it was already night. He could go no more and so he went into a house. There was a man who was also on the road. As night fell, he, too, went into this house.

They gave them a place in the same house, the two strangers together.

Mawu's messenger asked the other, "Where are you going?"

He said, "I am going where the sun sets."

Good. Mawu's messenger said, "It is life that gives a companion. I myself am going to the same place."

The following morning, at first cockcrow, in a house beside theirs where a sick child slept, the parents were crying.

Mawu's messenger went to ask them, "Why haven't you slept all night?"

They said, "We have a child here who is very sick."

Very well. Now, Mawu's messenger had a sack in which he carried some powder. He gave some of that powder to a man to give to the sick child.

And he went back quickly to the man who was sleeping in his house, and said, "Wake up! Wake up! We are leaving."

They took but a few steps away from the house, when all at once the people in the house began to shout, "Where is the stranger? Where is the stranger?

The child was dead.

So they went away. They went till . . . they came to Savalou. There in Savalou they spent the night. They took shelter in a house beside the road. At first cockcrow, Mawu's messenger took some flint and made a fire. And this fire he put to the straw of the house where he had slept. He said, now, to the other man, "Wake up, wake up! We must be going."

After they left, the house took fire. The people asked, "Where are the strangers? Where are the strangers?" But they were gone.

They ran away and continued their journey. As Mawu's messenger did that, his companion, who was a human being, was astonished. He did not know that the other was a *vodun*. So they reached Badahwedji where the sun sets. That is, they were almost there.

Now, there was a river that separated Badahwedji from where the two travelers were. In order to cross the river, one must put down a raft and pass on it. There was an old man from Badahwedji who was in the habit of coming to the riverbank for leaves. He gathered them and went back. Now he was crossing the river for the second time. So Mawu's messenger followed the old man. The old man went ahead. He went slowly, cautiously. Mawu's messenger came behind him and pushed him, so that he fell into the water.

When he did this, the man who came with Mawu's messenger ran away. Mawu's messenger saw him run and he called him back. "Come, come here," he said. He said, "That's not where you are going. You are going to this place. Here it is."

The other said, "What I saw on the road to here is too much. I am running away from it."

Mawu's messenger said: "Now, I'm not a man. I know you are astonished at all I did. But I'm not a human being. In the house where I killed the child, if that child had not died, its mother and father would have died when it took its first step. It is Mawu who sent me to destroy that child." He said: "In that house this mother and father have borne many children, and this one child could not be allowed to spoil their lives."

He said: "The family where I burned the house has rich relatives among them. But they buried all their money and their children are poor. So I burned the house, so that when they break the walls to make them anew and begin to dig the foundation, they will find the money."

He said: "I had the man fall into the river, because the king of Badahwedji is dead. To replace this king, a young man should be named. If that old man were alive, a young man could not be named. That is why Mawu sent me to throw him into the water. The people still think the old man will be their king. But if that man became king, there would be no more goats, no more cattle, no more children in that kingdom. Sagbata would come to their kingdom and kill them, because Mawu had ordained that one could not be king. With a young king, they will have goats, pigs, and children also."

Then he said: "I, I look into the hearts of men (literally, 'into men's stomachs'), and Mawu sends me to look at things. You must not be astonished. Year after year, if I do not change into a man, I change into headache and kill men. I change into serpents and burn houses. And when, in the course of life, you see such things, you will know that it is Mawu who sends them."

(DAHOMEY)

Unkulunkulu, the old, old one, is no longer known. He was the first man. He broke off in the beginning; he broke off the nations from the reed.

He sent the chameleon with the message LET NOT MEN DIE. And soon after the lizard with the message LET MEN DIE.

The old men say that Unkulunkulu is the first Umvelin-qangi (outcomer); for they say he came out first. They say he is the reed from which all men broke off. The old men say Unkulunkulu is (is not a fable); he made the ancients of long ago.

Before the arrival of the missionaries, if we asked, "By what were these stones made?" it was said: "They were made by Umvelinqangi. It is said that we men came out of a bed of reeds." When we asked, "By what was the sun made?" they said: "By Umvelinqangi." For we used to ask when we were little, thinking that the old men knew all things which are on the earth; yet forsooth they do not know; but we do not contradict them, for neither do we know.

It is said all men sprang from Unkulunkulu, who sprang up first. The earth was in existence before Unkulunkulu. He had his origin from the earth in a bed of reeds.

All things as well as Unkulunkulu sprang from a bed of reeds—everything, both animals and corn, everything came into being with Unkulunkulu.

He looked at the sun when it was finished (worked into form as a potter works clay) and said: "There is a torch which will give you light, that you may see." He looked down on the cattle and said: "These are cattle. Be ye broken off, and see the cattle and let them be your food; eat their flesh and their milk." He looked on wild animals and said: "That is such an animal. That is an elephant. That is a buf-falo." He looked on the fire and said: "Kindle it, and cook, and warm yourself; and eat meat when it has been dressed by the fire." He looked on all things and said: "So and so is the name of everything."

Unkulunkulu said: "Let there be marriage among men, that there may be those who can intermarry, that children may be born and men increase on earth." He said, "Let there be black chiefs; and the chief be known by his people, and it be said, 'That is the chief: assemble all of you and go to your chief.'"

It is not from the white men that we first heard of the king who is above. In summertime, when it thunders, we say: "The king is playing." (He is enjoying himself as the chiefs do on great festivals.) And if there is one who is afraid, the elder people say to him: "It is nothing but fear. What thing belonging to the king have you eaten?"

But he is not like that Unkulunkulu who, we say, made all things. But the former we call a king, for we say, he is above. Unkulunkulu is beneath; the things which are beneath were made by him.

We do not say that the king who is above springs from Unkulunkulu. We say that Unkulunkulu was first; we do not know what belongs to that king. We know much of what belongs to Unkulunkulu, for he was on this earth, and we can give an account of matters concerning him. The sun and the moon we referred to Unkulunkulu. But we did not say that the heaven belonged to this king, although he dwells there. For we said all was made by Unkulunkulu.

(AMAZULU)

14 THE BEGINNER OF THE EARTH

We were told by the elders that when God came to prepare the world he found three things in the land, a Dorobo, an elephant, and a serpent all of whom lived together. After a time the Dorobo obtained a cow.

One day the Dorobo said to the serpent: "Friend, why does my body always itch so that I have to scratch whenever you blow on me?"

The serpent replied: "O my father, I do not blow my bad breath on you on purpose."

At this the Dorobo remained silent, but that same evening he picked up his club and struck the serpent on the head, and killed it.

On the morrow the elephant asked the Dorobo where the third one was. The Dorobo replied that he did not know, but the elephant knew he had killed it and refused to admit his guilt.

During the night it rained heavily, and the Dorobo was able to take his cow to graze and he watered it at the puddles of rain. They remained there many days, and at length the elephant gave birth to a young one.

After a time all the puddles became dry except in one place. Now the elephant used to go and eat grass, and when she had had enough to eat, she would return to drink at the puddle, lying down in the water and stirring it up so that when the Dorobo drove his cow to water he found it muddy.

One day the Dorobo made an arrow, and shot the elephant, and killed it. The young elephant then went to another country. "The Dorobo is bad," it said. "I will not stop with him any longer. He first of all killed the snake and now he has killed Mother. I will go away and not live with him again."

On its arrival in another country the young elephant met a Masai who asked where it came from. The young elephant replied: "I come from the Dorobo's kraal. He is living in yonder forest and he has killed the serpent and my mother."

The Masai inquired: "Is it true that there is a Dorobo there who has killed your mother and the serpent?" When he had received a reply in the affirmative, he said: "Let us go there. I should like to see him."

They went and found the Dorobo's hut, which God had

turned upside down, and the door of which looked toward the sky. God then called the Dorobo and said to him: "I wish you to come tomorrow morning for I have something to tell you."

The Masai heard this, and in the morning he went in and said to God: "I have come." God told him to take an ax and to build a big kraal in three days. When it was ready, he was to go and search for a thin calf, which he would find in the forest. This he was to bring to the kraal and slaughter. The meat was to be tied up in the hide and not eaten. The hide was to be fastened outside the door of the hut, firewood was to be fetched, and a big fire lit, into which the meat was to be thrown. He was then to hide himself in the hut, and not to be startled when he heard a great noise outside resembling thunder.

The Masai did as he was bid. He searched for a calf, which he found, and when he had slaughtered it he tied up the flesh in the hide. He fetched some firewood, lit a big fire, threw in the meat, and entered the hut leaving the fire burning outside.

God then caused a strip of hide to descend from heaven, which was suspended over the calfskin. Cattle at once commenced to descend one by one by the strip of hide until the whole of the kraal was filled, when the animals began to press against one another, and to break down the hut where the Masai was.

The Masai was startled and uttered an exclamation of astonishment. He then went outside the hut and found that the strip of hide had been cut, after which no more cattle came down from heaven.

God asked him whether the cattle that were there were sufficient. "For," he said, "you will receive no more owing to your being surprised."

The Masai then went away and attended to the animals which had been given him. The Dorobo lost the cattle and has had to shoot game for his food ever since.

Nowadays, if cattle are seen in the possession of Bantu tribes, it is presumed that they have been stolen or found, and the Masai say: "These are our animals, let us go and take them, for God in olden days gave us all the cattle upon the earth."

(MASAI)

15 MANTIS CREATES AN ELAND

Kwammang-a had taken off a part of his shoe and thrown it away, and Mantis picked it up and went and soaked it in the water, at a place where some reeds grew. Mantis went away, then he came back again, went up to the water, and looked. He turned away again, for he saw that the Eland was still small.

Again he came, and found the Eland's spoor where it had come out of the water to graze. Then Mantis went up to the water, while Eland went seeking the grass which it eats. He waited, sitting by the water; he was upon the water's bank, opposite Eland's assegai (spear), and soon Eland came to drink there. He saw Eland as it came to drink. He said, "Kwammang-a's shoe's piece!" And young Eland walked up as when its father trilled to him. Mantis called, making his tongue quiver, as Bushmen still do in springbok hunting.

Then Mantis went to find some honey; he went to cut some honey. He came back and put the bag of honey down near the water and returned home. Then, before the sun was up, he came back to pick up the bag. He approached while Eland was in the reeds. He called to it: "Kwammang-a's shoe's piece!" And Eland got up from the reeds and walked up to its father. Mantis put down the bag of honey. He took out the honeycomb and laid it down. He kept picking up pieces of it, he kept rubbing it on Eland's ribs while he splashed them, making them very nice.

Then he went away and took the bag to seek for more honey to cut. When he came back he again laid the bag of honey down near the water and returned home. Once more he returned and picked up the bag, once more he went to the place and called Eland out of the water, saying, "Kwam-mang-a's shoe's piece."

The Eland stood shyly in the water and walked up to its father, for he had grown. His father wept, fondling him. He again rubbed Eland's ribs making them nice with honey-comb. Then he went away, while Eland walked back into the water, went to bask in the water.

Mantis did not come back for a time, and for three nights Eland grew, becoming like an ox. Then Mantis went out early. The sun rose as he walked up to the water. He called Eland, and Eland rose up and came forth, and the ground resounded as it came. And Mantis sang for joy about Eland. He sang:

> Ah, a person is here!
> Kwammang-a's shoe's piece!
> My eldest son's shoe's piece!
> Kwammang-a's shoe's piece!
> My eldest son's shoe's piece!

Meanwhile he rubbed Eland down nicely, rubbed down the male Eland. Then he went away and returned home.

The next morning he called young Ich-neu-mon, saying that young Ich-neu-mon should go with him and that they would be only two. Thus he deceived young Ich-neu-mon. And they went out and reached the water while Eland was grazing. They sat down in the shade of the bush by which Eland's assegai stood, where he kept coming to take it.

Mantis spoke: "Young Ich-neu-mon, go to sleep!" for he meant to deceive him. So young Ich-neu-mon lay down, as Eland came to drink, because the sun stood at noon and was getting hot. Meanwhile young Ich-neu-mon had covered up his head, because Mantis wished him to do so. But young Ich-neu-mon did not sleep; he lay awake.

Then Eland walked away, and young Ich-neu-mon said: "Hi, stand! Hi, stand, stand!"

And Mantis said: "What does my brother think he has seen yonder?"

And young Ich-neu-mon said: "A person is yonder, standing yonder."

And Mantis said, "You think it is magic; but it is a very small thing, it is a bit of father's shoe, which he dropped. Magic it is not." And they went home.

Then young Ich-neu-mon told his father Kwammang-a about it. And Kwammang-a said that young Ich-neu-mon must guide him and show him Eland; he would see whether Eland was so very handsome after Mantis had rubbed it down. Then young Ich-neu-mon guided his father, while Mantis was at another place, for he meant to go to the water later on.

Meanwhile they went up to Eland at the water, and Kwammang-a looked at it and he knocked it down while Mantis was not there. He knocked Eland down and was cutting it up before Mantis came. So when Mantis arrived, he saw Kwammang-a and the others standing there cutting up his Eland.

And Mantis said: "Why could you not first let me come?" And he wept for Eland; he scolded Kwammang-a's people, because Kwammang-a had not let him come first, and let him be the one to tell them to kill Eland.

And Kwammang-a said: "Tell Grandfather to leave off. He must come and gather wood for us, that we may eat, for this is meat."

When Mantis came, he said he had wanted Kwammang-a to let him come while Eland was still alive, and not to have killed it when he was not looking. They might have waited to kill Eland until he was looking on. Then he himself would have told them to kill it. Then his heart would have been comfortable. Now his heart did not feel satisfied about Eland whom he alone had made.

Then, as he went to gather wood, he caught sight of a gall there; it was Eland's gall. And he said to himself that he would pierce the gall open and that he would jump upon it. And the gall spoke: "I will burst, covering you over."

Just then young Ich-neu-mon said: "What are you looking at there, that you do not gather wood at that place?"

So Mantis left the gall, brought wood, and put it down. Then he again looked for wood at the place where the gall had been. He went up to the gall and again said he would pierce the gall open and that he would jump upon it. The gall again said it would burst, covering him all over. He said he would jump, and that the gall must burst when he trod on it and as he jumped.

Young Ich-neu-mon scolded him again and asked: "What can be yonder, that you keep going to that place? You do not gather wood, you just keep going to that bush. You are going to play tricks and not gather wood."

And Kwammang-a said: "You must make haste and let us go when you have called Grandfather, for the gall lies there; Grandfather has seen it. So you must make haste. When Grandfather behaves like this about anything, he is not acting honorably; he is playing tricks with this thing. So you must manage that we start, when you have called Grandfather, that we may leave the place where the gall is."

Then they packed the meat into the net, while Mantis untied his shoe and put the shoe into the bag. It was an arrow-bag which he had slung on next to the quiver. And so they carried the things and went along homeward. On the way Mantis said: "This shoestring has broken."

Then young Ich-neu-mon said: "You must have put the shoe away."

And Mantis said: "No, no, the shoe must really be lying there where we cut up Eland. So I must turn back and go fetch the shoe."

But young Ich-neu-mon said: "You must have put the shoe in the bag. You must feel inside the bag, feel in the middle of it and see whether you cannot find the shoe."

So Mantis felt in the bag, but he kept feeling above the shoe. He said: "See, the shoe is really not in it. I must go back and pick it up, for the shoe is truly yonder."

But young Ich-neu-mon replied: "We must go home, we really must go home."

Then Mantis said, "You can go home, but I must really go and get the shoe."

Thereupon Kwammang-a said: "Let Grandfather be! Let him turn back and do as he wants."

And young Ich-neu-mon said, "O you person! I do wish Mantis would for once listen when we speak."

Mantis only said: "You always go on like this! I must really go and get the shoe."

Then Mantis turned back. He ran up to the gall, reached it, pierced it, and made the gall burst. And the gall broke, covering his head; his eyes became big and he could not see. He groped about, feeling his way. And he went groping along, groping along, groping, until he found an ostrich feather. This he picked up, sucked it, and brushed off the gall from his eyes with it.

Then he threw the feather up and spoke: "You must now lie up in the sky; you must henceforth be the moon. You shall shine at night. By your shining you shall lighten the darkness for men, until the sun rises to light up all things for men. It is the sun under whom men hunt. You must just glow for men, while the sun shines for men. Under him men walk about; they go hunting; they return home. But you are the moon; you give light for men, then you fall away, but you return to life after you have fallen away. Thus you give light to all people."

That is what the moon does: the moon falls away and returns to life, and he lights up all the flat places of the world.

(BUSHMEN)

16 THE DOGON MYTH OF CREATION

According to the Dogon the human soul is double. When a child is born the water spirit draws twin shadows on the ground. The one destined to support the feminine side of

*the individual is laid out first on the ground where parturi-
tion takes place. The other, which will receive the masculine
side, is then sketched over the first. The newborn child is
laid face down with his four limbs touching the ground and
thereby takes possession of his souls. If the child is a boy
the female principle will dwell on the foreskin; in case of a
girl, the male principle will reside in the clitoris. These two
principles are present in the individual during all of childhood. Neither wins over the other. The purpose of the rites
of circumcision and excision is to force the individual to
lean definitely toward the one of the two principles for which
his body is the better suited. The sexual life of the individual
depends on this fixation. The uncircumcised boy like the
unexcised girl is both male and female. If they were to remain in the state of their first childhood, neither would feel
an inclination to procreate. The boy is circumcised in order
to reduce his femininity and place him definitely on the
male side. A girl is excised to make her a woman. The Dogon
myth of the creation of the world recounts the reason for
this situation and gives the prototype of the rites of circumcision and excision.*

In the beginning everything was generated by twin births:
the ideal unity of being was formed by a couple. But in fact
this rule has not worked ever since the first creative attempt
of the God Amma. For Amma, the sole and supreme male
god was forced to create a mate with whom he could unite
himself to produce further offspring. Amma brought an
earth woman to arise from a lump of clay. Her clitoris was
made of a termite hill. When Amma tried to unite with her,
the termite hill barred his way by asserting her masculinity.
Amma defeated the rebellious termite hill; he cut off the
obstacle and united himself with the excised earth.

This occurrence influenced the product of the union so
that it was born single, in the form of a jackal. Later the
god had further relations with the earth that were not disturbed and resulted in the birth of a spirit couple, *Nommo*,
whose body was made of the divine seed, that is to say, water.

These two creatures would little by little replace the god in insuring the progress of the universe.

It was then that the first product, the jackal, whose position was unusual because it could not procreate, committed incest with its mother, the earth, an event that was to upset the course of earthly things. The god Amma, having turned away from his wife, kneaded two clay balls out of which sprang the first human couple, who in turn procreated, giving birth to twins. But after the coming of these two beings the production of twins became a very rare exception. And it is since the birth of this first generation that the spirit couple *Nommo,* becoming the mentor of the world, minimized the inconvenience of this new situation by creating a double soul for each being, granted through contact with the ground.

However, the first human birth brought about an event of considerable significance. The woman kneaded by Amma had intercourse with the man without having been excised. Becoming pregnant, she gave birth to twins; at that time her pains were directed to her clitoris, which fell off and went away in the shape of a scorpion, whose venom was made of both the water and the blood of parturition.

Previously her mate had been circumcised and his foreskin was transformed into *nay,* a kind of lizard.

(DOGON)

17 WHY THE SUN AND THE MOON LIVE IN THE SKY

Many years ago the sun and the water were great friends, and both lived on the earth together. The sun very often used to visit the water, but the water never returned his visits. At last the sun asked the water why it was that he never came to see him in his house. The water replied that the sun's house was not big enough, and that if he came with his people he would drive the sun out.

The water then said, "If you wish me to visit you, you must build a very large compound; but I warn you that it will have to be a tremendous place, as my people are very numerous and take up a lot of room."

The sun promised to build a very big compound, and soon afterward he returned home to his wife, the moon, who greeted him with a broad smile when he opened the door. The sun told the moon what he had promised the water, and the next day he commenced building a huge compound in which to entertain his friend.

When it was completed, he asked the water to come and visit him the next day.

When the water arrived, he called out to the sun and asked him whether it would be safe for him to enter, and the sun answered, "Yes, come in, my friend."

The water then began to flow in, accompanied by the fish and all the water animals.

Very soon the water was knee-deep, so he asked the sun if it was still safe, and the sun again said, "Yes," so more water came in.

When the water was level with the top of a man's head, the water said to the sun, "Do you want more of my people to come?"

The sun and the moon both answered, "Yes," not knowing any better, so the water flowed in, until the sun and moon had to perch themselves on the top of the roof.

Again the water addressed the sun, but, receiving the same answer, and more of his people rushing in, the water very soon overflowed the top of the roof, and the sun and the moon were forced to go up into the sky, where they have remained ever since.

(EFIK-IBIBIO)

18 THE SUN AND THE CHILDREN

Once some children, at their mother's behest, very gently approached the sun's armpit, as the sun lay sleeping. They were to lift up the sun's armpit.

At the same time, another woman ordered her children to do the same thing. She told them that if they approached ever so gently and drew up the sun's armpit, then the rice of the Bushmen would become dry, and the sun, as it proceeded from place to place across the sky, would cause everything to become bright. For this reason it was that the old woman, their mother, coaxed her children to do as she asked. "But, children," she said, "you must wait for the sun, who is making us so cold, to lie down to sleep. Then approach him gently and, all together, lift him up and throw him into the sky." Thus, indeed, did both of the old women speak.

And so the children approached the sun. The first sat down and looked at him in order to determine whether, as he lay there, he was looking at them. Finally they saw him lying there very quietly, his elbow lifted up so that his armpit shone upon the ground. Before the children prepared to throw him up into the sky they remembered what the old woman, their mother, had said: "O children, going yonder, you must speak to him when you throw him up. You must tell him that he must be the sun altogether, so that he will proceed forward while he feels that he is altogether the sun —the sun who is hot and who, as he passes along the sky, causes the Bushman rice to become dry—the sun who is hot as he stands above in the sky."

Thus had their mother, the old woman, whose head was white, spoken. They had listened and were going to obey her.

When all was in readiness, they took hold of the sun, all of them together, lifted him, raised him, even though he was hot to touch, and threw him up in the sky, addressing him as they threw him up: "O sun, you must altogether stand fast and you must proceed along your way—you must stand fast while you are hot."

Then the children returned to their mother, and one of them went to her and said, "Our companion, who is here, this one, took hold of him. So did I. Then my younger brother and my still younger brother, they all took hold of him. 'Grasp hold of him firmly,' I said, 'and throw him up. Grasp the old man firmly and throw him up.' Thus I spoke to them. Then the children threw him up, the old man, the sun."

Then another one of those who had been present—a youngster indeed—he also spoke to her and said, "Oh, grandmother, we threw him up, the sun, and we told him what you had told us, that he should altogether become the sun, the sun who is hot, for us who are cold. And we addressed him thus: 'O my grandfather, sun's armpit! Remain there at that place. Become the sun who is hot so that the Bushman rice may dry for us, so that you may make the whole earth light, that the earth may become warm in the summer, that you may altogether make heat. For that reason, you must shine everywhere. You must take away the darkness. You must come indeed so that the darkness will go away.'"

And thus it is. The sun comes, the darkness departs; the sun sets, the darkness comes and then at night the moon comes. The moon comes out; it brightens the darkness and the darkness then departs. It has taken the darkness away and now it moves along, continually brightening the darkness. And then the moon sets and the sun, following, comes out. The sun now drives away the darkness, indeed drives away the moon as it stands there. The sun actually pierces the moon with his knife and that is why it decays. Therefore the moon said, "O sun! leave the backbone for the children!" And the sun did so.

Then the moon painfully went away, painfully returned home. He went home to become another, a moon which is whole. He again comes to life although it seemed that he had died. He becomes a new moon and feels as though he had put on a new stomach. He becomes large; he is alive again. Then he goes along at night, feeling that he is the moon once more. Indeed he feels he is a shoe, the shoe that Mantis threw into the sky, and ordered to become the moon.

That is what the sun has done—made all the earth bright. And thus it is that the people walk while the earth is light. Then people can see the bushes, can see other people. They can see the meat which they are eating. They can see the springbok, can hunt it in summer. It is when the sun shines, likewise, that they can hunt the ostrich. And so—because the sun brightens the earth, because he shines upon the path of men—the Bushmen steal up to the gemsbok, steal up to the kudu, travel about in summer, and go visiting one another. Because the sun shines hottest upon the path of men in summer, they always go shooting and hunting then, for they are certain to espy the springbok. It is in the summer that they lie contented in their little homes made of bushes, and they scratch up the earth. All this they do when the springbok comes.

The people of whom we are speaking were the first Bushmen, the men of the early race. It is they who first inhabited this earth and it was their children who worked with the sun, who threw the sun up and made him ascend so that he might warm the earth for them, and that they might be able to sit in the sun.

The sun, they say, was originally a man who lived on earth. In the beginning, he gave forth brightness for a space just around his own dwelling. As his shining was confined to a certain space just at and around his own house, the rest of the country seemed as if the sky were very cloudy—as it looks now, in fact, when the sun is behind thick clouds. This shining came from one of the sun's armpits as he lay with one arm lifted up. When he put down his arm, darkness fell everywhere; when he lifted it up again, it was as if day came. In the day, the sun's light used to be white, but at night it was red like a fire. When the sun was thrown up into the sky it became round and never was a man again.

The same is true of the moon. He, too, was once a man who could talk. But today neither the sun nor the moon talk. They just live in the sky.

(BUSHMEN)

19 THE SON OF THE WIND

The son of the wind was once a man. When he was a man he used to go shooting and to roll a ball but later he became a bird and flew, no longer walking as he used to do when he was a man. When he had changed into a bird, he flew up and dwelt in a mountain hole. The mountain hole was his dwelling, and out of it he would fly every day and, later on, return. In this hole he slept and, awakening in the morning, he would leave in order to seek food. He sought it everywhere and he ate, ate, ate, until he had his fill. Then he would return to his mountain hole to sleep.

But when he was a man he had been quiet and still.

On one occasion when he was rolling his ball, he called out to Na-ka-ti: "Na-ka-ti, there it goes!" And Na-ka-ti exclaimed, "O comrade, truly there it goes!" He called him comrade because he didn't know the other's name. Yet it was truly he who is the wind, who had said, "Na-ka-ti, there it goes!"

Not knowing his name, however, Na-ka-ti went to his mother to question her. "Mother," he said, "do tell me the name of our comrade over there. He calls me by my name but I do not know his and I would like to know it when I am rolling the ball back to him."

"No, I will not at this moment tell you his name. That I will only do and let you utter it after Father has made a strong shelter for our hut. And then, when I tell you his name, the moment I have uttered it, you must at once scamper away and run home, so that you can seek the shelter of the hut."

Again Na-ka-ti went over to play with his companion and to roll the ball. When they had finished, Na-ka-ti went once more to question his mother, and she exclaimed, "He is *erriten-kuan-kuan,* he is *gau-gaubu-ti!*"

The next day Na-ka-ti again went to roll the ball with his companion. He did not, however, utter his playmate's name, for his mother had cautioned him to be silent on that matter, even when he was called by name. She had said, "When the time comes for you to utter his name, you must run home at once."

Now once more Na-ka-ti went to roll the ball with his friend, hoping and hoping that his father would finally finish making the shelter for their hut. At last he saw that his father had sat down, that he had indeed finished. Therefore, when he beheld this, he exclaimed, "There it goes, O *erriten-kuan-kuan!* There it goes, O *gau-gaubu-ti!*" No sooner had he uttered it than he scampered away and ran home. His companion thereupon began to lean over, and then fall down. As he lay there he kicked violently upon the *vlei.* As he kicked, huts blew away, bushes vanished, and the people could not see because of the dust. Thus was the wind blowing.

When the mother of the wind came out of her hut to grab him and set him on his feet again, he struggled with her for he wished to continue to lie down. However his mother took hold of him firmly and set him on his feet.

And so, because of all this, we who are Bushmen are wont to say, "The wind seems to be lying down, for it is blowing fiercely. When the wind stands on its feet then it is quiet and still. Thus it acts. The noise it makes comes from its knee; that is what makes the sound. I had wished that it might blow gently for us, that we might go out, that we might ascend the place yonder, that we might behold the riverbed yonder, standing behind the hill. For we have driven the springbok

from this place. They have gone to yonder dry riverbed
standing behind the hill."

(BUSHMEN)

20 HOW THE LESSER GODS CAME INTO THE WORLD

There once was a certain woman who bore eleven children.
Every day when she got up and cooked food the children
ate it all and the mother did not get any of it. She pondered
long about the matter, and went off to the plantation and
spoke to the silk-cotton tree, saying, "I shall send my eleven
children to come beneath you here to pluck pumpkins; and
when they come, pluck off eleven of your branches and kill
those children of mine."

The silk-cotton tree said, "I have heard, and I shall do it
for you."

The mother then went home and said to her children,
"You must go to the plantation beneath the silk-cotton tree;
there are pumpkins there. Go pick them and come back."

The children set off. They went and reached the silk-
cotton tree. Number Eleven said, "Number One, stand still;
Number Two, stand still; Number Three, stand still; Number Four, stand still; Number Five, stand still; Number Six,
stand still; Number Seven, stand still; Number Eight, stand
still; Number Nine, stand still; Number Ten, stand still; and
I myself, Number Eleven, I have stood still."

Number Eleven then addressed them, saying, "Do you
not know the sole reason why Mother said we must go and
pick pumpkins?"

His brothers answered, "No."

Thereupon he said, "She has told this silk-cotton tree that
when we go there, he must pluck off branches and beat us.
Therefore all of you cut sticks and throw them against this
silk-cotton tree."

They cut the sticks and threw them against the silk-cotton

tree. *Pim! pen! pim! pen!* was the sound they made. The silk-cotton tree supposed that the children had come. He took off eleven of his branches and let them fall to the ground. Little Number Eleven said, "You have seen—had we gone on there, the silk-cotton tree would have killed us."

They picked up the pumpkins and took them to their mother. She cooked them. And at once the children had eaten all! Their mother said, "Ah! As for this matter, I cannot bear it! I shall take these children and give them to the sky god."

The next morning, when things became visible, she went and told the sky god all about it, saying, "The children to whom I have given birth eat so fast and so much that when I wish to eat, I can't get anything. Hunger is killing me. Therefore, I implore you, let the children be brought and killed, so that I may get something to eat."

The sky god said, "Is that really the case?"

The woman said, "I am speaking with a head, the inside of which is white."

So the sky god picked out messengers, and they went and dug a large pit in which they placed broken bottles. The sky god himself went and fetched a snake and a leopard, put them in the pit, and covered it over. And now the messenger went to call the children.

No sooner did they reach the place where the pit lay than Number Eleven said, "Number One, stand still; Number Two, stand still; Number Three, stand still; Number Four, stand still; Number Five, stand still; Number Six, stand still; Number Seven, stand still; Number Eight, stand still; Number Nine, stand still; Number Ten, stand still; and I myself, little Number Eleven, I have stood still. You must pass here, but you must not pass there."

His brothers said, "Why, when a wide path lies there, must we pass through the bush?"

Now, as they were going along, they all carried clubs. Number Eleven said, "Throw one of these clubs upon this path." They threw a club upon the path, and it fell through into the pit. *Yiridi* was the sound of its fall. Number Eleven said, "There you are! You see! Had we passed there, we should all of us have died."

So they took a bypath and went off to meet the sky god. The sky god had caused holes to be dug, covered over, and stools placed upon them, so that when the children came to sit on them, they would fall into the holes. Soon the children arrived before the face of the sky god. He spoke to them: "Stools are set there. You may go and be seated upon them."

Then Number Eleven said, "Who are we that we should be able to sit upon such very beautiful stools? So, sire, we are going to sit aside here."

Thereupon the sky god gazed at the children and he said to himself, "I shall send these children to Death's village."

The next morning, when things became visible, he called the children and said, "You must go to Death who lives yonder and receive from her a golden pipe, a golden chewing-stick, a golden snuffbox, a golden whetstone, and a golden flyswitch."

Number Eleven said, "You are our master, wherever you will send us, we shall go."

The sky god said, "Be off!"

So the children set out for Death's village. When they arrived there, Death said, "Why, when no one must ever come here, have you come here?"

They replied, "We were roaming about and came here quite by chance."

Death said, "Oh, all right then."

Now Death had ten children. With herself added, they made eleven. When things began to disappear—that is, when it became dark—Death divided up the children one by one and gave one to each of her children, while she herself and Number Eleven went to rest. When it was dark, Death then lit up her teeth until they shone red so that she might seize Number Eleven with them.

Number Eleven said, "Death, I am not yet asleep."

Death said, "When will you be asleep?"

Number Eleven said, "If you were to give me a golden pipe to smoke for a while, then I might fall asleep."

And Death fetched it for him.

A little while later, Death again lit up her teeth in order to go and seize Number Eleven with them.

Number Eleven said, "Death, I am not yet asleep."

Death said, "When will you be asleep?"

Number Eleven said, "If you were to bring me a golden snuffbox, I might go to sleep."

And Death brought it to him.

Again, soon afterward, Death was going to seize Number Eleven.

Number Eleven said, "I am not yet asleep."

Death said, "When will you be asleep?"

Number Eleven said, "If you were to go and fetch a golden chewing-stick for me so that I might chew it for a while, then I might fall asleep."

Death fetched it for him. A short time passed, and Death was about to seize him.

Number Eleven said, "Grandmother, I am not yet asleep."

And Death said, "Then when will you be asleep?"

Number Eleven said, "Grandmother, if you were to go and bring me a golden whetstone, then I might sleep."

And Death went and brought it. Again, soon afterward, Death rose up once more .

Number Eleven said, "Oh, Grandmother, I said I was not yet asleep."

Death said, "And what will be the day when you will be asleep?"

Number Eleven said, "If you were to go and take a calabash full of holes and go and splash water in it and boil some food for me to eat, then I might sleep."

Death lifted up a strainer and went off to the stream. When she splashed the water in it, the holes in the strainer let it pass through. Now Number Eleven said to his brothers, "Rise up and flee away." Then they rose up and fled, and Number Eleven went and cut plantain stems and placed them where his brothers had lain and took cloths and covered them over.

Now Death was at the stream splashing water. And Male

Death called to Female Death, saying, "Ho there, Death!"
She replied, *"Adwo."*

He said, "What are you doing?"

She replied, "Alas, is it not some small child whom I have
got! When I am about to catch him, he says, 'I am not yet
asleep.' He has taken all my things, and now he says I must
take a strainer and splash water."

Male Death said, "Ah, are you a small child? If you pluck
leaves and line the inside of the strainer and then splash
water, would it not be all right?"

Female Death said, "Oh, how true!"

She plucked leaves, placed them inside, and splashed the
water and went off. Number Eleven said, "Death, you have
come already? Boil the food." Death cooked the food; she
lit up her teeth in order to kill Number Eleven's brothers
and cook them for food. When she went, she did not exam-
ine them carefully, and she herself killed all her own ten
children.

The next day, very, very early, when things became visible, Death rose up and sat there by the fire. Number Eleven
said, "Grandmother, a tsetse fly is sitting on your breast."

Death said, "Fetch the flyswitch which is lying there and
kill it for me."

Number Eleven said, "Good gracious me! A person of
your consequence—when a tsetse fly settles on you and a
golden flyswitch lies there—you would use this old thing!
Let me fetch the golden flyswitch and come and kill it."

Death said, "Go and fetch it from the room."

Number Eleven went and brought it. He purposely drove
the fly away; he didn't kill it. Number Eleven said, "Oh,
today, where this tsetse fly will rest, there I shall rest with
him."

Then Number Eleven went to the room and took his bag
in which lay the golden pipe and all the things. He said,
"Grandmother Death, nothing will suffice save that I get the
tsetse fly, put it in this bag, and bring it to you."

Number Eleven set off—*yiridi! yiridi! yiridi!* He reached
the end of the town and said, "Ho, there, Grandmother

Death! Pardon my saying so, but if you were not a perfect fool, could I have relieved you of all your things, could my brothers with whom I came have found a way of escape, and could I have made you also kill all your ten children? As for me, I am going off."

Death said, "You, a child like this! Wherever you rest, there I shall rest!"

Number Eleven leaped off—*yiridi! yiridi! yiridi!* and Death, too, went to chase him.

As Number Eleven was going, he overtook his brothers who were sitting on the path. They were making a bird-trap. Number Eleven said, "Have you not gone yet? Death is coming, so let us find some way to escape."

Now Death came upon them. Number Eleven took medicine and poured it on his brothers, and they went on top of a silk-cotton tree. And Death stood at the foot of the silk-cotton tree. She said, "Just now I saw those children, and where have they gone?"

Number Eleven was sitting above. He said to his brothers, "I am going to make water upon her."

His brothers said, *"E!* she is seeking us to catch us, and we have fled and come and sit here and yet you say, 'I am going to make water on her.'"

Number Eleven would not listen, and he made water over Death.

Death said, "Ah, there you are! Today you have seen trouble." Death said, "You, child, who are sitting up there, *Kyere-he-ne, Kyere-he-ne!*" Thereupon one of the children fell down. *"Kyere-he-ne!"* A second one fell down. Soon there remained only Number Eleven.

Death said, "Child, *Kyere-he-ne!*" and Number Eleven leaped and descended on the ground, *kirim!* And Death then went on top of the silk-cotton tree.

Number Eleven said, "You, great big woman, you too *Kyere-he-ne!*"

And Death, also, came down, *tum!* She was dead.

Number Eleven went and plucked medicine, rolled it between his palms, and sprinkled it on his brothers, and they rose up. Number Eleven was going to throw the medicine away, when some of it dropped on Death, and Death awoke. She said, "You have killed me, and you have also awakened me. Today you and I will have a chase."

Then they all started to run off at once, *kiri! kiri! kiri!* Now Death was chasing them. As they were going, there lay before them a big river in flood. When Number Eleven and his brothers reached it, the brothers knew how to swim and they swam across. Number Eleven alone did not know how to swim. The children stood on the other side; they cried and cried and cried; their mouths became swollen up. As for Number Eleven, he turned into a stone.

Death reached the river. She said, "Oh, these children! You stand there! Let me get a stone to throw and hit your swollen mouths." Death, when she looked down, saw a stone lying there. She picked it up and threw it. As the stone was traveling, it said, "Winds take me and set me on the other side." It alighted on the other side. Number Eleven said, "Here I am!"

Death said, "Ah, that child! I have no further matter to talk to you about. All I have to say to you is this: Go and remain at home and change into one of the lesser gods, and if anyone whom I wish to take comes to where you are, do you inform me. If I so desire, I will leave him and make you a present of him; but what I wish in exchange you must receive it for me."

That is how the Abosom, the lesser gods, came into the world. They are descended from the small child Number Eleven.

(ASHANTI)

21 HOW KINTU WAS TESTED

When Kintu came first to Uganda he found there was no food at all in the country. He brought with him one cow and had only the food with which the animal supplied him. In the course of time a woman named Nambi came with her brother to the earth and saw Kintu. The woman fell in love with him and, wishing to be married to him, pointedly told him so. She had to return, however, with her brother to her people and her father, Gulu, who was king of the sky.

Nambi's relations objected to the marriage because they said that the man did not know of any food except that which the cow yielded, and they despised him. Gulu, the father, however, said that they had better test Kintu before he consented to the marriage, and he accordingly sent someone to rob Kintu of his cow. For a time Kintu was at a loss what to eat, but he managed to find different kinds of herbs and leaves which he cooked and ate. Nambi happened to see the cow grazing and recognized it, and complaining that her brothers wished to kill the man she loved, she went to the earth and told Kintu where his cow was, and invited him to return with her to take it away.

Kintu consented to go, and when he reached the sky he was greatly surprised to see how many people there were with houses and with cows, goats, sheep, and fowls running about. When Nambi's brothers saw Kintu sitting with their sister at her house, they went and told their father, who ordered them to build a house for Kintu and to give him a further testing to see whether he was worthy of their sister. An enormous meal was cooked, enough food for a hundred people, and brought to Kintu, who was told that unless he ate it all he would be killed as an impostor. Failure to eat it, they said, would be proof that he was not the great Kintu. He was then shut up in a house and left alone.

After he had eaten and drunk as much as he could, he was at a loss to know what to do with the rest of the food. Fortunately, he discovered a deep hole in the floor of the house, so he turned all the food and beer into it and covered it over so that no one could detect the place. He then called the people outside to come and take away the baskets. The sons of Gulu came in, but would not believe that he had eaten all the food. They, therefore searched the house but failed to find it.

They went to their father and told him that Kintu had eaten all the food. He was incredulous, and said that Kintu must be further tested. A copper ax was sent to Kintu by Gulu, who said, "Go and cut me firewood from the rock, because I do not use ordinary firewood."

When Kintu went with the ax, he said to himself, "What am I to do? If I strike the rock, the ax will only turn its edge or rebound." However, after he had examined the rock, he found that there were cracks in it, so he broke off pieces of it, and returned with them to Gulu who was surprised to get them. Nevertheless, he· said that Kintu must be further tried before they could give their consent to the marriage.

Kintu was next sent to fetch water and was told that he must bring only dew, because Gulu did not drink water from wells. Kintu took the waterpot and went off to a field, where he put the pot down and began to ponder what he must do to collect the dew. He was sorely puzzled, but upon returning to the pot, he found it full of water. So he carried it back to Gulu. Gulu was most surprised and said, "This man is a wonderful being; he shall have his cow back and marry my daughter."

Kintu was told to pick his cow from the herd and take it. This was a more difficult task than the others, because there were so many cows like his own that he feared he would mistake it and take the wrong one. While he was thus perplexed a large bee came and said, "Take the one upon whose horns I shall alight; it is yours."

The next morning Kintu went to the appointed place and stood and watched the bee, which was resting on a tree near him. A large herd of cows was brought before him, and he pretended to look for his cow, but in reality he was watching the bee which did not move. After a time, Kintu said, "My cow is not there." A second herd was brought and, again, he said, "My cow is not there." A third, much larger herd was brought, and the bee at once flew away and rested upon a cow which was a very large one, and Kintu said, "This is my cow." The bee then flew to another cow, and Kintu said, "This is one of the calves from my cow," and the bee went on to a second and a third cow which Kintu claimed as the calves which had been born during the cow's stay with Gulu.

Gulu was delighted with Kintu and said, "You are truly Kintu, take your cows. No one can deceive or rob you, you are too clever for that." He called Nambi and said to Kintu, "Take my daughter who loves you, marry her, and go back to your home." Gulu further said, "You must hurry and go back before Walumbe (Death) comes, because he will want to go with you and you must not take him; he will only cause you trouble and unhappiness."

Nambi agreed to what her father said and went to pack up her things. Kintu and Nambi then took leave of Gulu, who said, "Be sure, if you have forgotten anything, not to come back, because Death will want to go with you and you must go without him."

They started off home, taking with them, besides Nambi's things and the cows, a goat, a sheep, a fowl, and a plantain tree. On the way Nambi remembered that she had forgotten the grain for the fowl, and she said to Kintu, "I must go back for the grain for the fowl, or it will die."

Kintu tried to dissuade her, but in vain. She said, "I will hurry back and get it without anyone seeing me."

He said, "Your brother Death will be on the watch and will see you."

She would not listen to her husband, but went back and said to her father, "I have forgotten the grain for the fowl, and I have come to take it from the doorway where I put it."

He replied, "Did I not tell you that you were not to return if you forgot anything, because your brother Walumbe would see you and want to go with you? Now he will accompany you."

Nambi tried to steal away without Walumbe, but he followed her. When she rejoined Kintu, he was angry at seeing Walumbe, and said, "Why have you brought your brother with you? Who can live with him?"

Nambi was sorry, so Kintu said, "Let us go on and see

what will happen."

When they reached the earth Nambi planted her garden, and the plantains grew rapidly, and she soon had a large plantain grove in Manyagalya. They lived happily for some time and had a number of children, until one day Walumbe asked Kintu to send one of the children to be his cook.

Kintu replied, "If Gulu comes and asks me for one of my children, what am I to say to him? Shall I tell him that I have given her to be your cook?"

Walumbe was silent and went away, but he again asked for a child to be his cook, and again Kintu refused to send one of his daughters, so Walumbe said, "I will kill them."

Kintu, who did not know what he meant, asked, "What is it that you will do?" In a short time, however, one of the children fell ill and died, and from that time they began to die at intervals.

Kintu returned to Gulu and told him about the deaths of the children, and accused Walumbe of being the cause. Gulu replied, "Did I not tell you when you were going away to go at once with your wife and not to return if you had forgotten anything? But you allowed Nambi to return for grain. Now you have Walumbe living with you. Had you obeyed me you would have been free of him and would not have lost any of your children."

After some further entreaty, Gulu sent Kaikuzi, another brother, to assist Nambi, and to prevent Walumbe from killing the children. Kaikuzi went to the earth with Kintu and was met by Nambi, who told him her pitiful story. He said he would call Walumbe and try to dissuade him from killing the children. When Walumbe came to greet his brother they had quite a warm and affectionate meeting, and Kaikuzi told him he had come to take him back, because their father wanted him.

Walumbe said, "Let us take our sister too."

But Kaikuzi said he was not sent to take her, because she was married and had to stay with her husband. Walumbe refused to go without his sister, and Kaikuzi was angry with him and ordered him to do as he was told. Death, however, escaped from Kaikuzi's grip and fled away into the earth.

For a long time there was enmity between the two brothers. Kaikuzi tried in every possible way to catch his brother Walumbe, but he always escaped. At last Kaikuzi told the people to remain in their houses for several days and not to let any of the animals out, and he would have a final hunt for Walumbe. He further told them that if they saw Walumbe they must not call out or raise the usual cry of fear.

The instructions were followed for two or three days, and Kaikuzi got his brother to come out of the earth and was about to capture him, when some children took their goats to the pasture and saw Walumbe and called out. Kaikuzi rushed to the spot and asked why they called, and they said they had seen Death. Kaikuzi was angry, because Walumbe had again gone into the earth. So he went to Kintu and told him he was tired of hunting Death and wanted to return home. He also complained that the children had frightened Walumbe into the earth again. Kintu thanked Kaikuzi for his help and said he feared nothing more could be done, and he hoped Walumbe would not kill all the people.

From that time Death has lived upon the earth and he kills people whenever he can, and then he escapes into the earth at Tanda in Singo.

(BAGANDA)

22 THE SON OF KIM-ANA-U-EZE AND THE DAUGHTER OF SUN AND MOON

I often tell of Kim-ana-u-eze, who begat a male child. The child grew up, and he came to the age of marrying. His father said, "Marry."

He said, "I will not marry a woman of the earth."

His father asked, "Then whom will you marry?"

He answered, "*I!* If it must be, I shall marry the daughter of Lord Sun and Lady Moon."

But the people asked, "Who can go to the sky where the daughter of Lord Sun and Lady Moon lives?"

He simply said, "I, indeed; I want her. If it is anyone on earth, I will not marry her."

Thereupon he wrote a letter of marriage and gave it to Deer. But Deer said, "I cannot go to the sky."

Then he gave it to Antelope. Antelope also said, "I cannot go to the sky."

He gave the letter to Hawk. Hawk, too, said, "I cannot go to the sky."

He gave it to Vulture, but Vulture also said, "I can go halfway to the sky; however, all the way I cannot go."

Finally the young man said, "How shall I do it?" He put his letter in his box and was quiet.

The people of Lord Sun and Lady Moon used to come to get water on earth, and one day Frog came and sought out the son of Kim-ana-u-eze and spoke to him.

"Young master," he said, "give me the letter that I may take it."

The young master, however, said, "Begone! If people of life, who have wings, gave it up, how can you say, 'I will go there'? How can you get there?"

Frog said, "Young master, I am equal to it."

So Kim-ana-u-eze gave Frog the letter, saying, "If you cannot get there and you return with it, I shall give you a thrashing."

Frog started out and went to the well where the people of Lord Sun and Lady Moon were wont to come to get water. He put the letter in his mouth and got into the well and kept very still. In a little while, the people of Lord Sun and Lady Moon came to get water. They put a jug into the well, and Frog got into the jug. After they got the water, they lifted it up, not knowing that Frog had entered the jug. They arrived in the sky, set down the jug in its place and departed.

Then Frog got out of the jug. In the room where they kept the jugs of water, there was also a table. Frog spat out the letter and placed it on top of the table. Then he hid in the corner of the room.

After a while, Lord Sun himself came into the room where the water was; he looked at the table and saw the letter on it. He took it and asked his people, "Whence comes this letter?"

They answered, "Lord, we do not know." He opened it and read it. It ran thus: "I, the son of Na Kim-ana-u-eze Kia-Tumb'a Ndala, a man of earth, want to marry the daughter of Lord Sun and Lady Moon." Lord Sun thought to himself in his heart: "Na Kim-ana-u-eze lives on earth; I am a man who lives in the sky. He who came with the letter, who is he?" He put the letter away into his box and said nothing.

When Lord Sun finished reading the letter, Frog got into the jug again. After the water had been emptied out of the jugs, the water girls lifted them and went down to earth. They again arrived at the well and put the jugs in the water. Frog then got out and went under the water and hid himself. After the girls had finished the filling of the jugs they left.

The Frog came out of the water and went to his village. There he kept quiet and said nothing. When many days had passed, the son of Kim-ana-u-eze asked Frog, "O fellow, where did you take the letter, and how?"

Frog answered, "Master, I delivered the letter, but they have not yet returned an answer."

The son of Kim-ana-u-eze said, "O man, you are telling a lie; you did not go there."

Frog said, "Master, that same place where I went, that you shall see."

After six days, the son of Kim-ana-u-eze again wrote a letter to ask about the former letter, saying: "I wrote to you, Lord Sun and Lady Moon. My letter was delivered but you returned no answer whatsoever to me, saying neither 'We accept you' nor 'We refuse you.'" Having finished his letter, he sealed it. Then he called Frog and gave it to him. Frog started and soon arrived at the well. He took the letter into his mouth, got into the water, and squatted on the bottom of the well.

After a while, the water carriers came down and arrived at the well. They put the jugs into the water, and Frog got into a jug. When they had finished filling them, they lifted them up. They went up to the sky by means of a cobweb which Spider had woven. Soon they arrived there, and entered a house. There they set down the jugs and departed. Frog came out of the jug, spat out the letter, and laid it on the table. Then he hid in the corner.

After a while, Lord Sun passed through the room where the water was. He looked at the table and saw the letter on it. He opened and read it. The letter said: "I, son of Na Kim-ana-u-eze Kia-Tumb'a Ndala, I ask you, Lord Sun, about my letter that went before. You did not return me an answer at all."

Lord Sun said, "Girls, you who always go to fetch water, are you carrying letters?"

The girls said, "We, master? No."

Then doubt possessed Lord Sun. He laid the letter in the box and wrote to the son of Kim-ana-u-eze, saying: "You who are sending me letters about marrying my daughter: I agree, on condition that you in person, the man, come with your first present, so that I may know you." When he finished writing, he folded the letter and laid it on the table and went away. Frog now came out of the corner and took the letter. He put it in his mouth and entered the jug. Then he remained very quiet.

After a while, the water was emptied from the jugs, and the girls came and lifted them up. Then they went to the cord of Spider and descended to earth. They arrived at the well and put the jugs into the water. Frog got out of the jug and went to the bottom of the well. When the girls had completed the filling of the jugs, they returned to the sky. Frog then left the well and soon arrived in his village. He kept very quiet.

When evening came, he said, "Now I will take the letter." He spat it out and arrived at the house of the son of Kim-ana-u-eze. He knocked at the door, and the son of Kim-ana-u-eze asked, "Who is it?"

Frog answered, "I, Mainu, the frog."

The son of Kim-ana-u-eze got up from his bed where he was reclining and said, "Come in."

So Frog went in and delivered the letter. Then he departed. The son of Kim-ana-u-eze opened the letter and read it. What Lord Sun announced pleased him. He said to himself: "Why, it was the truth Frog told me when he said, 'You shall see where I went.'" Then he went to sleep.

The next morning, he took forty *macutas* (coins) and wrote a letter, saying: "You, Lord Sun and Moon, here is the first present; I remain on earth to seek for the wooing present. You up there, you tell me the amount of the wooing present." He finished the letter and called Frog. When he came, he gave him the letter and the money, saying, "Take this."

So Frog started. Soon he arrived at the well. He went to the bottom of the well and remained very quiet. After a while, the girls came down and put the jugs in the water, and Frog entered one of them. When the girls had finished filling them, they took them up. Again they went up to the sky by means of a cobweb. Soon they arrived in the room for the water. They set down the jugs and went away.

Then Frog got out of the jug and put the letter on the table, together with the money. Then he hid in the corner. Some time later, Lord Sun came into the room and found the letter on the table. He took it with the money and read the letter. Then he told his wife the news that had come from the prospective son-in-law. His wife assented.

Lord Sun said, "Who is coming with these letters? I do not know. How shall his food be cooked?"

His wife, however, answered, "No matter, we shall cook it anyhow and put it on the table where the letters have been found."

Lord Sun replied, "Very well."

So they killed a mother hen and cooked it. When evening came, they cooked mush. They set these eatables on the table and shut the door. Frog came to the table and ate the victuals. Then he went to the corner and kept quiet.

Lord Sun now wrote another letter saying: "You, son-in-law of mine, the first present which you have sent me I have received. For the amount of the wooing present, you shall give me a sack of money." When he had finished the letter, he laid it on the table and left the room. Then Frog came out of the corner and took the letter. Shortly afterward, he entered the jug and went to sleep.

In the morning the girls took the jugs and went down to the earth. They arrived at the well and put the jugs into the water. Frog then got out of the jug. When the girls had finished filling the jugs, they again went up to the sky.

Frog now got out of the water and soon arrived at his village. He entered his own house but waited quietly until sundown. When evening had come, he said, "Now I will take the letter." He started out and soon arrived at the house of the son of Kim-ana-u-eze. He knocked at the door and the son of Kim-ana-u-eze asked, "Who is it?"

Then Frog answered, "I, Mainu, the frog."

"Come in," he replied.

Frog went in; he gave him the letter and departed. The son of Kim-ana-u-eze opened the letter, read it, and then put it aside.

Six days passed; then he was ready with the sack of money. He called Frog, and when Frog had come, the son of Kim-ana-u-eze wrote the following letter: "You, my parents-in-law, the wooing present is enclosed. Soon I myself, I shall find a day to bring my wife home." He gave the letter to Frog, together with the money.

Frog then started and soon arrived at the well. Again he went in under the water and hid. After a while, the water carriers came down and arrived at the well. They put the jugs, as usual, in the water; Frog, as usual, entered a jug. When they had finished filling the jugs, they took them up, going up by means of Spider's cobweb. Soon they arrived in the sky. There they set down the jugs in the regular room and departed. Frog then got out of the jug and laid the letter down on the table, together with the money. Then he went into a corner and hid.

Soon Lord Sun came into the room and found the letter and the money. He took both and showed the money to his wife, Lady Moon.

Lady Moon thereupon said, "It is good."

Then they took a young hog and killed it. When they had cooked the food, they set it down on the table and shut the door. Frog came in then and ate it. When he had finished, he entered the jug and went to sleep.

The next morning the water carriers took the jugs and again went down to earth. They soon arrived at the well and dipped the jugs in the water. Frog then got out of the jug and hid. When they had finished filling the jugs, they again returned to the sky. Then Frog left the well and soon arrived at his village. He entered his house and went to sleep.

The next morning, he said to the son of Kim-ana-u-eze, "Young master, I gave them the wooing present, and they accepted it. They cooked me a young hog, and I ate it. Now, you yourself shall choose the day to fetch the bride home."

The son of Kim-ana-u-eze said, "Very well." Then twelve days elapsed.

Now the son of Kim-ana-u-eze spoke to Frog: "I need people to fetch the bride for me, but I cannot find them. All those to whom I speak say, 'We cannot go to the sky.' Now, what shall I do, Frog?"

Frog said, "My young master, be at ease; I shall find a way to go and bring her home for you."

But the son of Kim-ana-u-eze said, "You cannot do that. You could indeed carry the letters, but bring the bride home—that you are unable to do."

But Frog again said, "Young master, be at ease; be not troubled for naught. I indeed will be able to go and bring her home. Do not despise me."

The son of Kim-ana-u-eze said, "Well, I will try you."

Then he took some victuals and gave them to Frog.

Frog thereupon started. Soon he arrived at the well. Again he got into the well and hid. After a while, the water carriers came down and arrived at the well. They dipped the jugs in the water. Frog entered one of them. When they had filled them, they went back. Arriving at the proper room, they set down the jugs and departed. Then Frog got out of the jug and hid in a corner. When the sun had set and it was evening, Frog left the room of the water jugs and went to seek the room where the daughter of Lord Sun slept. He found it and saw her asleep there. First he took out one of her eyes and then the other. These he tied up in a handkerchief and went back to the room where the jugs were. He hid in a corner and slept.

In the morning, all the people got up, but not the daughter of Lord Sun. So they asked her, "Why do you not get up?"

And she answered, "My eyes are closed; I cannot see."

Her father and mother said, "What may be the cause of this? Yesterday she did not complain."

So Lord Sun called for two messengers and said to them, "Go to Ngombo to divine about my child who is sick, whose eyes are sick."

They started immediately and soon arrived at the Ngombo-man's. They gave him presents and Ngombo took our his paraphernalia. Now the people who came did not let him know anything about the disease; they simply said, "We have come to be divined."

Ngombo looked into his paraphernalia and said, "Disease has brought you. The one who is sick is a woman. The sickness that ails her concerns her eyes. You have come, being sent, you have not come of your own will. I have spoken."

The people said, "True. Now tell us what caused the ailment."

Ngombo looked again, and said, "She, the woman who is sick, is not yet married. She is only chosen. Her master, who bespoke her, has sent a spell saying, 'My wife, let her come; if she does not come, she shall die.' You, who came to divine, go, bring her to her husband that she may escape death. I have spoken."

The messengers agreed and got up. They went to Lord Sun and reported to him the words of Ngombo.

Lord Sun said, "All right. Let us sleep. Tomorrow they shall take her down to earth.

Frog, being in his corner, heard all that they were saying. Then all slept.

The next morning, Frog got into the jug. Again the water carriers came. Again they took up the jugs. Then they descended to the earth and soon arrived at the well. They put the jugs in the water, and Frog came out of one of them. He hid under the well. When the jugs were filled, the water carriers went up to the sky.

Then Lord Sun told Spider, "Weave a large cobweb, down to earth, for this is the day when my daughter will be taken down to the earth." Spider wove and finished the web. Thus time passed.

Frog now got out of the well and went to his village. He found the son of Kim-ana-u-eze and said to him, "O young master! Thy bride, today she comes."

The son of Kim-ana-u-eze said, "Begone, man, you are a liar."

Frog answered, "Master, this is the truth itself. This evening I will bring her to you."

Frog then returned to the well and got into the water and was silent.

Now the sun had set, and the daughter of Lord Sun was taken down to the earth. They left her at the well and then went back.

Frog now got out of the well and spoke to the young woman, saying, "I myself will be your guide. Let us go immediately so that I can bring you to your master." Then Frog returned her eyes to her and they started. Soon they entered the house of the son of Kim-ana-u-eze. Frog exclaimed:

"O young master! Your bride is here."

The son of Kim-ana-u-eze said, "Welcome, Mainu the frog."

And so the son of Kim-ana-u-eze married the daughter of Lord Sun and Lady Moon, and they lived on.

(AMBUNDU)

23 THE BLUE JAY WHO MARRIED THE DAUGHTER OF GOD

Long ago Blue Jay had a wife but after a time he went to God; he went to seek the Daughter of God also as his wife. God replied, "Since you ask for her, you must not take her to the earth, you must stay just here in the sky. Because, if you take her to the earth, she may not eat meat of zebra or gnu or kudu; of any large animal she may not eat. If you desire to carry her to earth, let her eat only of smaller animals." Blue Jay answered, "It is well, Chief."

So Blue Jay was allowed to bring the Daughter of God to earth. Upon his arrival on earth he told these things to his earthly wife, saying, "I was told by God that his child may not eat of zebra or gnu or kudu; she may not eat of any large animal." These things he told his wife and mother; when they heard them, his mother said, "It is well, my child." Nevertheless, his first wife was terribly jealous.

One day Blue Jay went off hunting. He went and killed a zebra and a young duiker. When he returned to his first wife, he ordered her, saying, "You must on no account give my wife the meat of the zebra. Let her eat only of the young duiker." His wife replied, "It is well."

Another day while Blue Jay was out walking, the old wife deceived her fellow, the Daughter of God, giving her zebra meat and saying, "Eat, it is young duiker." But she was simply deceiving her. As soon as the Daughter of God ate it, she died. Then Blue Jay returned; on his arrival he asked, "My wife! What has she died of?" The old wife replied, "I don't know."

Nevertheless God had seen her from the sky. Said he, "It is that one yonder who killed my child."

Thereupon Blue Jay returned to the sky; on arrival he

went to tell the news, saying, "My wife is dead, Chief." God answered, saying, "You forgot the orders I gave you that my child must not eat of zebra or gnu or kudu; nevertheless, there on earth she was given some. She ate and died." Then Blue Jay replied, "It may be so, Chief." God answered, "Return."

When thirty days had passed, God gathered together a small cloud. Then he opened wide his mouth and thundered. After a time he descended and swept open the grave in which his child was buried; he took her out and carried her to the sky. Nevertheless, Blue Jay did not survive; he took him away also. When he arrived midway he thrust him down to earth; but he never arrived: only some small bones reached the ground. He died just there midway. To this very day this is what Blue Jay does: when he flies he goes up into the air with a loud cry; on the point of descending he dies.

(BAILA)

24 THE SWALLOWING MONSTER

Once upon a time there appeared in our country a huge shapeless thing called Kho-dumo-dumo. It swallowed every living creature that came its way. At last it came through a pass in the mountains into a valley where there were several villages; it went to one after another, and swallowed the people, the cattle, the goats, the dogs, and the fowls. In the last village was a woman who had just happened to sit down on the ash heap. She saw the monster coming, smeared herself all over with ashes, and ran into the calves' pen, where she crouched on the ground. Kho-dumo-dumo, having finished all the people and animals, came and looked into the place, but could see nothing moving, for, the woman being smeared with ashes and keeping quite still, it took her for a stone. It then turned and went away, but when it reached the narrow path at the entrance to the valley it had swelled to such a size that it could not get through and was forced to stay where it was.

Meanwhile the woman in the calves' pen who had been expecting a baby shortly, gave birth to a boy. She laid him down on the ground and left him for a minute or two, while she looked for something to make a bed for him. When she came back she found a grown man sitting there, with two or three spears in his hand and a string of divining bones around his neck. She said, "Hallo, man! Where is my child?" And he answered, "It is I, Mother!" Then he asked what had become of the people, and the cattle and the dogs, and she told him.

"Where is this thing, Mother?"

"Come out and see, my child."

So they both went out and climbed to the top of the wall surrounding the narrow path and they saw the thing, as big as a mountain. "That is Kho-dumo-dumo," said the mother.

Her son Dit-ao-lane got down from the wall, fetched his spears, sharpened them on a stone, and set off to the end of the valley, where Kho-dumo-dumo lay. The beast saw him and opened his mouth to swallow him, but he dodged and went around its side—it was too unwieldy to turn and seize him—and drove one of his spears into it. Then he stabbed it again with his second spear, and it sank down and died.

He took his knife, and had already begun to cut it open when he heard a man's voice crying out, "Do not cut me!" So he tried in another place, and another man cried out, but the knife had already slashed his leg. Dit-ao-lane then began cutting in a third place, and a cow lowed, and someone called out, "Don't stab the cow!" Then he heard a goat bleat, a dog bark, and a hen cackle, but he managed to avoid them as he went on cutting, and so, in time, released all the inhabitants of the valley.

There was great rejoicing as the people collected their belongings, and all returned to their several villages praising their young deliverer, and saying, "This young man must be our chief." They brought him gifts of cattle, so that, between one and another, he soon had a large herd, and he had his choice of wives among their daughters. So he built himself a fine kraal and married and settled down, and all went well for a time.

But the unintentionally wounded man never forgot his grudge and long after his leg was healed, whenever he noticed signs of discontent among the people, he would drop a cunning word here and there to encourage those who were secretly envious of Dit-ao-lane's good fortune, as well as those who suspected him because, as they said, he could not be a normal human being, to give voice to their feelings.

So before long they were making plans to get rid of their chief. They dug a pit and covered it with dry grass—just as the Bapedi did in order to trap Huveane—but he avoided it. They kindled a great fire in the courtyard intending to throw him into it, but a kind of madness seized them; they began to struggle with each other and at last threw in one of their own party. The same thing happened when they tried to push him over a precipice; in this case he restored to life the man who was thrown over and killed.

Next they got up a big hunt, which meant an absence of several days from the village. One night when the party were sleeping in a cave they induced the chief to take the place farthest from the entrance, and when they thought he was asleep stole out and built a great fire in the mouth of the cave. But when they looked around, they saw him standing among them.

After this, he grew weary of defeating their stratagems and allowed them to kill him without offering any resistance. Some of the Basuto, when relating this story, add, "It is said that his heart went out and escaped and became a bird."

(BASUTO)

25 HOW THE LAME BOY BROUGHT
FIRE FROM HEAVEN

In the beginning of the world, Obassi Osaw made everything but he did not give fire to the people who were on
earth.

Etim 'Ne said to the Lame Boy: "What is the use of
Obassi Osaw sending us here without any fire? Go therefore and ask him to give us some." So the Lame Boy set
out.

Obassi Osaw was very angry when he got the message,
and sent the boy back quickly to earth to reprove Etim 'Ne
for what he had asked. In those days the Lame Boy had
not become lame, but could walk like other people.

When Etim 'Ne heard that he had angered Obassi Osaw,
he set out himself for the latter's town and said:

"Please forgive me for what I did yesterday. It was by
accident." Obassi would not pardon him, though he stayed
for three days begging forgiveness. Then he went home.

When Etim reached his town the boy laughed at him.
"Are you a chief," said he, "yet could get no fire? I myself
will go and bring it to you. If they will give me none, I will
steal it."

That very day the lad set out. He reached the house of
Obassi at evening time and found the people preparing
food. He helped with the work, and when Obassi began to
eat knelt down humbly till the meal was ended.

The master saw that the boy was useful and did not drive
him out of the house. After he had served for several days,
Obassi called to him and said: "Go to the house of my wives
and ask them to send me a lamp."

The boy gladly did as he was bidden, for it was in the
house of the wives that fire was kept. He touched nothing,

but waited until the lamp was given him, then brought it back with all speed. Once, after he had stayed for many days among the servants, Obassi sent him again, and this time one of the wives said: "You can light the lamp at the fire." She went into her house and left him alone.

The boy took a brand and lighted the lamp, then he wrapped the brand in plantain leaves and tied it up in his cloth, carried the lamp to his master, and said: "I wish to go out for a certain purpose." Obassi answered: "You can go."

The boy went to the bush outside the town where some dry wood was lying. He laid the brand amongst the dry wood, and blew till it caught alight. Then he covered it with plantain stems and leaves to hide the smoke, and went back to the house. Obassi asked: "Why have you been so long?" And the lad answered: "I did not feel well."

That night when all the people were sleeping, the thief tied his clothes together and crept to the end of town where the fire was hidden. He found it burning, and took a glowing brand and some firewood and set out homeward.

When earth was reached once more the lad went to Etim and said:

"Here is the fire which I promised to bring you. Send for some wood, and I will show you what we must do."

So the first fire was made on earth. Obassi Osaw looked down from his house in the sky and saw the smoke rising. He said to his eldest son Akpan Obassi: "Go, ask the boy if it is he who has stolen the fire."

Akpan came down to earth and asked as his father had bidden him. The lad confessed: "I was the one who stole the fire. The reason why I hid it was because I feared."

Akpan replied: "I bring you a message. Up till now you have been able to walk. From today you will not be able to do so any more."

That is the reason why the Lame Boy cannot walk. He it was who first brought fire to earth from Obassi's home in the sky.

(HAUSA)

26 HOW THE EARTH FOLK RECEIVED FIRE

Motu made a large garden and planted it with many bananas and plantain. The garden was in a good position so the fruit ripened quickly and well. Arriving one day at his garden he found the ripe bunches of bananas and plantain had been cut off and carried away.

After that he did not go once to his garden without finding that some of the fruit had been stolen, so at last he made up his mind to watch the place carefully, and hiding himself he lay in ambush for the thief.

Motu had not been in hiding very long before he saw a number of Cloud Folk descending, who cut down his bananas, and what they could not eat they tied into bundles to carry away. Motu rushed out, and, chasing them, caught one woman whom he took to his house, and after a short time he married her, and gave her a name which meant Favorite.

Although Favorite had come from the Cloud Land she was very intelligent, and went about her housework and farming just like an ordinary woman of the earth. Up to that time neither Motu nor the people of his village had ever seen a fire. They had always eaten their food raw, and on cold, windy, rainy days had sat shivering in their houses because they did not know anything about fire and warmth.

Favorite, however, told some of the Cloud Folk to bring some fire with them next time they came to visit her, which they did. And then she taught the people how to cook food, and how to sit around a fire on cold days.

Motu was very happy with his wife, and the villagers were very glad to have her among them, and, moreover, Favorite persuaded many of the Cloud Folk to settle in her husband's village.

One day Favorite received a covered basket and, putting it on a shelf in the house, she said to her husband, "We are now living with much friendship together; but while I am away at the farm you must not open that basket; if you do we shall all leave you."

"All right," replied the husband, "I will never undo it."

Motu was now very glad in his heart, for he had plenty of people, a clever wife, and the villagers treated him as a great man. But he had one trouble: Why did his wife warn him every day not to open the basket? What was in that basket? What was she hiding from him? And foolish-like he decided to open it. Waiting therefore until his wife had gone as usual to the farm he opened the basket, and—there was nothing in it, so laughingly he shut it up and put it in its place.

By and by Favorite returned, and, looking at her husband, she asked him: "Why did you open that basket?" And he was speechless at her question.

On the first opportunity, while Motu was away hunting, Favorite gathered her people and ascended with them to Cloud Land, and never again returned to earth.

That is how the earth folk received their fire and a knowledge of cooking; and that is also how Motu through being too inquisitive lost his wife, his people, and his importance as a big man in the village.

(CONGO)

27 FIRE FROM HEAVEN

Once on a time the spider spun a long, long thread, and the wind caught one end of the thread and carried it up to the sky. Then the woodpecker climbed up the thread and pecking at the celestial vault made those holes in it which we call stars. After the woodpecker, man climbed up the thread to the sky and fetched down fire. But some say that man found fire at the place where fiery tears had fallen from the sky.

(LOANGO)

28 THE DISLOYALTY OF DOMESTIC ANIMALS

At one time all the birds and animals lived in the sky. One day it was very rainy and cold—so cold that they were all shivering. The birds said to the Dog: "Go down and fetch us some fire to warm ourselves."

The Dog descended, but seeing plenty of bones and pieces of fish lying about on the ground he forgot to take the fire to the shivering birds.

The birds and animals waited and since the Dog did not return they sent the Fowl to make him hurry back with the fire.

The Fowl, however, on arriving below saw plenty of palm nuts, peanuts, maize, and other good things, so he did not tell the dog to take up the fire, nor did he take it up himself.

This is the reason why on some evenings you can hear a bird which sings notes like this: *Nsusu akende bombo! Nsusu akende bombo!* which means, "The Fowl has become a slave! The Fowl has become a slave!"

This is why you hear these birds jeer at and abuse the Fowl and Dog, because they left their friends to shiver in the cold while they enjoyed themselves in warmth and plenty.

(BANGALA)

29 LILALA HUMBA

The first king of the Hlengwe tribe married the daughter of
the chief of the Sono. At this time the Hlengwe did not
have fire but ate their food cold and raw. The Sono tribe,
however, had fire. One day the son of the king visited the
Sono tribe, and when he saw how comfortably they lived he
stole a glowing cinder and brought it back to his people in a
shell and taught them how to cook. When the chief of the
Sono perceived the theft he declared war on the Hlengwe.
The Hlengwe tribe had grown so strong since they ate
cooked food and could warm themselves by the fire that
they withstood and finally defeated the Sono. Ever since
then the Hlengwe have fire and the king's son is regarded
as the first man, bearing the name Lilala Humba, or, he
who brought a glowing cinder in a shell.

(THONGA, SOUTHEAST AFRICA)

30 HOW MAN STOLE FIRE FROM THE LIONS

In the beginning there was no fire and men suffered from
the cold. One day a man told his wife that he was going to
cross the river and go to the city of the lions. After he
crossed the river he came to the entrance of a cave where a
lion family was sitting around a big fire. The chief of the
family bade him enter and offered him a seat of honor,
opposite the mouth of the cave. In the course of the meal
the man kept edging toward the place nearest to the mouth
of the cave. When the meal was almost over he snatched a

burning brand from the fire and throwing the lion cubs into the flames ran out from the cave. When the lions saw that the stranger went off with a burning brand they began to pursue him. But they were delayed, having first to save their children from the fire. So that the man escaped and reached the other shore of the river, bringing to his people the gift of fire.

(BERGDAMA, SOUTHWEST AFRICA)

2

MYTHS OF PRIMEVAL TIMES: THE ORIGIN OF DEATH

31 THE PERVERTED MESSAGE

The Moon, it is said, once sent an insect to men, saying, "Go to men and tell them, 'As I die, and dying live; so you shall also die, and dying live.'"

The insect started with the message but while on his way was overtaken by the hare, who asked, "On what errand are you bound?" The insect answered, "I am sent by the Moon to men, to tell them that as she dies and dying lives, so shall they also die and dying live."

The hare said, "As you are an awkward runner, let me go." With these words he ran off, and when he reached men, he said, "I am sent by the Moon to tell you, 'As I die and dying perish, in the same manner you also shall die and come wholly to an end.'"

The hare then returned to the Moon and told her what he had said to men. The Moon reproached him angrily, saying, "Do you dare tell the people a thing which I have not said?"

With these words the Moon took up a piece of wood and struck the hare on the nose. Since that day the hare's nose has been slit, but men believe what Hare had told them.

(HOTTENTOT)

32 THE PERVERTED MESSAGE

And how did it happen?

It is God who created men. And since God had pity, He

said, "I do not wish men to die altogether. I wish that men, having died, should rise again." And so He created men and placed them in another region. But He stayed at home.

And then God saw the chameleon and the weaverbird. After He had spent three days with the chameleon and the weaverbird, He recognized that the weaverbird was a great maker of words compounded of lies and truth. Now of lies there were many, but of the words of truth there were few.

Then He watched the chameleon and recognized that he had great intelligence. He did not lie. His words were true. So he spoke to the chameleon: "Chameleon, go into that region where I have placed the men I created, and tell them that when they have died, even if they are altogether dead, still they shall rise again—that each man shall rise again after he dies."

The chameleon said, "Yes, I will go there." But he went slowly, for it is his fashion to go slowly. The weaverbird had stayed behind with God.

The chameleon traveled on, and when he had arrived at his destination, he said, "I was told, I was told, I was told. . . ." But he did not say what he had been told.

The weaverbird said to God, "I wish to step out for a moment."

And God said to him, "Go!"

But the weaverbird, since he is a bird, flew swiftly, and arrived at the place where the chameleon was speaking to the people and saying, "I was told. . . ." Everyone was gathered there to listen. When the weaverbird arrived, he said, "What was told to us? Truly, we were told that men, when they are dead, shall perish like the roots of the aloe."

Then the chameleon exclaimed, "But we were told, we were told, we were told, that when men are dead, they shall rise again."

Then the magpie interposed and said, "The first speech is the wise one."

And now all the people left and returned to their homes. This was the way it happened.

And so men become old and die; they do not rise again.

(AKAMBA)

33 THE PERVERTED MESSAGE

In primeval times, God had familiar intercourse with men and gave them all they needed. This state, however, came to an end when some women who were grinding their food became embarrassed by God's presence and told him to go away, and beat him with their pestles. God then withdrew from the world, and left its government to the spirits.

Afterward God send a goat from heaven to the seven human beings on earth with the following message: "There is something called death. One day it will kill some of you. Even if you die, however, you will not be altogether lost. You will come to live with me in the sky."

On the way, the goat lingered at a bush in order to eat, and when God discovered this he sent a sheep with the same message. But the sheep changed the message to the effect that men should die, and that as far as they were concerned this would be the end of all things. When the goat then arrived with her true message, men would not believe it. They had already accepted the message delivered by the sheep. Shortly afterward, the first case of death took place, and God taught men to bury their dead. He also told them that as a foil to death they should be given the capacity to multiply.

According to another version, God sent the sheep with eternal life as a gift to men. But the he-goat ran on ahead and gave them death as a gift from God. They eagerly accepted this gift, as they did not know what death was. The sheep arrived after a while, but it was too late.

(ASHANTI)

34 THE PERVERTED MESSAGE

In the old days men did not die, and except for the chiefs they passed their whole times as slaves. At last they grew weary of this eternal bondage and decided to send a messenger to Wuni to beg him to put an end to their servitude. They chose for this duty their friend the dog, and he departed on this errand. As he ran along the road which led to the dwelling place of Wuni he came to a village where there was an old woman cooking a pot of something over a fire. The dog thought it a good chance to get some food and sat down nearby gazing at his hoped-for meal. The old woman tried to chase him away but that merely made him more anxious to share some of the good things inside the pot. While he was thus waiting a young goat who had overheard the message of the men came along, and seeing the dog tarrying decided he would do a good thing if he himself took the message and delivered it to Wuni.

He therefore went on.

Now the dog had to wait a long time, and at last the pot was boiling. The old woman took it off and fetching a baby opened the lid of the pot, which after all was only full of water, with which she began to wash the infant. The dog was very annoyed and ran off down the road to Wuni. On his way he met the goat, who asked him where he was off to. The dog told him, and the goat replied that it was now quite unnecessary to proceed as he himself had given the message. The dog asked him what message, and when the goat told him that he had arrived at Wuni's compound and there told the god that men were tired of being slaves and now wanted to die, the dog was very upset and raced away to Wuni to correct the mistake. He came to the god, but the latter refused to listen to the new message, saying that he did not believe it and that he had already arranged for the death of men. Thus it is that death comes to all men nowadays and men remain slaves.

(DAGOMBA)

35 THE MARPLOT OR THE MESSAGE THAT FAILED

When Mawu created human beings it was his intention that they should have eternal life. But the Spider was of a contrary opinion. Mawu took a calabash, put it on the water, and said that in the same way as the calabash always remains on the surface, so man should always remain upon the earth.

The Spider threw a stone into the water with the words: "Let Mawu say, when a man dies may he vanish like this stone and never reappear." Mawu agreed to this.

When, later, the Spider's mother died, it wished that Mawu should change this order of things, but Mawu refused. If Mawu had changed his word human beings would have come back after death, like the moon which dies and comes back.

(FO)

36 DEATH IS THE BROTHER OF SLEEP

God once asked men if they knew what it meant to die. The men answered that they did not, therefore God asked them to meet in the palaver-house at six o'clock. There the same question was put to them, and once more they an-

swered in the negative. God told them to wait for a little
while. At eight o'clock he asked them again, and once more
got the same answer. However, the people were growing
tired of the prolonged waiting, and by ten o'clock they had
all gone to sleep. God then woke them up and said: "So,
now you know what it is like when someone dies, for sleep
and death are similar."

(EKOI)

37 THE SLEEP TEST

In the beginning, Nzambi slid down to earth on a rainbow,
and there created the animals and the trees. After this he
also created a man and a woman, and he told them to
marry and have children. Nzambi imposed only one prohibition upon men, that they should not sleep when the moon
was up. If they disobeyed this command, they would be
punished with death. When the first man had become old
and had poor eyesight, it once happened that the moon was
veiled behind the clouds, so that he could not see it shine.
He went to sleep and died in his sleep. Since then all men
have died, because they are unable to keep awake when the
moon is up.

(LUNDA)

38 THE SLEEP TEST

Nkengo saw how men died daily in swarms. One day he
called out to the Cloud Folk and told them to throw down a
rope to him. His request granted, Nkengo seized the rope
and was hauled up to them. Up there he had first to wait a

day and a night. The following morning they said to him: "You have come here to receive lasting life and escape from death. You cannot make your request for seven days, and in the meantime you must not go to sleep."

Nkengo managed to stay awake for six days but on the seventh he fell asleep. The people in Cloud Land were wroth with him; they drove him out and lowered him down to the earth again. The people there asked him how he had fared. He told them what had happened, how he had failed to keep awake and been driven away with the words: "Get away with your dying; you shall not receive lasting life, for every day there shall be death among you!" Nkengo's friends laughed at him for having tried to gain eternal life and failed by going to sleep. And this is the reason why death remains in the world.

(NGALA, CONGO)

39 THE SLEEP TEST

Kalumba the Creator knew that Life and Death wrapped up in grasscloth and tied to a pole as for burial, would be coming along the road to try to reach men. He therefore charged the Dog and the Goat to keep watch by the roadside and to allow Life to pass, but not Death. The two animals at first quarreled with each other as to which of them was the most suitable sentinel. The Dog asserted that he could stay awake, while the Goat considered that the Dog would fall asleep at his post. After disputing the point for a while, the Goat went away and left the watch to the Dog. The latter made a fire, but then went to sleep. Then Death got past. The following day the Goat kept watch. He stayed awake and captured Life. Thus Death had been allowed to reach men on account of the Dog's negligence, while Life, on the other hand, had been captured; and the people said: "If Goat had watched, Death would have been caught."

(LUBA)

40 THE WRONG CHOICE

A little man with two bundles, a big one and a little one, came to a man who happened to be working in the forest and told him to choose one of the bundles. "This one," he said, taking up the big bundle, "contains looking glasses, knives, beads, and cloth; and this one," he said, taking up the little bundle, "contains everlasting life." The man did not venture to choose himself, however, but went and asked the other people in the town. While he was away, some women came to the place and were told to make the same choice. The women tried the edges of the knives, draped themselves in the cloth, admired themselves in the mirrors, and without more ado they chose the big bundle. The little man disappeared with the other one. When the forest worker returned, he found only the women, who were busy sharing out the contents of the big bundle. But men had now lost eternal life, and death remained on the earth. And this is why people say: "Oh, if those women had only chosen the small bundle, we folk would not be dying like this!"

(NGALA)

41 MAN CHOOSES DEATH

One day God asked the first human couple who then lived in heaven what kind of death they wanted, that of the moon

or that of the banana. Because the couple wondered in
dismay about the implications of the two modes of death,
God explained to them: the banana puts forth shoots which
take its place and the moon itself comes back to life. The
couple considered for a long time before they made their
choice. If they elected to be childless they would avoid
death, but they would also be very lonely, would themselves
be forced to carry out all the work, and would not have
anybody to work and strive for. Therefore they prayed to
God for children, well aware of the consequences of their
choice. And their prayer was granted. Since that time man's
sojourn is short on this earth.

(MADAGASCAR)

42 THE THREE CALABASHES

Shortly after Leza had created the first two human beings,
Mu-longa and Mwi-nam-buz-hi, he summoned to his presence the honeybird May-imba, and gave it three calabashes,
all of them closed at both ends. He told May-imba to take
these to the man and the woman, without opening them on
the way. May-imba was then to tell the human couple that
they might open the two calabashes which contained seed.
The third, however, was not to be opened until Leza himself had come to the earth and given instructions concerning its contents.

On the way, May-imba could not contain his curiosity,
and opened the calabashes. The first two contained seed of
different kinds, and when May-imba had examined the contents he put them back and closed the calabashes.

He opened the third. In this calabash were death, sickness, all kinds of beasts of prey, and dangerous reptiles.
These unpleasant things came out, and May-imba could not

catch them. Then Leza appeared and helped the bird to look for them. They did, it is true, find the lion in its lair, the snake in its hole and so forth, but they were unable to capture them.

Leza said to May-imba: "You have sinned greatly and the responsibility is yours." The terrified bird flew into the woods and no longer lived among men.

Leza then said to Mu-longa and his wife: "May-imba is a great sinner. I told him that on no account was the third gourd to be opened until I came; but he disobeyed me. Thereby he has brought you much trouble, sickness, death; and the risk from lions, leopards, snakes, and other evil animals and reptiles. This I cannot help now, for these things have escaped and cannot be caught; so you must build yourselves huts and shelters to live in for protection from them."

(KAONDE)

43 DEATH AS A PUNISHMENT

God had created the first human beings, two sons and one daughter. God stood on an intimate footing with his children, but without showing himself, and he had commanded them never to see him. If they did so, misfortunes would come upon them. They were then enjoying a pleasant existence. They did not need to work. God helped them with everything. All things came to them without effort on their part.

But the daughter had been entrusted with the task of placing wood in front of God's hut. One evening when she had put the pitcher of water outside the hut, she was overcome with curiosity to see her father. She hid behind a post and was able to see his arm, adorned with heavy brass rings, as he stretched it out to take the pitcher. Then God discovered her. He summoned the people, reproached them, and said that they must hereafter live alone. He himself would withdraw. But he taught them the art of forging weapons and tools and all they needed to be able to make their own way. The woman was to be the servant of the man. She was to give birth to her children with pain and carry out all the heavy work. Thus God left them. At the same time they also lost happiness and peace, and they had to work in order to live.

Death, with which they had hitherto been unacquainted, was also sent to them as a punishment. The woman's first-born child was given the name *Kukua kende,* "Death comes." The child died two days after birth. Since then no man escapes death, the avenger. Thus death came into the world.

(SUA)

44 DEATH AS A PUNISHMENT

There originally lived on earth only an old married couple. The sky was at that time so close that they could touch it with their hands. The man and his wife tilled the fields and lived happily together. One day the woman suggested that they should throw a stone at the sky, but the man forbade this. The sky would collapse and fall upon them. One day when the man was out, however, the woman threw a stone, and in the same instant the sky was far away. She heard a voice from the sky saying: "Because you did not obey your husband, from this time on all men must die."

(EWE)

45 DEATH AS A PUNISHMENT

Nyambe originally lived together with human beings, who were at that time happily ignorant of both pain and death. When they grew old they needed only to spend nine days near a little tree called Singo to get back their youth and begin life anew. But then people began to become wicked and forgot to reverence Nyambe.

Nyambe gathered the people about him and told the strongest among them to break a bundle of sticks that was tied together. No one succeeded. "You see," Nyambe said to them, "there is advantage in unity. Why have you deserted me? As your punishment I will withdraw myself far from you; you will no longer have the same ways and all of you, men, women, and children will know suffering and death." He thereupon pulled up the lifetree Singo and took it with him toward the setting sun.

(KOKO)

46 THE FORBIDDEN FRUIT

God created the first human being Ba-atsi with the help of the moon. He kneaded the body into shape, covered it with a skin, and poured in blood. When the man had thus been given life, God whispered in his ear that he, Ba-atsi, should beget children, and upon them he should impress the following prohibition: "Of all the trees of the forest you may eat, but of the Tahu tree you may not eat." Ba-atsi had many children, impressed upon them the prohibition, and

then retired to heaven. At first men respected the com-
mandment they had been given, and lived happily. But one
day a pregnant woman was seized with an irresistible desire
to eat of the forbidden fruit. She tried to persuade her husband to give her some of it. At first he refused, but after a
time he gave way. He stole into the wood, picked a Tahu
fruit, peeled it, and hid the peel among the leaves. But the
moon had seen his action and reported it to God. God was
so enraged over man's disobedience that as punishment he
sent death among them.

(EFE)

47 THE FORBIDDEN FRUIT

The god Ruwa, it is true, did not create man; he let the first
human beings out of a mysterious vessel by breaking it and
ordered things so that men could make a livelihood. He
gave them a banana grove, and in the grove of their principal elder he planted a great number of sweet potatoes and
yams, in the middle a sort of yam called Ula or Ukaho. He
then gave men permission to eat of all this, but not of Ula.
"Neither you nor your people may eat it, and if any man
eats it, his bones shall break and at last he shall die," he said
to the elder of the village. He then went his way, but came
on a visit every morning and evening.

One day a stranger came and asked for something to eat.
The elder told him that he might eat of the fruits in the
banana grove, only not of Ula. The stranger replied that
that same morning Ruwa had instructed him to ask for a
cooking pot, to cook Ula and eat it, and that the elder and
his people should do the same. So the Ula yam was cooked,
and the people began to eat.

While they were eating, Ruwa's minister recognized the
smell and hastened to the spot. He took the pot and the

yams with him to Ruwa, who became very wrathful and
sent his minister to pronounce the following sentence:
"Because you were deceived by a stranger and ate my Ula,
I shall break your bones and burst your eyes, and at last
you shall die." The minister then returned to Ruwa. Since
then, no one has seen him, nor has Ruwa sent any more
messages to men, who began to be broken, and their eyes to
be closed, and afterward they died.

(DJAGA)

48 HOW MAN LOST ETERNAL YOUTH

The god Ruwa had decreed that men should change their
skins like the snake and become young when they had
attained a great age. "But not one of your people may see
you when you cast your skin, you must be alone at such a
time. And if your child or grandchild see you, in that hour
you shall die altogether and not be saved again."

When the elder had become old and knew that the time
had come for him to cast his skin, he sent his granddaughter
to fetch water in a calabash, in the bottom of which he had
made a lot of small holes, so that she should be forced to be
away for a sufficiently long time. She plugged the holes,
however, and returned after a short time and surprised him
in the middle of the act, whereupon he cried out: "I have
died, all of you will die, I have died, all of you shall die. For
you, granddaughter, entered while I cast my skin. Woe is
me, woe is you!"

Then the people drove the girl into the woods. There she
became a wife and gave birth to children. These are the
baboons and the monkeys, the apes and the Colobus monkeys; and the baboons and their like are called "People of
the Forest" or "Children of the Curse."

(DJAGA, KILIMANJARO)

49 DEATH IN EXCHANGE FOR FIRE

Formerly men had no fire but ate all their food raw. At that time they did not need to die for when they became old God made them young again. One day they decided to beg God for fire. They sent a messenger to God to convey their request. God replied to the messenger that he would give him fire if he was prepared to die. The man took the fire from God, but ever since then all men must die.

(DARASA, GADA)

50 THE BEGINNING OF DISORDER

The first human beings did not know death. When they grew old they were changed into snakes, or into spirits called Gyi-nu, and entered into another world where a secret language was spoken. One day, however, the oldest of the An-dum-bulu[1] went to the Gyi-nu and heard them speak the secret language which they had been taught by the god Amma. Then he began to speak this language himself. An An-dum-bulu who had not yet undergone the metamorphosis heard him, and asked him to teach him the secret language. The new Gyi-nu did this, at the same time warning his pupil that with the knowledge of the secret language death would enter into the world of the An-dum-bulu; the oldest one among them would succumb first and then it would be necessary to dance the Sigui[2] in way of

[1] The An-dum-bulu are the first ancestors; spirits represented as hairy men with long beards. The Gyi-nu are spirits with one arm, one leg, and green hair. They live in trees and give sickness.

[2] The Sigui is an expiatory feast, during which the Dogon secret language is spoken. It is celebrated to obtain the pardon of the dead.

reparation. The secret language was reserved for the Gyi-nu. To teach it to others meant the beginning of disorder.

According to another tradition, the order of the world was broken in the following way. A man was about to undergo his metamorphosis (for death had not yet entered into the world of men) and he betook himself to a grotto in order to join his soul that had gone to the Yeban in advance.[1] He met one of his sons, however, who questioned him at the entrance. The old man did not answer but returned with his son to the village, angered at having been surprised. This contact with a human being took place after he had left the world of men. He thus became impure for the Yeban, his metamorphosis could not be consummated, and he died. It is said that he was the first to die in the human stage. His name was Lebe.

(DOGON)

[1] Yeban are spirits in which men were transformed before death entered the world. They are tiny with big heads and make women pregnant.

PART TWO

TALES

3

TRICKSTER TALES

51 HOW SPIDER READ THE SKY GOD'S THOUGHTS

The Sky God begat three children, who were Esum (Darkness), Osrane (Moon), and Owia (Sun). When his three children grew up, the sky god made them go to separate villages. The first one built his village, the second one also built his village, and the third one, he too built his village. And there they lived.

Now their father loved Sun most. And while the sky god was reigning there, he blackened a stool and said to his attendants, "Who knows what my thoughts are?" Ananse the spider said, "As for me, I know them." At the time when he said, "As for me, I know them," the sky god made all the attendants rise up. There and then the spider also rose up, saying he was going to the villages of the sky god's children.

When Ananse reached the path, he said to himself, "I do not know his thoughts and yet I said, 'I know them.'" And he plucked some feathers out of every bird, stuck them on himself and flew off, alighting on a *gyedua* tree in the sky god's village. And when the people saw the bird, they all made a great commotion which sounded like *Ye-e-e-e!* And the sky god came out of the house and came under the *gyedua* tree and said, "Were Ananse here, he would have known the name of this bird. I had decided that Owia, Sun, is the one I wanted to make a chief, so I asked who knew what was in my head and Ananse said that he did. Now I have gone and pulled up the yam known as 'Kintinkyi,' and he who knows its name and utters it, to him I shall give it, my blackened stool. That is why Ananse has gone off to bring my children. Had he been here, he would have known the name of this bird."

Then the bird flew off, and Ananse pulled out the feathers and threw them away, and set out till he reached the village of Night. To Night he said, "Your father said that you must come with me." And Night replied, "It is well, I and you will go." Then Ananse said, "I am going on to fetch Moon and Sun." But Night said to him, "Let me first seek for something to give you to eat." Spider replied, "Ho!" Night thereupon went out and brought some roasted corn and gave it to Ananse. When he had finished chewing it, he set out for Moon's village. When he reached it, he said, "Your father says you must come along with me." And Moon replied, "It is well, I shall go." Then Ananse said, "I shall go on to Sun's village in order to bring him." But Moon said, "Let me first get you something to eat." And Ananse replied, "Ho!" So Moon mashed up some yam for him to eat. Then Spider set out for Sun's village. When he reached Sun's village, he said to him, "Your father says you must come along with me." And Sun said, "It is well, I and you shall go, but let me get you something to eat first." Ananse replied, "Ho!" So Sun went and caught a sheep. When he came back, he said to Ananse, "I would have wished, had my father come here, that he should have seen what I was doing; if it were good, or if it were bad, in either case he would have seen. Since, however, he has not come and you have come, it is as if Father had come. Therefore here is this, my sheep, that I shall kill so you may eat."

And he killed the sheep and prepared it beautifully for Spider to eat. After the meal Ananse said, "Let us go on a fallen tree." When they got there, Ananse said to Sun, "Your father has blackened a stool at his home. He wishes you to succeed to that stool, so he has pulled up a yam and if you know its name, he will take the stool and give it to you. Now this yam is called 'Kintinkyi.' And in order that you may not forget its name, I shall cut a short drum for you, and make a *mpintini* drum to go with it, so that when they beat the short drum and the *mpintini* drum then you will never forget this word, for the short drum will speak out and say:

> 'Firi bomo!
> Firi bomo!'

Then the *mpintini* drum will say:

> 'Kintinkyi bomo!
> Kintinkyi bomo!' "

So they set off to go to the sky god's town. First they reached Moon's village and took him along; then they reached Night's village and took him along. All the way they played the *mpintini* drum. When they reached the outskirts of the town Ananse saw a man, and he sent him off to tell the sky god that they were coming. Thereupon the sky god called an assembly together, and soon Ananse and the others arrived and saluted everyone. Ananse now gave the spokesman the news, saying, "The chief's errand on which I was sent I have performed; I have brought them." And the sky god said, "My children, the reason I caused you to be sent for is this: I have blackened the stool standing there and I have also pulled up the yam over there. I shall now take this stool and give it to him who sees and names the yam. Because my eldest child is Night, let him try first." Then Night said, "It is called 'Pona.' " And all the people shouted, *"Ye-e-e-e."* Again the sky god spoke, "My second child is Moon, therefore let him give its name." And Moon said, "It is the yam called 'Asante.' " The people shouted, *"Ye-e-e-e."* Again the sky god spoke, "My child, the third one, is Sun, therefore let him name it."

Now, I forgot to say that the dance music was going on:

Kintinkyi bomo!
Kintinkyi bomo!

and Ananse was turning cartwheels.

Then Sun rose up and stood there, and took hold of the
yam, and he said, "Oh, as for this, since ever I began
to walk beside my father and was very small, he used
to tell me its name, and I have not forgotten; it is called
'Kintinkyi.'" And the tribe shouted applause three times,
"E!-E!-E!"

Then his father rose up and stood there and said, "You,
Night, you are the eldest, but the words which I told you
you have allowed yourself to forget, because you did not
pay attention to my words. Because of this, it is now decreed
that wicked things only will be done during your time. And
you, Moon, the words with which you and I walked and I
told you, you too, did not follow. It is decreed therefore
that only children will play during your reign. As for you,
Sun, when I said words to you, you did not forget; you listened to my advice, so you are to be the chief. Should anyone have any matter to settle, let it be heard in your time.
Household cases, however, may be heard in the evening.

"So take the path which I have set you and if Moon
wishes to trespass upon it, may Kon-ton-ku-rowie, the circu-
lar rainbow seen at times around the sun, throw itself
around you, so that Moon may not be able to come and
touch you. Again, if the rainclouds gather, the sky god's
bow will be cast on the sky that your children who are
under you may see when I have cast it so that the waters
will not overflow and carry them away.

"One more thing. These words which were formerly
known as the 'Sayings of the Sky God,' now since Ananse,
the spider, has been able to read these words in my head, let
them be known henceforth as 'The Sayings of Spider.'"

(ASHANTI)

52 HOW SPIDER OBTAINED THE SKY GOD'S STORIES

Kwaku Ananse the spider once went to Nyan-konpon, the
sky god, in order to buy the sky god's stories. The sky god
said, "What makes you think *you* can buy them?" The spider
answered and said, "I know I shall be able." Thereupon the
sky god said, "Great and powerful towns like Kokofu,
Bekwai, Asumengya, have come, but they were unable to
purchase them, and yet you who are but a mere masterless
man, you say you will be able?"

The spider said, "What is the price of the stories?" The
sky god said, "They cannot be bought for anything except
Onini the python; Osebo the leopard; Mmoatia the fairy;
and Mmoboro the hornet." The spider said, "I will bring
some of all these things, and, what is more, I'll add my old
mother, Nsia, the sixth child, to the lot."

The sky god said, "Go and bring them then." The spider
came back and told his mother all about it, saying, "I wish
to buy the stories of the sky god, and the sky god says I
must bring Onini the python; Osebo the leopard; Mmoatia
the fairy; and Mmoboro the hornet; and I said I would add
you to the lot and give you to the sky god." Now the spider
consulted his wife Aso, saying, "What is to be done that we
may get Onini the python?" Aso said to him, "You go off
and cut a branch of a palm tree, and cut some string-creeper
as well, and bring them." And the spider came back with
them. And Aso said, "Take them to the stream." So Ananse
took them; and, as he was going along, he said, "It's longer
than he is, it's not so long as he; you lie, it's longer than he."

The spider said, "There he is, lying yonder." The python,
who had overheard this imaginary conversation, then asked,
"What's this all about?" To which the spider replied, "Is it

not my wife Aso who is arguing with me that this palm
branch is longer than you, and I say she is a liar." And
Onini the python, said, "Bring it, and come and measure me."
Ananse took the palm branch and laid it along the python's
body. Then he said, "Stretch yourself out." And the python
stretched himself out, and Ananse took the rope-creeper
and wound it and the sound of the tying was *nwenene!
nwenene! nwenene!* until he came to the head.

Ananse the spider said, "Fool, I shall take you to the sky
god and receive the sky god's tales in exchange." So Ananse
took him off to Nyame, the sky god. The sky god then said,
"My hand has touched it, there remains what still remains."
The spider returned and came and told his wife what had
happened, saying, "There remain the hornets." His wife
said, "Look for a gourd, and fill it with water and go off with
it." The spider went along through the bush, when he saw a
swarm of hornets hanging there and he poured out some of
the water and sprinkled it on them. He then poured the
remainder upon himself and cut a leaf of plantain and covered his head with it. And now he addressed the hornets,
saying, "As the rain has come, had you not better come and
enter this, my gourd, so that the rain will not beat you;
don't you see that I have taken a plantain leaf to cover myself?" Then the hornets said, "We thank you, Aku, we thank
you, Aku." All the hornets flew, disappearing into the gourd,
fom! Father Spider covered the mouth and exclaimed,
"Fools, I have got you, and I am taking you to receive the
tales of the sky god in exchange."

And he took the hornets to the sky god. The sky god said,
"My hand has touched it; what remains still remains."

The spider came back once more, and told his wife, and
said, "There remains Osebo the leopard." Aso said, "Go and
dig a hole." Ananse said, "That's enough, I understand."
Then the spider went off to look for the leopard's tracks,
and, having found them, he dug a very deep pit, covered it
over, and came back home. Very early next day, when
objects began to be visible, the spider said he would go off,
and when he went, lo, a leopard was lying in the pit. Ananse

said, "Little father's child, little mother's child, I have told you not to get drunk, and now, just as one would expect of you, you have become intoxicated, and that's why you have fallen into the pit. If I were to say I would get you out, next day, if you saw me, or likewise any of my children, you would go and catch me and them." The leopard said, "O! I could not do such a thing."

Ananse then went and cut two sticks, put one here, and one there, and said, "Put one of your paws here, and one also of your paws here." And the leopard placed them where he was told. As he was about to climb up, Ananse lifted up his knife, and in a flash it descended on his head; *gao!* was the sound it made. The pit received the leopard and *fom!* was the sound of the falling. Ananse got a ladder to descend into the pit to go and get the leopard out. He got the leopard out and came back with it, exclaiming, "Fool, I am taking you to exchange for the stories of the sky god." He lifted up the leopard to go and give to Nyame, the sky god. The sky god said, "My hands have touched it; what remains still remains."

Then the spider came back, carved an Akua's child, a black flat-faced wooden doll, tapped some sticky fluid from a tree and plastered the doll's body with it. Then he made *eto*, pounded yams, and put some in the doll's hand. Again he pounded some more and placed it in a brass basin; he tied string round the doll's waist, and went with it and placed it at the foot of the odum tree, the place where the fairies come to play. And a fairy came along. She said, "Akua, may I eat a little of this mash?" Ananse tugged at the string, and the doll nodded her head. The fairy turned to one of the sisters, saying, "She says I may eat some." She said, "Eat some, then." And she finished eating, and thanked her. But when she thanked her, the doll did not answer. And the fairy said to her sister, "When I thank her, she does not reply." The sister of the first fairy said, "Slap her crying-place." And she slapped it, *pa!* And her hand stuck there. She said to her sister, "My hand has stuck there." She said, "Take the one that remains and slap her

crying-place again." And she took it and slapped her, *pa!*
and this one, too, stuck fast. And the fairy told her sister,
saying, "My two hands have stuck fast." She said, "Push it
with your stomach." She pushed it and her stomach stuck
to it. And Ananse came and tied her up, and he said, "Fool,
I have got you, I shall take you to the sky god in exchange
for his stories." And he went off home with her.

Now Ananse spoke to his mother, Ya Nsia, the sixth
child, saying, "Rise up, let us go, for I am taking you along
with the fairy to go and give you to the sky god in exchange
for his stories." He lifted them up, and went off there to
where the sky god was. Arrived there he said, "Sky god,
here is a fairy and my old woman whom I spoke about, here
she is, too." Now the sky god called his elders, the Kontire
and Akwam chiefs, the Adonten, the Gyase, the Oyoko,
Ankobea, and Kyidom. And he put the matter before them,
saying, "Very great kings have come, and were not able to
buy the sky god's stories, but Kwaku Ananse the spider has
been able to pay the price: I have received from him Osebo
the leopard; I have received from him Onini the python;
and of his own accord, Ananse has added his mother to the
lot; all these things lie here." He said, "Sing his praise."
"Eee!" they shouted. The sky god said, "Kwaku Ananse,
from today and going on forever, I take my sky god's stories
and I present them to you, *kose! kose! kose!* my blessing,
blessing, blessing! No more shall we call them the stories of
the sky god, but we shall call them spider stories."

This, my story, which I have related, if it be sweet, or if it
be not sweet, take some elsewhere, and let some come back
to me.

(ASHANTI)

53 HOW DISEASES CAME TO THE ASHANTI

Now there lived Kwaku Ananse the spider, and he went to
Nyankonpon the sky god and said, "Grandsire, take your

sheep called Kra Kwame, the one which you keep to sacrifice to your soul on a Saturday, and let me kill and eat it, that I may go and bring you a beautiful girl in exchange."

The sky god gave him the sheep, and Ananse set out and returned to his village and killed the sheep and ate it. The spider then went to a certain village. In that village there was not a single male—all were women. Ananse married them all and he and they lived there.

One day a hunter came and saw them. When he left, he went and said to the sky god, "As for Ananse and that sheep of yours which he received, he has killed it and given it to some women to eat and then married them."

The sky god said, "Is it true?"

The hunter said, "Grandsire, it is the truth."

The sky god then sent messengers, telling them to go to that village and bring to him all the women who were there.

The messengers went off, met the women, and, with the exception of one woman who was ill, took them all to the sky god.

Ananse said, "You who remain, what can I do with you? You can't do anything for me."

The sick woman said, "Go and bring me a gourd cup." Ananse went and brought a gourd cup.

She said, "Bathe me, and take the water you have used and pour it into this gourd."

Ananse bathed her body and poured the water he had used into the gourd. She then became very beautiful; there was no woman like her in the tribe. Then Ananse married her again, although she was already his.

Now the hunter came again, and he saw this woman. He went off and reported to the sky god, saying, "Ananse has made a fool of you, he sent you the ugly women and has kept the beautiful one for himself."

The sky god sent messengers and directed them to go to the village where the spider was and to bring the woman to him.

They delivered the message of the sky god to Ananse. He

said, "Would he not like me to come also?"

The messengers said, "The sky god said we must take the woman to him."

Ananse said, "That is she sitting there, take her away."

After she had been taken, Ananse went and got the gourd into which all the diseases he had taken from the woman had been poured, and he stretched a skin over the mouth of it. Then he stretched a skin over another gourd and gave it to his child Ntikuma, and Ananse beat on the drum he had made and sang:

> *Y'odende dende den,*
> *Y'odende den.*
>   Aso Ya-e!
> *Y'odende dende den.* Aso Ya-e!
>   Your eyes are red in vain!
> *Y'odende den.* Aso Ya-e!
>   You are bandy-armed!
> *Y'odende*
>   Is that Aso Ya?
> *Y'odende dende den.* Aso Ya-e!
>   You are knock-kneed!
> *Y'odende den.* Aso Ya-e!
>   Your nose is a lump on your face!
> *Y'odende den.* Aso Ya-e!
>   Your feet are large as paddles, like those of a slave!
> *Y'odende den.* Aso Ya-e!
>   Your head is like a cow!
> *Y'odende dende den,*
> *Y'odende den.*

Ntikuma drummed and sang:

> *Beautiful maiden,*
> *Beautiful maiden!*

And Afudotwedotwe or Belly-Like-to-Burst and Nyi-wankonfwea or Thin-Shanks, Ananse's children, danced.

Anene the crow ran with speed and told the sky god, "Ananse has a dance which is fitting for you but not for a spider."

Immediately the sky god sent messengers there to Ananse to go and bring him this dance.

Ananse said, "This dance of mine, we perform it only in the harem, and if the sky god agrees then I shall bring it along."

The messengers returned and told the sky god. The sky god said, "That is nothing, let him bring it to the harem." Ananse went with the drums to the harem, and the sky god came and danced, and all his wives danced.

Now, there remained the one who had been sick. When she saw that Ananse had stretched a skin over the gourd in which were all her diseases, because of that she said she would not dance. And now the sky god forced her, and she came; and when she was about to dance, Ananse lifted up the gourd and struck the woman with it, and the diseases scattered with a sound like *tese!*

That is how syphilis, stomachache, headache, leprosy, Guinea worm, smallpox, yaws, fits, diabetes, and madness came among the tribe. Once there was no sickness among mankind. It was the sky god who was the cause of Ananse's bringing diseases among the tribe.

(ASHANTI)

54 SPIDER PASSES ON A DEBT

There was once a certain Woman who had a Daughter, and, when she was going to give her in marriage, the Daughter said that she had no basins and no plates and that she would not be married without them. So the Mother, who had a Bull, took it to the Slaughtermen and asked them to buy it, ten basins and ten plates was the price. But they said that they could not give that for it.

Now the Spider heard, and he came up and said that he would buy the Bull, and that when the marriage was about to be performed he would bring ten plates and ten basins. So the Woman handed over the Bull to the Spider, and he took it home and killed it.

When he had cooked it, he poured the broth into a pot, and took it and placed it in the road, and he climbed a tree above, and hid there. Now the Goat was passing, and he was very thirsty, so he came up and put his nose into the pot, and immediately the pot caught hold of his nose. Then the Spider slid down and said "Good." And he continued:

"The Spider is the Buyer of the Old Woman's Bull
For ten large basins and ten large plates;
The payment is upon you now, O, He-Goat."

And the He-Goat replied "Very well, I agree."
So he went to the river to drink water, and there a Crab seized his nose, and then he said:

"The He-Goat is the Drinker of the Spider's broth;
The Spider is the Buyer of the Old Woman's Bull
For ten large basins and ten large plates;
The payment is upon you, O Crab."

And the Crab replied "Very well, I agree.
Now when the Daughter came to the stream, she trod upon the Crab, and the Crab said:

"The Daughter has stepped on the poor little Crab;
The Crab is the Catcher of the He-Goat's beard;
The He-Goat is the Drinker of the Spider's broth;
The Spider is the Buyer of the Old Woman's Bull
For ten large basins and ten large plates;
The payment is upon you, O Daughter."

And the Daughter said "Very well, I agree."
So the Daughter took the water which she had come to

get, and was going home, when the Slipperiness caused her to fall, and she spilt the water. Then she said:

"Slipperiness made the Daughter fall;
The Daughter is the Stepper on the poor little Crab;
The Crab is the Catcher of the He-Goat's beard;
The He-Goat is the Drinker of the Spider's broth;
The Spider is the Buyer of the Old Woman's Bull
For ten large basins and ten large plates;
The payment is upon you, O Slipperiness."

And the Slipperiness said "Very well, I agree."

Now the Slipperiness stayed on the ground, and soon afterward a White Ant came, and made a passage across the wet place. Then the Slipperiness sang:

"The White Ant has built on the Slipperiness;
The Slipperiness made the Daughter fall;
The Daughter is the Stepper on the poor little Crab;
The Crab is the Catcher of the He-Goat's beard;
The He-Goat is the Drinker of the Spider's broth;
The Spider is the Buyer of the Old Woman's Bull
For ten large basins and ten large plates;
The payment is upon you, O White Ant."

And the White Ant said "Very well, I agree."

After a little while a certain Bird came and built a nest upon the White Ant's hill, and then the White Ant said:

"The Bird has alighted on the White Ant's hill;
The White Ant built on the Slipperiness;
The Slipperiness made the Daughter fall;
The Daughter is the Stepper on the poor little Crab;
The Crab is the Catcher of the He-Goat's beard;
The He-Goat is the Drinker of the Spider's broth;
The Spider is the Buyer of the Old Woman's Bull
For ten large basins and ten large plates;
The payment is upon you, O Bird."

And the Bird said "Very well, I agree."

Now the Bird stayed there, and one day a Boy who was shooting came along, and when he saw the Bird sitting on the Anthill he shot it. Then the Bird said:

"The Boy is the Shooter of the poor little Bird;
The Bird alighted on the White Ant's hill;
The White Ant built on the Slipperiness;
The Slipperiness made the Daughter fall;
The Daughter is the Stepper on the poor little Crab;
The Crab is the Catcher of the He-Goat's beard;
The He-Goat is the Drinker of the Spider's broth;
The Spider is the Buyer of the Old Woman's Bull
For ten large basins and ten large plates;
The payment is upon you, O Boy."

And the Boy said "Very well, I agree."

So the Boy went home, and just as he had opened his mouth to tell his Mother about it, she covered him with blows. Then the Boy said:

"The Mother is the Beater of the poor little Boy;
The Boy is the Shooter of the poor little Bird;
The Bird alighted on the White Ant's hill;
The White Ant built on the Slipperiness;
The Slipperiness made the Daughter fall;
The Daughter is the Stepper on the poor little Crab;
The Crab is the Catcher of the He-Goat's beard;
The He-Goat is the Drinker of the Spider's broth;
The Spider is the Buyer of the Old Woman's Bull
For ten large basins and ten large plates;
The payment is upon you, O Mother."

And the Mother said "Very well, I agree."

Now it happened soon afterward that a certain Blacksmith burned one of the Mother's cloths, and then she said:

"The Blacksmith is the Burner of the Mother's cloth;

The Mother is the Beater of the poor little Boy;
The Boy is the Shooter of the poor little Bird;
The Bird alighted on the White Ant's hill;
The White Ant built on the Slipperiness;
The Slipperiness made the Daughter fall;
The Daughter is the Stepper on the poor little Crab;
The Crab is the Catcher of the He-Goat's beard;
The He-Goat is the Drinker of the Spider's broth;
The Spider is the Buyer of the Old Woman's Bull
For ten large basins and ten large plates;
The payment is upon you, O Blacksmith."

Then the Blacksmith said "Very well, I agree."
Immediately all the Blacksmiths started work, and
made ten basins and ten plates, and took them to the
Woman. The Woman took them, and gave them to the Boy.
The Boy took them, and gave them to the Bird. The Bird
took them, and gave them to the White Ant. The White Ant
took them, and gave them to the Slipperiness. The Slipperiness took them, and gave them to the Daughter. The Daughter took them, and gave them to the Crab. The Crab took
them, and gave them to the He-Goat. The He-Goat took
them, and gave them to the Spider. And the Spider took
them, and gave them to the Old Woman.

That is an example of the Spider's cunning. He himself
ate the flesh of the Bull, but he made others make the payment for him, he gave nothing in return for what he had got.

(HAUSA)

55 SPIDER PAYS HIS DEBTS

The Spider had contracted a number of debts, he had borrowed from every Beast of the forest, and he took counsel

with himself as to what he should do, for he had no money
with which to pay. So he gave out that on the Friday all the
Creditors should come and receive payment.

When Friday had come, while it was still early in the
morning, the Hen arrived to collect her debt. And when
she had come the Spider said, "Good, I will pay you at
once, but wait a minute or two while I prepare you some
food." So the Hen was waiting inside the hut, and soon the
Wildcat came. Then the Spider said, "Good, the repayment
is in the hut, go and take it." So the Wildcat went and
entered the hut, and seized the Hen, and twisted her neck.

Just as he was about to go off, the Dog arrived, and the
Spider said, "Good, the repayment is in the hut, go and
take it." So the Dog went and seized the Wildcat, and bit
him, and killed him. Just as he was about to go, the Hyena
arrived, and the Spider said, "Good, the repayment is in
the hut, go and take it." So the Hyena ran in and seized the
Dog, and ate him up. Just as she was about to leave, lo! the
Leopard appeared, and the Spider said, "Good, the repayment is in the hut, go and take it." So the Leopard sprang
upon the Hyena, and killed her. Just as she was about to
leave who should arrive but the Lion, and he came upon the
Leopard.

So they began to fight, and while they were fighting and
fighting, the Spider took some pepper and poured it into
their eyes. When he had done this, he took up a big stick and
began to beat them, and he beat them until they were dead,
both of them. Then the Spider collected the meat in his
house, and said that he had extinguished his debts.

(HAUSA)

56 THE RACE

A frog challenged a deer to a race. Before the day appointed
for the contest, the frog entered into a league with all his

companions and arranged that they should station themselves at regular intervals along the course, and that each should wait in readiness to answer the calls of the deer as he raced along toward the goal. The race started. The deer thought to outstrip the frog with ease, and soon called back in mocking tones to ask where the frog was. To his surprise the answer, "Here I am," came from the opposite direction to what he expected. He raced along once more and repeated the challenge. Again a voice answered from in front of him, and once more he was deceived and thought he was being left behind in the race. The strategy was repeated all along the course until the deer fell down exhausted and died.

(IBO)

57 THE RABBIT AND THE ANTELOPE

It was during an almost rainless "hot season," when all who had no wells were beginning to feel the pangs of thirst, that the rabbit and the antelope formed a partnership to dig a deep well so that they could never be in want of water.

"Let us finish our food," said the antelope, "and be off to our work."

"Nay," said the rabbit; "had we not better keep the food for later on, when we are tired and hungry after our work?"

"Very well, hide the food, rabbit; and let us get to work, I am very thirsty."

They arrived at the place where they purposed having the well, and worked hard for a short time.

"Listen!" said the rabbit; "they are calling me to go back to town."

"Nay, I do not hear them."

"Yes, they are certainly calling me, and I must be off. My

wife is about to present me with some children, and I must name them."

"Go then, dear rabbit, but come back as soon as you can."

The rabbit ran off to where he had hidden the food, and ate some of it, and then went back to his work.

"Well!" said the antelope, "what have you called your little one?"

"Uncompleted one," said the rabbit.

"A strange name," said the antelope.

Then they worked for a while.

"Again they are calling me," cried the rabbit. "I must be off, so please excuse me. Cannot you hear them calling me?"

"No," said the antelope, "I hear nothing."

Away ran the rabbit, leaving the poor antelope to do all the work, while he ate some more of the food that really belonged to them both. When he had had enough, he hid the food again, and ran back to the well.

"And what have you called your last, rabbit?"

"Half-completed one."

"What a funny little fellow you are! But come, get on with the digging; see how hard I have worked."

Then they worked hard for quite a long time. "Listen, now!" said the rabbit, "surely you heard them calling me this time!"

"Nay, dear rabbit, I can hear nothing; but go, and get back quickly."

Away ran the rabbit, and this time he finished the food before going back to his work.

"Well, little one, what have you called your third child?"

"Completed," answered the rabbit. Then they worked hard and as night was setting in returned to their village.

"I am terribly tired, rabbit; run and get the food, or I shall faint."

The rabbit went to look for the food, and then calling out to the antelope, told him that some horrid cat must have been there, as the food was all gone, and the pot quite clean. The antelope groaned, and went hungry to bed.

The next day the naughty little rabbit played the antelope

the same trick. And the next day he again tricked the antelope. And the next, and the next, until at last the antelope accused the rabbit of stealing the food. Then the rabbit got angry, and dared him to take casca, a purge or emetic.

"Let us both take it," said the antelope, "and let him whose tail is the first to become wet be considered the guilty one."

So they took the casca and went to bed. And as the medicine began to take effect upon the rabbit, he cried out to the antelope:

"See, your tail is wet!"

"Nay, it is not!"

"Yes, it is!"

"No, but yours is, dear rabbit; see there!"

Then the rabbit feared greatly, and tried to run away. But the antelope said: "Fear not, rabbit; I will do you no harm. Only you must promise not to drink of the water of my well, and to leave my company forever."

Accordingly the rabbit left him and went his way.

Some time after this, a bird told the antelope that the rabbit used to drink the water of the well every day. Then the antelope was greatly enraged, and determined to kill the rabbit. So the antelope laid a trap for the silly little rabbit. He cut a piece of wood and shaped it into the figure of an animal about the size of the rabbit; and then he placed this figure firmly in the ground near to the well, and smeared it all over with birdlime.

The rabbit went as usual to drink the waters of the well, and was much annoyed to find an animal there, as he thought, drinking the water also.

"And what may you be doing here, sir?" said the rabbit to the figure.

The figure answered not.

Then the rabbit, thinking that it was afraid of him, went close up to it, and again asked what he was doing there.

But the figure made no answer.

"What!" said the rabbit. "Do you mean to insult me? Answer me at once, or I will strike you."

The figure answered not.

Then the little rabbit lifted up his right hand, and smacked the figure in the face. His hand stuck to the figure.

"What's the matter?" said the rabbit. "Let my hand go, sir, at once, or I will hit you again."

The figure held fast to the rabbit's right hand. Then the rabbit hit the figure a swinging blow with his left. The left hand stuck to the figure also.

"What can be the matter with you, sir? You are excessively silly. Let my hands go at once, or I will kick you."

And the rabbit kicked the figure with his right foot; but his right foot stuck there. Then he got into a great rage, and kicked the figure with his left. And his left leg stuck to the figure also. Then, overcome with rage, he bumped the figure with his head and stomach, but these parts also stuck to the figure. Then the rabbit cried with impotent rage. The antelope, just about this time, came along to drink water; and when he saw the rabbit helplessly fastened to the figure, he laughed at him, and then killed him.

(BAKONGO)

58 THE HARE

Hare, that wily trickster, went to live with Gray Antelope. One day he said to her, "Suppose we go and till our fields and plant some beans!" So off they went and set to work. Antelope stole Hare's beans, and Hare stole Antelope's beans, but Hare did most of the stealing.

Hare set a trap in his field, and Antelope was caught by the leg. In the early morning the cunning rascal went out and found Antelope caught in the trap. "Don't you think you deserve to be killed," said he, "now that I have found you out?"

"No! No!" she cried. "Let me go, and we will go back to my house where I will give you a hoe." So he let her go, and she gave him the hoe.

Hare then packed his beans, harvested all his fields, and made ready to be off. "Good-bye," he said to Antelope. "I won't stay with you any longer. You are a thief!"

Hare soon came across the great lizard Varan lying at the edge of a waterhole. It was the chief's waterhole, where they drew their water, and he had been placed there on guard to find out who it was that was continually disturbing it and making it muddy. "What are you doing here?" said Hare.

"I am watching this hole to see who it is that muddies the chief's water."

"I'll tell you what," said Hare, "we had much better go and till a field together."

"How can I dig?" said Varan. "I can't stand on my hind legs and hold the hoe in my forepaws."

"That doesn't matter! Just come along. I will tie the hoe to your tail and you will be able to dig beautifully."

So the hoe was tied on, but when this was done Varan could not move. Then Hare ran back to the hole, drank his fill of water, and finished by stirring it up well, making it as muddy as possible. After this he walked all over Varan's fields and regaled himself on his groundnuts. In the heat of the day he came back and said, "Ho! An army has passed through the country. I hear that the warriors have dirtied the water in the hole. I hear, too, that they have ravaged all your crop of groundnuts!"

"Untie me!" said Varan. "I can't budge."

"All right, but only on condition that you don't go and accuse me, Hare, of having stirred up the water."

"But who told you this story about those soldiers who did all the mischief?"

"Don't ask me so many questions. If you do, I won't untie you!"

"Very well! I'll be quiet, but take away this hoe. It hurts me!"

"Listen! First of all, I'll go and draw some water for you. You must be thirsty."

"No, I'm not thirsty. Only let me go!"

"If you are not thirsty, all right! I won't untie the hoe."

"Oh, very well, I am thirsty. Hurry up, and come back as fast as you can."

Hare went to Varan's village, took the wooden goblet from which he always drank, drew some water, and once again stirred up the hole. He took a drink to Varan, and said to him, "If anyone asks you whether I have disturbed the water, you must say that you did it. If you don't promise me this, I won't untie you."

"All right. Very well."

Then Hare ran to call the chiefs—Lord Elephant, Lord Lion, and the rest. They all came and asked Varan, "Who has been drawing our water and making it all muddy?"

"It is I," said Varan.

And Hare, the rascal, added, "Yes, I found him committing this crime and I tied him up to a hoe, so that he couldn't run away."

The chiefs congratulated Hare. "Ah! you have been very clever! You have discovered the villain who has been muddying our pool!" And they immediately killed Varan.

The wily trickster Hare took the hoe and then went to look for Gray Antelope. She was on sentry duty, on the edge of a pool, for guards were placed at all the pools to prevent anyone from approaching, as the water still continued to be muddied during the night. Hare, not being able to get anything to drink, said to Antelope, "What are you doing there so close to the water?"

"I am guarding the chief's pool."

"You will get thin and die of hunger, if you stay like that at the edge of the pool. Listen! You would do much better to come with me and till a field. Then, in time of famine, you would have something to eat."

"Let us go!" said Antelope.

Hare set to work in grand style. He gave Antelope a hoe and told her to dig. "I can't get on my hind legs," said she, "and hold the hoe with my forelegs."

"Let me have a look at your forelegs. I'll tie the hoe to them, and you will be able to dig all right."

Antelope tried, but she couldn't do it.

"Never mind," said Hare. "Wait a minute." He ran back to the pool, quenched his thirst, and muddied the water. Then he filled a calabash and hid it in the bush. On returning to Antelope, he said, "Hello! Haven't you done any hoeing yet?"

"No, I can't manage it."

"Would you believe it! An army has passed by, and they have stirred up the pool."

"No! Truly? Untie me, Hare!"

"I won't untie you unless you swear that what I said is true."

"Very well! Untie me."

Off Hare went to get the calabash to give her a drink, and he made her promise to confess that it was she who had disturbed the water. Then he called the chiefs, who killed Antelope.

But there was one creature that outdid Hare in cunning and that was Tortoise. She mounted guard at the pond. Hare arrived there. "You will die of hunger, if you stay at the edge of the pool with nothing to do. We had much better go and till a field together."

"How can I hoe with such short legs?" asked Tortoise.

"Oh! That will be all right. I'll show you how to do it."

"Eh! No thank you! I think not!"

"Well then! Let's go and help ourselves to some of the wild boar's sweet potatoes."

"No," said Tortoise uncompromisingly. "No pilfering!"

However, before long Tortoise began to feel hungry, so much so that when Hare again proposed a marauding expedition, she overcame her scruples and they went off together to root up the sweet potatoes. Then they lighted a fire of grass in the bush and roasted them.

"Tortoise," said Hare, "just go and see if the owners of

these fields are anywhere about, as we must not let them catch us."

"Yes, but let us both go. You go one way and I'll go the other."

Off went Hare, but Tortoise, instead of following his example, stayed behind and crawled into Hare's sack. Hare soon came back, filled up his bag with sweet potatoes, threw it over his back, and ran away to escape the proprietors, shouting at the top of his voice, "Hi, Tortoise! Look out! They will catch you! I'm off! Fly!"

He ran as hard as he could to escape capture. Tortoise, inside the sack, ate the sweet potatoes. She picked out all the best ones and finished the lot. She said, being satisfied, *"Kutlu."* After a while Hare was tired out and lay down quite exhausted. He felt the pangs of hunger.

"'Aha!" said he to himself. "I will have a good feed!" He sat down in a shady spot, opened his sack, put his hand inside, and pulled out one very small sweet potato. "This is much too small for me," said he, and putting his hand in again, felt a nice big one. "Oho! Here's a beauty!" When he had pulled it out of his bag, what was his surprise to find that his potato turned out to be Mistress Tortoise!

"Hello! Why! It's you!" he cried in disgust and threw her on the ground. She scuttled away as fast and as far as she could. Then Hare began to wail, "When I think that I have been carrying her all this time!" He felt very crestfallen.

Continuing his travels, Hare next met King Lion, surrounded by his courtiers. He at once asked permission to swear allegiance to the king and to settle in that country. But every day he went out to steal other folk's groundnuts. When the owners of the fields came to look at their crops, they exclaimed, "Who can it be that digs up our groundnuts?"

Hare went off to find King Lion and said to him, "Sire, your subjects are not what they should be, for they are in the habit of stealing."

"Indeed!" said Lion. "Go and keep watch, and if you discover anyone stealing, catch him."

Hare went off to take up his position in the fields, but Lion followed him and surprised him in the very act of feasting on groundnuts. "Ha! Ha! You tell me that my subjects are not honest folk, while it is you who do the thieving!"

"Not at all! I was only keeping a lookout! Come here, and I will show you the footprints of your subjects, for I know them well!"

So they went to a large shady banyan tree. Hare made a strong string of one of the long tendrils and said to Lion, "As you think I don't speak the truth, just sit down here and you will soon see the thieves passing by. I shall while away the time by making you a crown of wax."

"All right," said Lion, "make me a crown."

Hare began by parting Lion's mane down the middle and arranging the hairs carefully, one by one, on either side of his neck, as if he were preparing a spot on the top of his head for a crown. Then he made holes through the bark of the tree, on both sides of the trunk, and passed the hairs of the mane right through them, some on one side, some on the other. This done, he tied all the hairs securely together at the back of the tree with the string he had made, and he said to Lion, "I've finished the job. Jump up quickly and you will see one of your subjects stealing in the fields!"

Lion tried to jump up. He couldn't! He half killed himself struggling to get on his feet!

Hare ran to the village. "Come," he shouted, "and see who it is who ravages your fields!" He had previously torn up a lot of groundnut leaves and thrown them down close to the Lion. The villagers hurried to the spot.

"There! Don't you see him? Haven't I found him out, eh?" Lion didn't dare to say a single word.

Then his subjects cut great staves and beat him to death. "Ah! Hare, you are very clever, and we are grateful!" they said.

Hare cut Lion up into pieces. Then he took the skin and wrapped himself in it. Thus disguised, he went to Lion's village and entered the queen's hut. He said, "I am not well," and shut himself up, refusing to see anyone. He gave orders

to the servants to kill an ox because he was ill. Then he had
a second one slaughtered, then a third.

The women said to him, "Are you going to move to
another place, since you are killing all your oxen?"

"No," said Hare. "I have no intention of moving any
more. I am killing them because I know very well that I
shall never get over this illness." So he had a general slaugh-
tering of all Lion's oxen, goats, and sheep, to the very last
head of cattle. When all were killed, he said to the queen,
"Haven't you got my money in your keeping?"

"Yes," she replied.

"Well, bring it all out and put it together with my royal
mat and all my valuables on the village square."

The lion's skin had now acquired a rather loathsome odor,
the flies were settling upon it in swarms, and Hare was by
no means comfortable inside of it.

"What sort of complaint have you got?" asked the queen.
"It is something that smells very nasty."

"Oh! I have only got some sores. I must go and find a
doctor. Good-bye, I shall start at once."

Lion's wife replied, "Then I will go with you, my husband."

"No," said he. "No occasion for that, for I know exactly
where I must go."

He went out to the square, picked up the mat in which all
the money and valuables had been packed, and then, throwing off the lion's skin, he tore away as fast as his legs could
carry him with all the village in pursuit.

Hare came to a burrow, and in he ran. The pursuers got
a hooked stick to pull him out. They tried to hook him and
managed to get hold of his leg. "Oh, pull away!" cried he.
"Pull away! You've only got hold of the root of a tree!"

So they left off pulling. They tried again, and this time
they really hooked a root.

"Hi! hi!" he yelled. "Hi! hi! Take care! You're hurting
me! You're killing me! Ow! Ow!"

They all pulled as hard as they could, and they pulled and
pulled until the hook broke and they all fell over backward.

They said, *"Qaa."* Finally they were tired out and said, "Oh! Let us give it up and leave him where he is!" So they stopped up the burrow with a bunch of grass and went away.

The south wind now sprang up and blew the grass deeper into the burrow. "I am done for," said Hare to himself, as he fancied they were succeeding in getting nearer to him. He was suffering the pangs of hunger and was terribly thirsty, but did not dare to leave the burrow, supposing his enemies to be close at hand. At length he cried out, "Have pity on me and let me go, my good fathers, I beseech you!" He crept cautiously toward the entrance of the burrow, and found only a bunch of grass. Then he made off at once, leaving all his treasures behind him, not even giving them a single thought.

He ran on and on. He became thin and ill. He ate grass, but it did not remain in his insides; it passed through him immediately. He came to the home of Gray Antelope. "Say, Antelope, suppose we sew one another up! You stitch me up, but not completely, you know! It will keep the grass much longer in our insides when we browse, and we shall get much more nourishment out of it." Antelope consented, and partially stitched up Hare. Hare sewed her up entirely. Antelope swelled and died. Fortunately for her, however, she fell in a field belonging to a woman who picked her up, put her in her basket on the top of her head, and carried her to the village to be eaten. She gave her to her husband to cut up. He set to work and began by cutting the stitches that Hare had sewn. All that was in Antelope's interior at once came out, she jumped to her legs, and galloped away.

She met Hare, and she said to him, "All right! I've found you out now! Never again do I call you my friend!"

Hare, being thirsty, was looking for a pool but could not find one. At last he came to one where no one was on guard. Tortoise was really in charge, but she was in the water. Hare walked in. "What luck! How nice and cool it is!" said he, quenching his thirst and swimming about. Tortoise snapped at one of his legs, then at another.

"Hello! Let me go! I'll promise you a goat if you will let go!"

They came out of the pool together, and Hare said to her, "Come along to my house, and get your goat." They reached his home, but no goat! Nothing! Hare did not give her anything. Then he remembered the money that he had left in the burrow and said, "Let us go and see Chameleon. He has my valuables, for he borrowed a lot of money from me. I'll just run around and fetch my brother; he knows all about the business and will be my witness." Having said this, Hare ran off. Tortoise arrived at Chameleon's abode and said, "Give me Hare's money which he says you have!"

"What! I haven't anything belonging to Hare!" Whereupon Chameleon blew into Tortoise's eyes. She swelled, and swelled, and died.

That's the end.

Hare came to Lord Lion's village and this Chief took him into his service. The Lion went hunting every day, and it was the Hare's duty to look after the Lion's children, and teach them their lessons. When the Lion returned from hunting, he stopped some distance from the village and sent meat by the Hare for his three little children, saying to him: "Give the little ones the tender meat, for they are young, and you can eat the bones!"

The Hare told the children: "Your father says you are to eat the bones, for they are hard and will make you strong, and I will eat the meat." Thus he regaled himself.

Then he taught them a nice little game. He collected a lot of wood, made a fire, and said: "I will teach you how to jump. You know that your father catches animals by springing upon them, so you too had better learn how to spring properly." He began first: "I will show you the way I jump, and you must do just as I do." He easily cleared the fire in one bound, but when the little Lion cub tried, he jumped right into the flames and was burnt. Then the Hare ate him up.

When the Lion returned in the evening, he said to the

Hare: "Show me my little ones."

He had stopped, as usual, a short way off, so the Hare lifted up one of the cubs saying: "Here is No. 1"; then another: "Here is No. 2"; and, lifting the same one twice: "Here is No. 3."

" 'Tis well!" said the Lion. The next day the Hare repeated his game with the fire. Another cub perished, and was eaten. In the evening he lifted up the one cub that was left three times, and the Lion was quite satisfied. The day following the third cub was cooked and made away with. Then the Hare climbed into a thorny tree and scratched his skin so badly that he was bleeding in several places.

The Lion came back toward nightfall: "What is the matter with you?" said he.

"Alas! my grandfather, a whole band of enemies have been here! They have killed all your children! Just see the wounds their assagais have made all over my body!" He had also taken care to make a quantity of marks on the ground: "You can see their footprints all around. I will go and find out which way they have gone, and we will pursue them!"

The Hare ran off to the mountains, where he found an enormous boulder, so poised that it would require only the slightest push to send it crashing down the steep slope. "This will do!" said he, "it is just exactly what I want!" He went back to the Lion and said to him: "Come along, and hide yourself just where I tell you to. If you hear a great noise, don't look up, don't even raise your head. It will be the enemy coming along, and, if you make any movement, they may see you, and run away. You can kill them when they pass close by you. Here is the spot! Hide yourself in here!" He placed him just below the rocking boulder. Then up he climbed.

"Look out! Here they come!" He pushed the rock; down it fell, crushing the Lion. The Hare came hurriedly down the slope, cut off the Lion's claws, and decamped.

He went farther on, taking with him the jawbone of the Lion he had killed, built an immense enclosure with stakes, and put the jawbone at the entrance. Then he sent this proclamation all through the land: "Come and see! A new and wonderful thing! Teeth growing out of the ground! Quantities of them!" He summoned everyone with his trumpet, and all the animals came into the enclosure, without noticing that there was no way out of it.

He closed the entrance and all were prisoners. Then he said to them: "It is well, you are in the Chief's enclosure. I will go and tell him you have arrived. He will soon be here." He went and decked himself out in a dress entirely covered with small pieces of looking glass: it was so resplendent that it quite dazzled the eyes of all who looked at him. "Here is the King," said they all, on seeing him approach.

Then he addressed them and proclaimed this law: "Know ye all! Hawks, Lions, Tigers, that from henceforth no beast of the field is allowed to kill any other one, or to eat his flesh. Nothing is to be eaten but grass." He appointed a shepherd to see that the animals did not kill each other. The Lions and Tigers grew thin on this diet: it made them ill, and none but the herbivorous animals were in good health.

One day the Hare, having sent all the animals away, took off his glittering coat, and began to browse near the enclosure. Now it happened that a Lion, who was unwell and could not go with the others, had remained behind. He saw the Hare browsing close by, and, casting a glance around to make sure no one was watching, with a single bound he was upon him and devoured him! In the evening all the animals returned, but as the King did not put in an appearance for eight or ten days, their spirits began to revive. They plucked up courage and flew at each other's throats: a terrible carnage was the result; the stakes of the enclosure rotted and all the survivors dispersed. Among these was one of the Hare's brothers, who at once stepped into the shoes of the deceased deceiver and continued his evil ways.

One day the Hen invited the Hare to drink some beer at her house. There he saw the Hen cooking and the Cock roosting with his head under his wing. "Where is his head?" he asked the Hen.

"Oh! he cut it off and sent it round to invite our friends to come. It is only his body that you see there: his head will soon come back."

"No! really! You don't say so? Honor bright?"

"Why certainly!"

"What sort of drugs do you use for this wonderful operation?"

"Oh! none at all! You just take a knife, sharpen it well, and cut your head off!"

"Ah! is that all? I must try it!"

Later on the Hare asked the Hen to drink beer with him. He cut off his head and killed himself. Henceforth the Hen was the most cunning of all the animals!

That is the end!

The Hare and the Baboon built a village together. One day, when they were tipsy, the Hare said to the Baboon: "Let us go and kill our wives!" The idea pleased the Baboon immensely, so they set off to kill them. The Hare went inside the hut and began to hit the big basket, telling his wife at the same time to shriek and cry out. The Baboon heard the cries, and was satisfied that the Hare was indeed killing his wife. So he took a big stick and belabored his wife so that she died, while the Hare had not done his wife any harm, having only belabored the big basket!

One day the Baboon overheard the Hare talking to his wife. He was greatly astonished. "Ha! ha!" he said. "The rascal has played a trick on me; I have killed my wife, and he never killed his!"

Another day the Hare proposed to the Baboon that they should go and steal groundnuts in other folks' fields. The Baboon was quite agreeable, as he was suffering from hunger, having no wife to till his land, or to give him any good food. When they got to the fields they began helping themselves to the groundnuts, dug them up, and ate them.

While they were thus employed the Hare said: "Grandfather, don't tire yourself digging up these groundnuts; leave them alone; just sit down in the shade and I will dig them up for you." The Baboon was very pleased, and took a seat under a shady tree which was close by: then the Hare dug up groundnuts and threw them down in front of the Baboon in such quantities that he was completely hidden behind the pile. He ate them greedily, and with great gusto.

When the Hare saw that the pile was big enough, he went behind the Baboon and said: "Will you let me kill the fleas in your tail?"

"Certainly, little one!" said he.

So the Hare set to work, pretending to be killing fleas, and all the while he was digging a deep hole, as deep as the tail was long, in which he intended to fix it when he should get an opportunity! He tried to put the tail in the hole, but in doing so hurt the Baboon who said: "You are hurting me, Grandson!"

"No," replied the Hare, "I'm not hurting you; I am only playing with your tail!" When the Hare saw that the Baboon had nearly finished his groundnuts, he hurried off to fetch a fresh supply in order to divert the Baboon's attention, while he continued his digging operations.

Once more he tried to insert the tail in the hole; but the Baboon called out: "What are you doing, Grandson?"

"I'm not doing anything, Grandfather!" said he, and continued digging until he had made the hole quite as deep as was necessary. Then he succeeded in putting the entire tail in the hole, right up to the stump; he filled in the earth all round it, and hammered it down with a stick as hard as he could. He tried to pull it out but couldn't, it was so securely fixed in. Seeing the Baboon had again nearly finished his groundnuts, he got another lot, and went behind him to put the finishing touches to his handiwork.

When all was completed to his entire satisfaction, he ran off and clambered to the top of an anthill, and began to shout at the top of his voice: "Hello! Here's the Baboon eating up other folks' groundnuts!"

Hearing this the Baboon scolded the Hare, and told him

not to make such a noise: "My grandson, you must not shout like that before I have finished my groundnuts! You can shout as much as you like when I have done, and we will then run away together."

But the Hare would not obey him, and went on shouting as loud as he could until, at last, the women of the fields heard him and people came running up with their bows and arrows and guns. Then the Hare came down from his ant-hill and took to his heels. As for the Baboon, he was in a great fright, dropped the groundnuts, and tried to make off; but he couldn't move, as his tail was hard and fast in the ground! When he saw the folks approaching nearer and nearer, he made the most frantic efforts to get loose, throwing himself first on one side and then on the other, until finally, groaning with pain and terror, with one tremendous bound, he wrenched his tail free; but it was only the bone! With a skeleton tail waving and dripping blood he rushed away. He jumped and dodged, fearing lest an arrow or a bullet should hit him, until he got safely into the wood.

When he reached home he found the Hare seated in his wife's hut, but he made no remark. During the night the Hare went back to the spot where they had been eating groundnuts and unearthed the remains of the tail, which he took home to his wife telling her to cook it; this she did with great care, beginning by rubbing off all the hairs; she then stewed it with some groundnuts. She also cooked some flour. When everything was done to a turn, she dished up the food on separate plates, one containing the flour, and the other the savory stewed tail. Then the Hare sent his son to call the Baboon, who came with much pleasure, as he knew he was being asked to a meal.

On his arrival he went into the hut, sat down and was served with the flour and its seasoning, the stew. He enjoyed the food, took some of the meat and ate it. "Why!" said he, "here is meat! Wherever did you get it, my grandson?" He had no idea it was his own tail! He ate it, emptied the plate, and went home.

Some days later, the Hare told his wife to make some

beer, which she did; when it was properly brewed, he invited all the countryside to come to a beer drinking. They all came and drank beer. Grandfather Baboon was among the guests. While they were all enjoying themselves, the Hare raised his hand for silence and requested permission to make a few remarks. When all the noise had subsided, he raised his voice, and asked: "Have any of you ever seen anyone who devoured his own tail?"

They all said: "No, we have never seen such a person!" The Baboon also declared he had never even heard of such a thing.

"Well" said the Hare, "Shall I tell you who it is?"

"Yes, do! We should much like to know," said they.

Then the Hare exclaimed: "It is he, the Baboon! He has eaten the tail that he lost over there in the groundnut field!" The Baboon was very angry, and left the gathering with a scowling face; he went home muttering to himself: "I wonder how I can manage to get the better of that rascal? I must try, for he is always making a fool of me, and annoys me horribly."

After some weeks, during which the Baboon had been cogitating how he could be revenged on the Hare, he hit upon a plan. "I'll go and get a wife," said he to himself, "and then I shall be able to trick him, and starve him to death!" So he began at once by making proposals to a girl in a distant village, and, when the time came to go and fetch her, he asked the Hare to accompany him on his journey. They each packed up their provisions and started. The Hare, when preparing for the trip, put his eatables in the bottom of his wallet, and three stones on top of them; then he closed the package.

The Baboon, who wanted to deceive the Hare and get him to throw away his provisions, packed one stone with the eatables in his bag. When they were well on their way, they came to the bank of a river where they sat down to rest, and beginning to feel hungry, thought they might as well have something to eat. Then said the Baboon: "Let us throw our provisions into the water to see them float down the stream, for we are quite close to the village of my future parents-in-law." Now this was not true: the village was still a long way off.

The Hare was quite willing to throw away the food, so the Baboon began and threw his stone into the water; the Hare followed suit and also threw away a stone. Now, in the Baboon's bag only eatables were left, as he had put only one stone on top, while the Hare, having put into his bag three stones, and having only thrown one away, had still two remaining.

"Go on, my friend," said the Hare, "throw away another stone!" The Baboon had no more to throw, so he had to throw away his flour. The Hare then threw in his second stone. Continuing the game the Baboon flung his "seasonings" into the river, and had nothing left to eat. The Hare tossed his third stone into the water, but had all his provisions untouched.

So the Baboon, failing to trick the Hare, was himself a martyr to the pangs of hunger; for they were nowhere near the village of his relatives-in-law; they had still four nights to sleep on the way! They jogged along on their journey and, whenever they stopped for a meal, the Baboon would seat himself at some distance from the Hare and watch him eating; he longed to share the provisions, but the Hare never offered him any, for the Baboon himself had stipulated that neither should ask the other for any of his eatables.

When they had trudged on for four days they arrived at the village, where they were well received. In the meanwhile the Baboon had arranged that if, when swallowing the good things provided, he should scald his throat, the Hare must run back and get the medicine for burns, to relieve the pain. Now this was only a dodge to get rid of the Hare, while he himself would eat up all the food, and the Hare find none on his return. However, the Hare suspected some trick and therefore stuck an arrow into the ground at the foot of the tree which cures scalds and burns. Before reaching the village he said: "Oh! I have left one of my arrows over there; I must run back and fetch it."

"Don't you go digging up the roots of that tree that I showed you; you must only do that if I happen to send you for some when we are having our meal." So the Hare ran back to the spot where he had left his arrow. "He wants to trick me, does he?" said he to himself, and he dug up a root and put it carefully into his bag, so that the Baboon should not see it.

On his return the Baboon questioned him as to what had kept him so long: "You didn't dig up any roots of that tree, did you?" said he.

"Oh no!" replied the Hare. "I didn't take a single one!" And so they came to the village.

When food had been put before them and they had commenced eating, the Baboon cried out: "I have burnt my throat! Oh! Oh!" Then the Hare hurried off and got the remedy out of his bag: he had not very far to go. The Baboon was furious, and shouted: "I told you not to dig up the medicine, but only to do so if I should send you for it!"

"But, Grandfather," replied the Hare, "I did not like to keep you waiting in pain such a long time!" When the Baboon found he could not trick the Hare, he hurried up his wedding and his return home, for he was very unhappy: he lost all his appetite owing to his fit of rage on seeing how short a time was needed for the Hare to fetch the medicine. On the other hand the Hare regaled himself heartily. The Baboon couldn't get over the disappointment; he grew thinner and thinner and was nearly dying.

When they once more reached their home, they were each possessed of a wife, so they both started off to build their villages in different places.

The Hare used to go hunting to procure meat, but the Baboon was too lazy to hunt for himself, so lived by stealing meat from the Hare, and this is how he managed it: whenever the Hare had killed some game and cooked it in the open, the Baboon smeared himself all over with mud, and came rushing out of the marshes toward the Hare's village. Then the Hare and his wife and the little ones all fled away, for they were afraid of this great black beast. Now it was only the Baboon who frightened the Hare: he took the game and gave it to his wife.

Thus it went on for several days, until at last the Hare concluded that he must look carefully into the matter. So, on a certain occasion when the Baboon carried on his thieving in the same way, the Hare remained hidden in his village; only his wife and children ran away. He hid in the hut so as to watch closely the animal who stole his meat and see how he could fight him. The Baboon crept up to the pot in which the meat was cooking, for the folks of the village had not yet begun their breakfast. He lifted the cover, pulled out a piece of meat, and ate it up. Then the Hare let fly an arrow and shot him right in the stomach. The Baboon ran off and went home to his wife. He was very ill.

A day or two later, the Hare went to see his grandfather, and on arriving, greeted him with: "How do you do, Grandfather?" Now, before entering the hut, the Hare had heard groans, but as soon as he stepped inside all was quiet, for the Baboon was afraid his visitor might suspect that it was he who had been hit with the arrow. The Hare had, however, already recognized the Baboon as the culprit, and said to him: "Well, Grandfather, I hope you are feeling all right?"

"No," replied the Baboon. "I am not very well: I feel a pain in my side, which shoots right through me."

"I knew it was you who stole my meat," said the Hare, "so I shot you with an arrow." So the Baboon died and his wife lived in want and misery. That's the end!

Here is a different version of the way in which the Baboon worked his vengeance, or tried to do so, on the Hare for having made him eat his own tail.

The Baboon set to work picking up all the Hare's excrement for several days, until he had collected quite a large quantity. The Hare, noticing this maneuver, said to himself: "All right! We shall see!" He caught a fowl and pulled off one of its legs without killing it: the fowl survived.

The Baboon invited the Hare to dinner, and the latter

went quite happily with the fowl's leg in his pocket. "Here is the plat du jour," said the Baboon, pointing to the pot in which the Hare's excrement was cooking.

"Thanks! Thanks!" said the Hare, who, as soon as his host's head was turned, dug a hole in the ground into which he emptied the contents of the pot, and began eating the hen's leg that he had brought with him. The Baboon returned.

"This chicken is very good" said the Hare, gnawing the bone. And so they parted.

A few days later, when the village was full of men playing *tshuba* the Baboon arrived on the scene, very cocky and called out: "Let me ask a question. Has anyone here ever seen a person feasting on his own excrement?"

"Why certainly not," said everyone present.

"Well! I know someone who has so feasted! It is the Hare."

"Are you quite sure of that?" said the accused, and holding up in sight of all assembled, the one-legged fowl, which he had taken care to bring with him, he told the whole story. So the laugh was turned against the Baboon; everybody made fun of him, and the villagers caught him by his blackened and twisted-up stump of a tail, and chopped it off! That's the end!

One day the Hare said to the Gray Antelope: "Let us go and sow peas."

"I don't like peas, I prefer wild beans," said the Antelope. So the Hare went by himself to sow peas. When they began to sprout, he noticed that they were disappearing, so he hid himself in the field and caught the Antelope digging up his peas. "Aha!" said he. "You are a thief. Pay the fine!" She gave him a hoe and he went off.

He met some women, who were digging clay with sticks. He said to them: "Haven't you got any hoes?"

"No," said they, "we haven't a single one."

"Then take this one," said he, "you can give it back to me later on." When they had finished, the last one who used the hoe broke it. Then the Hare sang the following words:

> Clay Diggers, give back my hoe, my friends,
> My hoe which the Antelope gave me,
> The Antelope who paid the fine for my peas.

The women took one of their pots, and gave it to him.

He left, and met some men who were harvesting honey; they were doing so in a piece of tree bark.

"Haven't you got any pot to put your honey into?" said he.

"No," said the men, "we haven't any." So he gave them his pot. The last one who handled it, broke it. When it was broken the Hare sang:

> Honey Harvesters, give me back my pot.
> My pot which the Clay Diggers gave me;
> The Clay Diggers paid for my hoe,
> My hoe which the Antelope gave me,
> The Antelope who paid the fine for my peas.

They took some of their honey, and gave it to him.

He came to a village, and there he saw women pounding maize flour. He said to them: "Haven't you any honey to mix with your flour?"

"No," said they, "we have none." So he gave them his honey, saying: "Take it, but be careful to leave me some of it." But the last one finished it all. Then he sang:

> Pestle Pounders, give me back my honey,
> The honey which the Honey Harvesters gave me;
> The Honey Harvesters paid for my pot,
> The pot which the Clay Diggers gave me;
> The Clay Diggers paid for my hoe,
> The hoe which the Antelope gave me,
> The Antelope who paid the fine for my peas.

They took some of their dough, and gave it to him.

He went on, and met some boys herding goats. "Haven't you anything to eat?" said he. "Your lips look very dry."

"No," they replied, "we have no food at all." So he gave them the dough, saying: "Eat away! but leave some for me." The last one ate the last bite. Then sang the Hare:

> Goatherds, give me back my dough,
> The dough which the Pestle Pounders gave me;
> The Pestle Pounders paid for my honey,
> The honey which the Honey Harvesters gave me;
> The Honey Harvesters paid for my pot,
> The pot which the Clay Diggers gave me;
> The Clay Diggers paid for my hoe,
> The hoe which the Antelope gave me,
> The Antelope who paid the fine for my peas.

They took a goat, and gave it to him.

He met some young men tending the oxen while feeding. He said to them: "Your lips seem very dry; haven't you anything to eat?"

"No," said they, "we have nothing." So he said: "Take this goat, but be sure to leave some for me." The last one devoured the last mite. Then the Hare sang:

> Cattlemen, give me back my goat
> The goat which the Goatherds gave me;
> The Goatherds paid for my dough,
> My dough which the Pestle Pounders gave me;
> The Pestle Pounders paid for my honey,
> My honey which the Honey Harvesters gave me;
> The Honey Harvesters paid for my pot,
> My pot which the Clay Diggers gave me;
> The Clay Diggers paid for my hoe,
> The hoe which the Antelope gave me,
> The Antelope who paid the fine for my peas.

They gave him an ox.

Still going on, he met some people who were tilling the

fields. They were working for beer. "Your lips look very dry," said he to them; "haven't you anything to eat?"

"No!" said they. He gave them his ox saying: "You must leave a little of the meat for me." They went home with the ox, cooked it, and ate every mouthful; nothing was left. Then the Hare came and sang:

> Workers-for-beer, give back my ox,
> My ox which the Cattlemen gave me;
> The Cattlemen paid for my goat
> My goat which the Goatherds gave me;
> The Goatherds paid for my dough,
> My dough which the Pestle Pounders gave me;
> The Pestle Pounders paid for my honey,
> My honey which the Honey Harvesters gave me;
> The Honey Harvesters paid for my pot,
> My pot which the Clay Diggers gave me;
> The Clay Diggers paid for my hoe,
> My hoe which the Antelope gave me,
> The Antelope who paid the fine for my peas.

They seized him and beat him. When he was quite unconscious, they took him out of the village, thinking he was dead. But he regained his senses and climbed up a tree which was in the middle of the village, just on the spot where they were all drinking beer; no one noticed him and, when he reached the top of the tree, he attracted in his direction all the light beer, and the water in the wells, in such a way that it all ran away into the ground, and folks soon found that there was nothing to drink. The little ones cried for water and there was none. The men and the women started out to fetch water, but they could not find any; even the rivers were all dried up! The little ones died and so did both women and men! Just a few survived. These went to the Hare and said to him: "My Lord, we ask for water, as we are dying of thirst."

"Pull up this reed by the roots," said he. All the men, even the strongest, tried hard to pull up the reed, but could not succeed.

"Now," said the Hare, and with one finger he pulled it out of the ground, and forth flowed water and beer, light and strong.

Then said he: "Give me five old women." He plunged them into the pond and drowned them. After this they allotted to him a small province, where he reigned as chief.

(THONGA)

4

EXPLANATORY TALES

59 HOW IT CAME ABOUT THAT CHILDREN WERE FIRST WHIPPED

They say that once upon a time a great famine came, and that Father Ananse the spider, and his wife Aso, and his children Ntikuma, Nyiwankonfwea (Thin-Shanks), Afu-dotwedotwe (Belly-Like-to-Burst), and Tikonokono (Big-Big-Head), built a little settlement and lived in it. Every day the spider used to go and bring food—wild yams—and they boiled and ate them.

Now one day Father Ananse went to the bush and he saw that a beautiful dish was standing there. He said, "This dish is beautiful."

The dish said, "My name is not 'Beautiful.' "

The spider then asked, "What are you called?"

It replied, "I am called 'Fill-Up-Some-and-Eat.' "

The spider said, "Fill up some so that I may see." The dish filled up with palm-oil soup, and Ananse ate it all.

When he had finished, he asked the dish, "What is your taboo?"

The dish replied, "I hate a gun wad and a little gourd cup."

The spider took the dish home and went and placed it on the ceiling. He went off to the bush and brought food, and Aso, when she had finished cooking, called Ananse. He said, "Oh, yours is the real need. As for me, I am an old man. What should I have to do with food? You and these children are the ones in real need. If you are replete, then my ears will be spared the sounds of your lamentations."

When they had finished eating, Ananse the spider passed behind the hut and went and sat on the ceiling where the dish was. He said, "This dish is beautiful."

It replied, "My name is not 'Beautiful.' "

He said, "What is your name?"

It said, "I am called 'Fill-Up-Some-and-Eat.' "

Ananse said, "Fill up some for me to see." And it filled up a plateful of groundnut soup, and Ananse ate. Every day when he arose it was thus.

Now Ntikuma noticed that his father did not grow thin in spite of the fact that they and he did not eat together, and so he kept watch on his father to see what the latter had got hold of. When his father went off to the bush, Ntikuma climbed up on top of the ceiling and saw the dish. He called his mother and brothers and they, too, went on top. Ntikuma said, "This dish is beautiful."

It said, "I am not called 'Beautiful.' "

He said, "Then what are you called?"

It said, "My name is 'Fill-Up-Some-and-Eat.' "

He said, "Fill up a little that I may see." And the dish filled up to the brim with palm-oil soup.

And now Ntikuma asked the dish, "What do you taboo?"

The dish said, "I hate a gun wad and a small gourd cup."

Ntikuma said to Afudotwedotwe, "Go and bring some for me."

And he brought them, and Ntikuma took the gun wad and touched the dish and also the little gourd cup and touched the dish with it. Then they all descended.

Father Spider meantime had come back from the bush with the wild yams. Aso finished cooking them. They called Ananse.

He replied, "Perhaps you didn't hear what I said—I said that when I come home with food, you may partake, for you are the ones in need." Aso and her children ate.

Father Spider washed and then climbed up on the ceiling. He said, "This dish is beautiful." Complete silence! "This

dish is beautiful!" Complete silence! Father Spider said,
"Ah! It must be on account of this cloth not being a beautiful one; I shall go and bring the one with the pattern of the
Oyoko clan and put it on." And he descended to go and
fetch the Oyoko-patterned cloth to wear. He put on his
sandals and again climbed up on the ceiling. He said, "This
dish is beautiful." Complete silence! "This dish is beautiful."
Complete silence! He looked round the room and saw that
a gun wad and a little gourd cup were there.

Ananse said, "It's not one thing, it's not two things—it's
Ntikuma." Ananse smashed the dish, and came down. He
took off the Oyoko-patterned cloth, laid it away, and went
off to the bush. As he was going, he saw that a very beautiful
thing called Mpere, the whip, was hanging there. He said,
"Oh, wonderful! This thing is more beautiful than the last.
This whip is beautiful."

The whip said, "I am not called 'Beautiful.' "

The spider said, "Then what are you called?"

It said, "I am called 'Abiridiabrada,' or 'Swish-and-Raise-
Welts.' "

And Ananse said, "Swish a little for me to see." And the
whip fell upon him *biridi, biridi, biridi!* Father Spider cried,
"Pui! pui!"

A certan bird sitting nearby said to Ananse, "Say
'Adwobere, cool-and-easy-now.' "

And Ananse said, *"Adwobere,* cool-and-easy-now."

And the whip stopped beating him. And Ananse brought
this whip home; and he went and placed it on the ceiling.

Aso finished cooking the food and said, "Ananse, come
and eat."

He replied, "Since you are still here on earth, perhaps
you have not a hole in your ears and don't hear what I said
—I shall not eat." Ananse climbed up above and went and
sat down quietly. Soon he came down again and he went
and hid himself somewhere.

Then Ntikuma climbed up aloft. He said, "Oh, that
father of mine has brought something home again!" Ntikuma
called, "Mother, Nyiwankonfwea, Afudotwedotwe, come

here, for the thing father has brought this time excels the last one by far!" Then all of them climbed up on the ceiling. Ntikuma said, "This thing is beautiful."

It replied, "I am not called 'Beautiful.' "

He said, "What is your name?"

It said, "I am called 'Swish-and-Raise-Welts.' "

He said, "Swish a little for me to see." And the whip descended upon them and flogged them severely.

Ananse stood aside and shouted, "Lay it on, lay it on! Especially on Ntikuma, lay it on him!" Now when Ananse had watched and seen that they were properly flogged, he said, *"Adwobere,* cool-and-easy-now." Ananse came and took the whip and cut it into small pieces and scattered them about.

That is what made the whip come into the tribe. So it comes about that when you tell your child something and he will not listen to you, you whip him.

(ASHANTI)

60 HOW ALL STORIES CAME AMONG MEN

Mouse goes everywhere. Through rich men's houses she creeps, and visits even the poorest. At night, with her little bright eyes, she watches the doing of secret things and no treasure chamber is so safe but she can tunnel through and see what is hidden there.

In the old days she wove a story child from all that she saw, and to each of these she gave a gown of different colors—white, red, blue, and black. The stories became her children and lived in her house and served her, because she had no children of her own.

Now in the old days a sheep and a leopard lived in the same town. In course of time Leopard became pregnant and

Sheep also. Sheep bore a daughter and Leopard a son.

There was a famine in all the land, so Leopard went to Sheep and said, "Let us kill our children and eat them." Sheep thought, "If I do not agree, she may kill my child in spite of me," so she answered "Good."

Then Sheep went and hid her own babe, and took all that she had and sold it for a little dried meat. This she cooked and set before Leopard, and they both ate together. Leopard killed her own child, and ate that also.

In another year both became pregnant once more. This time again the townsfolk were hungry. Leopard came as before and said, "Let us kill these children also." Sheep agreed, but she took her second child and hid her in the little room where the first child was, then went out, and begged till someone gave her a few pieces of dried meat. These she cooked and set before Leopard as she had before.

Some years afterward Leopard went to Sheep and said, "Come; today you shall feast with me."

Sheep went, and found a great calabash on the table. She opened it and found it full of food, and by it three spoons laid ready.

She was astonished and questioned Leopard. "Formerly we used two spoons, you and I. Why should there be three today?"

Leopard laughed and opened the door of the inner room. "Come daughter, let us eat." Her daughter came, and they all ate together. Then the mother said, "When my first child came, I killed and ate him because we were very hungry; but when I learned how you had saved your child, I thought, 'Next time I also will play such a trick on Sheep.' Therefore I saved my daughter alive."

After that Sheep went home and tended her two children. Years passed by, and all the daughters began to grow up. Leopard put her child into the fatting house. Then she went to Sheep and said, "Give me one of your daughters to stay with mine in the fatting house. She is alone and cannot eat."

Now Sheep and both her daughters were quite black, but there were some young goats in the house which served them as slaves. These were white, so before Sheep sent her daughter to Leopard's house, she rubbed her all over with white chalk, then dyed one of the young goats black, and sent them together.

When they both arrived at the house, Leopard thought that the goat was Sheep's daughter. All three of the young ones were placed in the fatting house. During the night Leopard entered the room, took Goat and killed her, then cooked the meal and gave her own daughter to eat, thinking it was the daughter of Sheep whom she had slain.

Next day Leopard went to Sheep and said, "Give me your other child, that our three daughters may be in the fatting house together."

Sheep consented, but before this child went she advised her what to do.

When therefore the second lamb reached the fatting house she took out a bottle of rum and gave it to Leopard's daughter, saying "Drink this. It is a present which my mother has sent to you." So Leopard's child drank and fell asleep. The two young sheep kept awake until their companion slept. They then got up, carried her from her own bed, and laid her on one of those prepared for themselves.

It was very dark in the room when Leopard came in to kill the young sheep. She killed her own daughter instead. She was pleased and thought, "Now I have finished with the children whom Sheep hid from me." Next morning, very early, she went out to the bush to get palm wine that she might drink it with her daughter while they feasted on the young sheep.

No sooner had she left the house than the two sheep ran out. One of them went home to her mother's house, but the other followed after Leopard. The latter was at the top of a high palm tree, so Sheep's child stopped some way off and called in a loud voice:

"Last night you tried to kill me as you did the young goat, but you made a mistake, and killed your own child instead."

No sooner had Leopard heard this than she jumped from the tree and ran after the young sheep.

The latter ran to the crossroads, and when Leopard reached the place she could not tell which way Sheep had gone. After thinking a while she took the wrong road and ran on.

Now when Sheep had run a long way she met the Nimm woman walking along with her Juju round her waist. The woman looked as if she had come a long way, and Sheep said, "Let me carry your Juju for you."

To this the Nimm woman agreed. When they came to her house she was very tired and her head hurt her.

Sheep said, "Let me fetch water and firewood while you rest."

The Nimm woman was very thankful and went into her house to lie down.

When the young Sheep had done as she promised, she went into the other part of the house where the Nimm shrine was. On it she saw the "medicine." This she took and rubbed over herself.

Next day the Nimm woman said, "Will you go and fetch me my 'medicine' which stands on the shrine of Nimm?"

Sheep asked her, "Do you know that I was 'born' into your medicine last night?"

At this the Nimm woman was very angry and sprang up. Sheep ran, and the Nimm woman followed her. In her hurry to escape, Sheep ran against the door of the house where Mouse lived. The door was old and it broke and all the stories on earth and all the histories ran out. After that they never went back to dwell with Mouse any more, but remained running up and down over all the earth.

(EKOI)

61 WHY ONE NEVER TELLS A WOMAN THE TRUTH

Hunter saw Agbanli as he was hunting. As Hunter spied on her, she changed into a young girl. She took off her skin and put it into a hole. When she changed into a young girl, she took her gumbo to sell in the market. Formerly, it was Deer who sold gumbo. After she left, Hunter took her skin. But she went on her way, not knowing that her skin had been taken away by Hunter.

At night Hunter came there before she herself returned. As she came back from market, she went to the place where she had hidden her skin, but the skin was not there. She looked everywhere.

Now Hunter came toward her. He said, "My girl, what are you looking for?"

Agbanli said, "If I tell you, you must never tell anyone."

Hunter said, "No. I will never tell it."

The girl said, "I lost my skin."

Hunter said, "If I bring it to you, what will you give me as a reward?"

The girl said, "If you will tell no one about it, I will become your wife."

Hunter promised her. He said, "If you will surely become my wife, I will tell no one, and you shall have your skin."

Agbanli said, "All right."

Hunter had this skin at his house. He took Agbanli with him as his wife. Coming home, the hunter went to his first wife, and said, "Now you must be careful with this new wife I brought. She is not a girl, she is really *agbanli;* and you must not quarrel with an animal."

After the fourth day, while the Hunter was away, the two wives began to quarrel. The first woman said, "What airs you put on. You are only an antelope."

The girl began to cry. She thought, "Hunter promised he would tell it to no one, all the same he told."

Hunter came back home. The young girl said to him, "Did I not forbid you to tell anyone?"

Hunter said, "What did you hear?"

She said, "Today, while quarreling with your wife, she told me I am only an antelope.

> *"O my skin, my skin,*
> *How are things with me,*
> *Now that Hunter has taken my skin?"*

Hunter said to her, "Say nothing."

The next day Hunter left again for the bush. After the fifth day, the women began to quarrel again.

The senior wife of the hunter said, "You had better find your skin again. It is buried in back of my house. I do not want to be annoyed by *agbanli* in my own house."

But when she went to look for the skin, it was not there. As she did not find her skin, she went to tell her husband's other wife, "You will never again see an antelope change into a woman for your husband. You will remain alone here."

Hunter came home. The girl told him what happened. He told her again not to be angry. On the third day the husband returned to the bush. He spent ten days on his hunt. The women began to quarrel for the third time. As they quarreled, the other woman went and found the other's skin and threw it at her.

"Take your skin and get out of my house! You are not a girl to marry!"

She took her skin, and, turning her back, changed back into an antelope. At once she ran away. On the way she met her husband. He took his gun and aimed it at the antelope. He did not know it was his wife. She raised herself on her hind legs and made a sign to him with her paws not to shoot. She gestured to him to come to her.

Hunter refused. She motioned again. Again he refused. "I, I have never before been called by an animal."

She said, "I beg you. Come to me first. You must not shoot before you come."

Hunter approached the animal.

She said, "It is I who changed into a young girl for you. I came back here, but it is not my fault. You told your wife to return my skin to me."

Hunter said, "I beg you to change again into a woman,

and to come home with me once more. We will talk this over at home. I want to judge which of you was at fault."

She said, "I do not want to go home with you again. If I go now, she will say again to me what I had forbidden you to tell. You, too, cannot keep a secret."

When she said this, there were two birds up a tree. The two birds were called Adjahè and Ayohè. The two birds did not know that these were a hunter and an antelope talking together. The Adja bird said to the Ayo bird, "People are too foolish. If they would take our excrement and would put with it a leaf of this tree and a little water and then would put that on the head of an animal, that animal would change into a woman." The Ayo bird said the same thing. Hunter heard these words. Then the two birds flew away.

Hunter gathered the things the birds had talked about and approached the antelope. He put the mixture on her head, and she changed into a young woman again. The skin fell off. The two now returned home.

Seeing them come, the wife said, "Is that Agbanli you are bringing again?"

> The Adja-bird has seen the Ayo bird,
> They said, "It is hard to understand things;
> Men who eat with five fingers,
> It is hard to understand their ways."

When they came home, Hunter forbade his wife to quarrel with this new wife.

That is why one never tells the truth to women.

(DAHOMEY)

62 WHY THOSE WHO DIE DO NOT RETURN TO LIFE

Dosi[1] had twins. She looked after them well, but one died. It was the boy who died. The girl remained. Now Dosi, who

[1] This name, given to a female twin, indicates that the mother herself belonged to this category.

has this daughter, never goes out of her house. The little girl does everything for her. She goes to market; she does all. When the girl is in the market and sees cooked meat, she buys it.

Now, one day in this market she saw a hunter with smoked meat for sale. Though the hunter had much meat, the girl said, "I'll buy all of it." So he sold her all his meat at a very good price.

When the girl bought all this meat, a woman said to her, "Take this meat to that other market. They have no meat there at all. You can sell it dear." So the girl went there, and she sold the meat at a high price.

At night she came home and told her mother how she found the meat in the market, and how she sold it. She earned much money. Her mother said, "Good. Next market day, do the same thing."

The hunter always came to this market. Three times the girl bought meat from him. For the third time she bought the meat and sold it dear in the other market. But when she came home with the money for her mother, her mother was dead.

By this time the girl had some money. So she called together many people and said, "I am my mother's only child. I have no brothers, I have no sisters. I must, therefore, see to it that my mother has a proper burial." So she bought much to drink, and called together many people for the funeral.

When all the funeral rites for her mother were finished, she again began to trade in the market. She went back to the same market, and saw the same hunter who came there with his smoked meat. The girl said to him, "Now I am alone at home. I had only my mother, and now she is dead."

The hunter said, "The next time you come to market, I will go home with you." The next market day, the hunter had all his belongings with him. He said, "I am ready. Take me to your house." When the hunter found himself alone with the girl, he made her his wife. And when he hunted, he brought the meat home to her and she sold it in the market dear.

One day the girl went to the market of Ku.[1] There she saw a woman who looked like her dead grandmother. The old woman knew her at once, but when the girl greeted her, the old woman vanished. When she went home, she told her husband about the woman she saw in the market. "I am sure she was my grandmother. When I greeted her, she vanished."

Good. When she said this her husband said, "That market must be the market of the dead. But go again and make sure."

When market day came around again,[2] the girl went there once more. This time she saw her brother Zinsu, who had died years before. But when she came near to him to say "Good day," he vanished. The girl started for home to tell the hunter about this. On the way she saw her dead mother. Now, she still had a piece of meat in her calabash. So when she saw her mother, she called to her to give her the food. But her mother did not answer her, and she, too, vanished.

This time the girl said nothing at home, but went back again the next market day. When she got there, she looked for the three she had seen—her grandmother, her brother, and her mother. When she found them, she said to her grandmother, "I knew you at once. Why did you vanish? It frightened me." She gave some of her meat to the grandmother; and to her mother and brother she gave some as well.

They told her, "When you go home, you must not tell anyone that you saw us here, or that we talked together." So the girl said nothing to anyone.

Now this girl had a friend, her best friend. So she went to her, and told her how she had seen her grandmother, her mother, and her brother in the market. Her friend said to her, "You are lying. No one sees the dead. I'll go to the market with you."

[1] Death; i.e., she went to the market of the dead.
[2] Dahomean markets operate on a four-day cycle.

But the girl refused to take her. She said, "No one must go with me." Good. The friend pleaded with her until she agreed to take her. In the market, she saw only Zinsu, her brother. The others were not there.

Zinsu said, "We forbade you to bring anyone here. You brought your friend. Very well. She stays here. You can go." But the friend did not want to stay. She followed the girl down the road. So Zinsu cut off her head.

Then the girl said to her brother, "It is my fault that my friend had her head cut off. I brought her here to this market. Since you killed her, kill me, too." So she, too, died.

Now in those days, when anyone died, if you whistled a whistle, you found out where they were. When the friend did not come home, her family and the husband of the girl whistled and whistled. But they heard nothing. That is how it happens that, to this day, when one is once dead, he is never seen again. Before that, if you whistled, you saw them. It is the girl who did that by going to the market of the dead.

(DAHOMEY)

63 WHY THE CROCODILE DOES NOT EAT THE HEN

There was a certain hen; and she used to go down to the river's edge daily to pick up bits of food. One day a crocodile came near to her and threatened to eat her, and she cried: "Oh, brother, don't!"

And the crocodile was so surprised and troubled by this cry that he went away, thinking how he could be her brother. He returned again to the river another day, fully determined to make a meal of the hen.

But she again cried out: "Oh, brother, don't!"

"Bother the hen!" the crocodile growled, as she once more turned away. "How can I be her brother? She lives in a town on land; I live in mine in the water."

Then the crocodile determined to see Nzambi about the question, and get her to settle it; and so he went his way. He

had not gone very far when he met his friend Mbambi (a
very large kind of lizard). "Oh, Mbambi," he said, "I am
sorely troubled. A nice fat hen comes daily to the river to
feed; and each day, as I am about to catch her and take her
to my home and feed on her, she startles me by calling me
'brother.' I can't stand it any longer; and I am now off to
Nzambi, to hold a palaver about it."

"Silly idiot!" said the Mbambi. "Do nothing of the sort, or
you will only lose the palaver and show your ignorance.
Don't you know, dear crocodile, that the duck lives in the
water and lays eggs? The turtle does the same; and I also lay
eggs. The hen does the same; and so do you, my silly friend.
Therefore we are all brothers in a sense." And for this reason
the crocodile now does not eat the hen.

                                                    (BAKONGO)

64 WHY THE LEOPARD HUNTS THE ANTELOPE

The leopard one day bet his life to the antelope that if he
hid himself the antelope would never find him.

"Well," said the antelope, "I accept your bet. Go and
hide yourself."

And the leopard went into the woods and hid himself.
Then the antelope looked for him, and after a little while
found him. And the leopard was very angry with the antelope, and told him to go and hide himself, and see how easily
he would find him. The antelope agreed to this, but told the
leopard that he would have his life.

After some time the leopard set out to seek the antelope.
He searched the woods through and through, but could not
find him. At last, thoroughly worn out, he sat down, saying:
"I am too fat to walk any more; and I am also very hungry.
I will pick some of these nonje nuts, and carry them to my
town and eat them."

So he filled the bag he carried under his arm, and returned to his town. Once there, he determined to call his people together and continue his search for the antelope after breakfast.

So he knocked his gong, and ordered all his people to assemble, from the babe that was born yesterday to the sick men who could not walk and must be carried in a hammock. When they were all there, he ordered his slaves to crack the nonje nuts. But out of the first nut they cracked jumped a beautiful dog.

Now, the leopard was married to four princesses. To one by common consent, to another by the rites of Boomba, to the third by the rites of Funzi, and to the fourth by those of Lembe. Each of his wives had her own cooking shed.

Now, when the little dog jumped out of the nut, it ran into the first wife's shed. She beat it, so that it ran away and entered the shed of the wife after the rites of Boomba. This wife also beat the dog, so that it took refuge with the wife after the rites of Funzi. She also beat the little dog; and thus it fled to the wife after the rites of Lembe. She killed it.

But as the dog was dying, it changed into a beautiful damsel. And when the leopard saw this beautiful maiden he longed to marry her, and straightway asked her to be his wife.

The beautiful girl answered him and said: "First, kill those four women who killed the little dog."

The leopard immediately killed them. Then the maid said: "How can I marry a man with such dreadful looking nails. Please have them taken out."

The leopard was so much in love with the maiden that he had his claws drawn.

"What fearful eyes you have got, my dear leopard! I can never live with you with those eyes always looking at me. Please take them out."

The leopard sighed, but obeyed.

"I never saw such ugly ears; why don't you have them cut?" The leopard had them cut.

"You have certainly the clumsiest feet that have been

seen in this world! Can you not have them chopped off?"

The leopard in despair had his feet taken off.

"And now my dear, dear leopard, there is but one more favor that I have to ask you. Have you noticed how ugly your teeth are, how they disfigure you? Please have them drawn."

The leopard was now very weak, but he was so fascinated by the girl and so hopeful now that he would obtain her by this last sacrifice, that he sent to the cooking shed for a stone and had his teeth knocked out.

The maiden then saw that the leopard was fast dying. So she turned herself into the antelope, and thus addressed him:

"My dear leopard, you thought to kill me to avoid giving your life to me, as promised, when I found you. See now how I have outdone you. I have destroyed you and your whole family." And this is why the leopard now always kills the antelope when he meets one.

(BAKONGO)

65 WHY THERE ARE CRACKS IN TORTOISE'S SHELL

Mr. Tortoise, who was married to Mrs. Tortoise, had in Vulture a friend who was constant in visiting him. But, having no wings, Tortoise was unable to return the visits, and this upset him. One day he bethought himself of his cunning and said to his wife, "Wife!"

Mrs. Tortoise answered, "Hello, husband! What is it?"

Said he, "Don't you see, wife, that we are becoming despicable in Vulture's eyes?"

"How despicable?"

"Despicable, because it is despicable for me not to visit Vulture. He is always coming here and I have never yet been to his house—and he is my friend."

Mrs. Tortoise replied, "I don't see how Vulture should think us despicable unless we could fly as he does and then did not pay him a visit."

But Mr. Tortoise persisted. "Nevertheless, wife, is it despicable."

Said his wife, "Very well, then, sprout some wings and fly and visit your friend Vulture."

Mr. Tortoise answered, "No, I shan't sprout any wings because I was not born that way."

"Well," said Mrs. Tortoise, "what will you do?"

"I shall find a way," he replied.

"Find it then," said Mrs. Tortoise, "and let us see what you will do."

Later Tortoise said to his wife, "Come and tie me up in a parcel with a lump of tobacco and, when Vulture arrives, give it to him and say that it is tobacco to buy grain for us." So Mrs. Tortoise took some palm leaf and made him into a parcel and put him down in the corner.

At his usual time, Vulture came to pay his visit and said, "Where's your husband gone, Mrs. Tortoise?"

"My husband has gone some distance to visit some people, and he left hunger here. We have not a bit of grain in the house."

Vulture said, "You are in trouble indeed, not having any grain."

Mrs. Tortoise replied, "We are in such trouble as human beings never knew." And she went on: "Vulture, at your place is there no grain to be bought?"

"Yes," said he, "any amount, Mrs. Tortoise."

She brought the bundle and said, "My husband left this lump of tobacco thinking you would buy some grain with it for us and bring it here."

Vulture willingly took it and returned to his home in the heights. As he was nearing his native town he was surprised to hear a voice saying, "Untie me, I am your friend Tortoise. I said I would pay a visit to you."

But Vulture, in his surprise, let go his hold of the bundle

and down crashed Tortoise to the earth, *pididi-pididi*, his shell smashed to bits, and he died. And so the friendship between Tortoise and Vulture was broken: and you can still see the cracks in Tortoise's shell.

(BAILA)

66 WHY THE ELDERS SAY WE SHOULD NOT REPEAT SLEEPING-MAT CONFIDENCES

They say that once upon a time Nyankonpon Kwame the sky god had cleared a very large plantation, and had planted okras, onions, beans, garden-eggs, peppers, and pumpkins. The weeds in the garden became thick and nettles grew up. The sky god then made a proclamation by gong-gong to the effect that his plantation was overgrown with weeds, and that anyone who could weed it without scratching himself might come forward and take his daughter Abena Nkroma, the ninth child, in marriage. This one, when he went to try, scratched himself where the nettles tickled, and they hooted at him; that one went and was also hooted; all men went and tried; they failed.

Now Kwaku Ananse the Spider said, "As for me, I am able." Now the sky god's plantation was situated on the side of the path, and that path was the one people used to take, going to the market every Friday. Now the Spider, because he knew this fact, used only to go and clear the weeds every Friday. For when he was hoeing, and the people who were passing by used to greet him with, "Hail to you at your work, Father Spider!" he used to answer, "Thank you, Aku." They continued, "A plantation which no one has been able to clear, do you mean to say you are weeding it?"

The Spider would answer, "Ah, it's all because of one girl that I am wearing myself out like this. Her single arm is like this." And he would slap and rub his arm where it was

tickling him, and when he did so, would get relief from the
irritation. Someone else would pass again and hail him at
his work; and he would take his hand and slap where the
place was that was itching. For example, if his thigh, he
would say, "That single girl, they say her thigh is like this,"
slapping and rubbing his own. In this manner he finished
clearing the plantation.

Then he went off to tell the sky god how he had finished
the weeding of his farm. The sky god asked the messenger,
saying, "Has he really finished?" The messenger said, "Yes."
The sky god asked him, "Did he scratch himself?" He said,
"No, he did not scratch himself." The sky god took Abena
Nkroma and gave her to Ananse in marriage.

One night Ananse and his bride went to rest, and the
bride questioned him, saying, "However was it that you of
all people were able to clear father's plantation of weeds, a
plantation such that, whosoever went on it, turned back,
but which you were able to clear?" Then the Spider said,
"Do you suppose that I am a fool? I used to hoe, and when
anyone passed by and asked me, saying, 'Ananse, are you
clearing this farm which no one else has ever been able to
clear,' thereupon, I would slap with my hand any place on
my skin that was tickling me, and scratch it, and declare to
the person that, for example, your thigh was like the thigh
of a buffalo, and that it was beautiful and polished. That is
how it came about that I was able to weed it." Thereupon
Abena the ninth child said, "Then tomorrow I shall tell
father that you scratched yourself after all." The Spider
spoke to her, saying, "You must not mention it, this is a
sleeping-mat confidence." Abena the ninth child said, "I
know nothing whatever about sleeping-mat confidences, and
I shall speak." Abena Nkroma took her sleeping-mat away
from beside Ananse and went and lay down at the other end
of the room. Now Ananse's eyes grew red, and he went and
took his musical bow, and he struck the strings and sang:
"Abena, the ninth child, this is not a matter about which to
quarrel. Let us treat it as a sleeping-mat confidence. 'No,' she
says. She has a case against me, but someone else has a case

which is already walking down the path."

Then the Spider got up, and went and lay down. After Ananse had lain there for some time, then he rose up. He said, "Abena Nkroma"—not a sound—save the noise of the cacada chirping—*dinn!* Ananse said, "I've got you." He took a little gourd cup and splashed it full with water, and poured it over Abena Nkroma's sleeping-mat. Then Ananse went and lay down.

After he had lain down a while, he said, "Ko! Abena Nkroma, whatever is this? You have wet the sleeping-mat, you shameless creature, surely you are not at all nice; when day comes and things become visible, I shall tell everyone. It was true then, what they all said, that when anyone went to that plantation he used to say, 'A girl who wets . . . ! I am not going to clear a nettle plantation for such a person.' " Then Abena said to him, "I implore you, desist, and let the matter drop." The Spider said, "I will not leave it, my case came first; 'you said you would tell your father; I said, 'Desist'; you said, 'No.' Because of that I will drop the case." And Abena the ninth child said, "Leave my case, and your case, too, about which I spoke, I shall drop it; for if you do not leave mine, my eyes will die for shame." Then Ananse said, "I have heard, since you so desire, let it be a sleeping-mat confidence, so the matter ends there."

That is how the elders came to say, "Sleeping-mat confidences are not to be repeated." This my story which I have related, if it be sweet, or if it be not sweet, some you may take as true, and the rest you may praise me for telling of it.

(ASHANTI)

67 HOW IT CAME ABOUT THAT SOME PEOPLE ARE GOOD-LOOKING AND OTHERS ARE NOT

They say there once was a woman and that she went to a certain palm tree which stood there in the water that she might consult it about childbearing. And when she went, the palm tree said, "I shall give you what you want, but the child with whom I shall present you, when he rises up, will never do any work." She said, "I agree to that."

It was not two days, it was not three days, when she conceived and gave birth. He was not long of growing up, he was grown up at once. And his mother told him, saying, "Among the whole of the tribe's taboos, there are none which you need observe save the palm tree, you must never climb one." He said, "Mother, I have heard."

Now, one day the mother left him there to go to the farm. He went and called his sweetheart, and he and she began to play, and he caught hold of her waist beads and they broke. Then she said, "Go and bring me some palm tree fiber that I may restring them." The boy went off and bought some and brought it. The girl said, "I don't want that. I want some from a palm tree which stands in the water." So the child set out in search of some. As he went, there was a palm tree standing in the water. Up he climbed, *kra! kra! kra!* until he reached the neck of the tree. He took out his knife, and as soon as he touched it the palm tree split in two, and the boy's stomach went inside, and the palm tree closed up again. There he was, it was squeezing him.

Soon after, his mother came. When she reached the water, she saw a shadow upon it, and she said:

"Whose shadow is this lying on the water like that of my child Akwasi Kwasaman?"

He said, "Mother, it's I."

She said, "Why is the palm tree squeezing you?"

He said, "I went to strip off palm fiber to go and give to my lover and the palm tree squeezed me."

The mother said, "You, this palm tree, squeeze him, squeeze him, my child Kwasaman. Palm tree, squeeze him, squeeze him, squeeze him, palm tree squeeze him."

And the mother went off. And the father also came, and he said: "Whose shadow is it that lies on this water like that of my son Kwasaman?"

He said, "Father, it is I."

The father said, "Why is the palm tree squeezing you?"

He said, "I went to strip off palm fiber to go and give to my lover and the palm tree squeezed me."

The father said, "You, this palm tree, squeeze him, squeeze him, my child Kwasaman. Palm tree, squeeze him, squeeze him, palm tree squeeze him."

And the father went off home and told the Head of the village, and the Head of the village, too, called all the people; and they came to the foot of the palm tree, and the Head of the village lifted up his voice, saying:

"Whose shadow is it that lies on the water like that of my grandchild Akwasi Kwasaman?"

He said, "Grandfather, it is I."

The Head of the village said, "Why is the palm tree squeezing you?"

He said, "I went to strip off palm fiber to go and give to my lover and the palm tree squeezed me."

The Head of the village said, "You, this palm tree, squeeze him, squeeze him, squeeze him, my grandchild Kwasaman. Palm tree squeeze him, squeeze him, palm tree squeeze him."

And the Head of the village went off, and all the villagers sang the same song telling the palm tree to squeeze him. And now his lover came along, and she said:

"Whose shadow is it that lies upon the water, like that of my lover Akwasi Kwasaman?"

He said, "It is I, your real lover."

She said, "Why is the palm tree squeezing you?"

He said, "I went to break off palm fiber for you, and the palm tree squeezed me."

She said, "Palm tree release him, release him, release him. Palm tree release my lover, Akwasi Kwasaman. Palm tree release him, release him, release him, palm tree release him."

When she spoke thus, the palm tree opened out a little, and her lover's stomach came out a little. And she raised her voice once more, saying:

"Whose shadow is it that lies upon the water, like that of my lover Akwasi Kwasaman?"

He said, "It is I, your real lover."

She said, "Why is the palm tree squeezing you?"

He said, "I went to break off palm fiber for you, and the palm tree squeezed me."

She said, "Palm tree release him, release him, release him. Palm tree release my lover, Akwasi Kwasaman. Palm tree release him, release him, release him, palm tree release him."

And now her lover came forth all at once, and he came and clung on the bosom of his sweetheart, and they melted away; and they changed into oil. And the people who went there quickly and rubbed some on their faces, are they who are very beautiful; but they who did not get any, they are those who are not nice-looking. This, my story, which I have related, if it be sweet or if it be not sweet, take some elsewhere, and let some come back to me.

(ASHANTI)

68 HOW THE ANIMALS GOT THEIR COLOR

The color of all the animals is said to have been painted on by the meercat. The meercat said to the animals, "If anyone will kill a buck and bring me the meat I will paint color on him."

The hyena heard him, so he went and killed a buck; he ate all the meat himself and took the bones to the meercat.

The meercat said, "Lie down." The hyena knelt down, and the meercat painted ugly marks on him, saying, "If anyone cheats me, I do the same to him."

The leopard went out hunting and killed a buck and brought it to the meercat unskinned. The meercat told him to kneel down and painted him a beautiful color, saying, "If anyone keeps his word with me I will do the same to him."

The story is finished.

(BAVENDA)

69 HOW THE ANIMALS GOT THEIR TAILS

It is said that animals were created without tails by their maker. The Maker one day called them to come and select what tails would suit them. The first group of animals appeared and selected the long and best tails. The second group came and received good tails. The last group were the hares, who are very lazy, and they told the other animals to pick out tails for them. The other animals, having taken the best tails for themselves, brought the short and ugly tails for the hares. If you want a thing well done, do it yourself.

The story is finished.

(BAVENDA)

70 WHY THE HAWK DEVOURS THE DOVE AND THE VULTURE

The dove, the vulture, and the hawk lived together in peace and friendship. All had their mothers. One day the dove's mother became ill and died soon after. The dove told the vulture and the hawk, and they felt pity and sympathy; they spent a few days mourning at the dove's home.

A few days later the vulture's mother died, and he told the dove and the hawk and they came and mourned with him.

Soon after this the hawk likewise sent a message that his mother, who was a very old lady, was dead. As his friends came to him he said, "My mother is no more." The vulture replied, "Was she a queen?" and the dove said, "Are we to mourn for such a miserable old thing?" The hawk was very angry with them for not mourning with him too, and in a rage he killed the dove and the vulture. From that day the hawk kills and devours the dove and the vulture. That is all.

(BAVENDA)

5

DILEMMA STORIES AND MORAL FABLES

71 WHY THE CHIEF OF THE SMITHS WAS UNABLE TO CREATE HUMAN BEINGS

A very long time ago there was a king who called Walukaga, chief of the smiths, and gave him a great quantity of iron and said, "I want you to make a real man for me, one who can walk and talk, and who has blood in his body, and who has brains."

Walukaga took the iron and went home, but he was at a loss what to do, and no one could advise him how to set about making a real man. He went about among his friends telling them what the king had said, and asked what he had better do. No one was able to give him any advice. They all knew that the king would not accept anything short of an honest trial, and would punish the man for not carrying out his commands.

On the way home one day Walukaga met a former friend who had gone mad, and who lived alone on some wasteland. Walukaga did not know that he was mad until he met him. When they approached each other, Walukaga greeted his old friend, and the madman asked him where he had come from. Walukaga reasoned for a moment and then said to himself, "Why should I not tell him my story? Even though he is mad, he used to be my friend." So he answered, "I have come from some friends where I have been trying to get advice."

The madman asked what advice he wanted, and Walukaga told him all the king had said, and about the work he had given him to do, and how he had given him the iron, and then added, "What am I to do?"

The madman answered, "If the king has told you to do this work, go to him and say that, if he really wishes to have a nice man forged, he is to order all the people to shave their heads and burn the hair until they have made up a thousand loads of charcoal, and he is to get one hundred large pots of water from the tears of the people with which to slake the fire and keep it from burning too fiercely."

Walukaga returned to the king and said to him, "My lord, if you wish me to make this man quickly and well, order the people to shave their heads and burn their hair, and make a thousand loads of charcoal out of it for me to work the iron into the man. Further, make them collect a hundred pots full of tears to act as water for the work, because the charcoal from wood and the ordinary water from wells are of no use for forging a man."

The king agreed to the request and gave the order to all the people to shave their heads and burn their hair into charcoal, and to collect all the tears. When they had all shaved their heads and burnt their hair, there was scarcely one load of charcoal, and when they had collected all the tears there were not two pots full of water.

When the king saw the results of his endeavors, he sent for the smith Walukaga and said to him, "Don't trouble to make the man, because I am unable to get the charcoal or the tears for the water."

Walukaga knelt down and thanked the king. He then added, "My lord, it was because I knew you would be unable to get the hair for charcoal and the tears for the water that I asked for them; you had asked me to do an impossible thing."

All the people present laughed and said, "Walukaga speaks the truth."

(BAKONGO)

72 HOW A STORY IS TOLD

Perhaps it may interest you to know how a story is told.

Imagine, then, a village in a grove of graceful palm trees. The full moon is shining brightly upon a small crowd of people seated round a fire in an open space in the center of the village. One of them has just told a story, and his delighted audience demands another. Thus he begins:

"Let us tell another story; let us be off!"

All then shout: "Pull away!"

"Let us be off!" he repeats.

And they answer again: "Pull away!"

Then the storyteller commences.

There were two brothers, Clever One and Foolish One. And it was their habit to go out shooting to keep their parents supplied with food. Thus one day they went together into the mangrove swamp, just as the tide was going down, to watch for the fish as they nibbled at the roots of the trees. Foolish One saw a fish, fired at it, and killed it. Clever One fired also, but at nothing, and then ran up to Foolish One and said: "Fool, have you killed anything?"

"Yes, Clever One, I am a fool; but I killed a fish."

"Indeed, you are a fool," answered Clever One, "for when I fired I hit the fish that went your way; so that the fish you think you killed is mine. Here, give it to me."

Foolish One gave Clever One the fish. Then they went to their town, and Clever One, addressing his father, said: "Father, here is a fish that your son shot, but Foolish One got nothing."

Here the crowd join in, and sing over the last sentence two or three times.

Then the narrator continues.

The mother prepared and cooked the fish, and the father and Clever One ate it, giving none to Foolish One.

Then they went again; and Foolish One fired, and with his first shot killed a big fish.

"Did you hear me fire?" says Clever One.

"No," answers Foolish One.

"No?" returned Clever One. "See then the fish I killed."

"All right," says Foolish One. "Take the fish."

When they got home they gave the fish to their mother; and when she had cooked it, Clever One and his father ate it, but gave none to Foolish One. But as they were enjoying the fish, a bone stuck in the father's throat. Then Clever One called to Foolish One and bade him go for a doctor.

"No," says Foolish One, "I cannot. I felt that something would happen." And he sings:

> "Every day you eat my fish, you call me Fool,
>   And would let me starve."

The crowd here join in, and sing Foolish One's song over and over again.

"How can you sing," says Clever One, "when you see that our father is suffering?"

But Foolish One goes on singing:

> "You eat and eat unto repletion;
>   A bone sticks in your throat;
> And now your life is near completion,
>   The bone is still within your throat.
>
> "So you, smart brother, killed the fish,
>   And gave the food to eat?
> Nay! but now he's dead perhaps you wish
>   You'd given the fool to eat."

The crowd go on singing this until they are tired; and the storyteller continues.

While yet Foolish One was singing, the father died. Then

the neighbors came and joined the family circle, and asked Foolish One how it was that he could go on singing now that his father was dead.

And Foolish One answered them, saying: "Our father made us both, one a smart man, the other a fool. Foolish One kills the food, and they eat it, giving none to Foolish One. They must not blame him, therefore, if he sings while they suffer. He suffered hunger while they had plenty."

And when the people had considered the matter, they gave judgment in favor of Foolish One, and departed.

The father had died, and so had been justly punished for not having given Foolish One food.

He who eats fish with much oil must suffer from indigestion.

And now I have finished my story.

All answer, "Just so!"

"Tomorrow may you chop palm kernels," says the narrator, as he gets up and walks away.

A lady telling a story begins by shouting out the words: "Viado! Nkia? (An antelope! How big?)"

The crowd answer: "Nzoka (two fathoms)."

Then the narrator begins.

Once there was a man who had a wife, but he fell in love with another woman. His wife was heavy with child, but he neglected her. He used to go out fishing; but instead of giving his wife the fish, he gave it to his lover. When he shot an antelope he gave his wife none of it. If he trapped a bird it went to the wicked woman.

The narrator sings:

> "The poor starved wife
> Brought forth a son,
> She gave it life,
> Poor weakly one!"

Then all join in this song in tones of disgust.

The son grew up and complained to his mother that

while he had eaten of the produce of her farm he had not yet eaten any food killed by his father, or even worn a cloth given by him.

One day a friend gave him a knife, and he immediately, unknown to his mother, went to the woods and hills to cut some muchinga, or native string. He tried to kill some game by throwing his knife at it, but to no purpose. So before he left for home he set a trap to catch some bird or other. He grieved at his bad luck.

Next morning he went out again, and to his intense relief found a guinea fowl in his trap. He ran away home with his prize, and, while yet afar off, shouted to his mother:

"Mother, get the fundi (tapioca) ready!"

"Fundi, my son! How is this? You return too early for mealtime and call for fundi. Your father has taken no notice of me and has brought me no food: whence then, my son, hast thou got food for me to cook?"

"Never you mind, Mother, get the fundi ready."

The mother prepared the fundi, and the son laid the bird at her feet. When she saw that her son could bring her food, she no longer thought of her troubles or her husband. When the food was ready, the mother called her son and named him Zinga (to continue to live), for now they could eat and live without the help of a father.

About this time the husband had grown tired of his concubine and sent her away, so that having no one to cook for him, he remained in his shimbec (house) hungering.

When he heard that his son now went out hunting and had plenty of food, he sneaked out of his shimbec and clapped his hands and begged his son to give him food.

He sang:

> "My son, can it be true
>   That you me food deny?
>   Upon my knees I sue,
>   My son, let me not die."

All present repeat this song plaintively.
Then the mother replied:

> "You first denied us food;
>   We starved and nearly died;
>   We will not give him food
>   Who kept that girl supplied."

Another day, when the son had been lucky and caught a bird, after killing and cleaning it, he said: "Mother, time was when we nearly died of hunger, but now we have plenty; and now that I am a man you shall need neither cloth nor food."

And as they were feeding, the father, very thin and weak, crawled out of his shimbec, and cried:

> "Oh, Zinga, my son, Zinga,
>   Will you let your father die?
>   Oh, Kengi, my wife, Kengi,
>   Here starving do I lie."

All around sing this song in a supplicating tone.

When the son heard his father crying so bitterly, he was greatly moved, and prayed his mother to put some food upon a plate and send it to him; but the mother refused, saying that he deserved none.

Then the son wept and sang:

> "Mother, Father wronged us
>   When he starved us;
>   Let us feed him now he asks us,
>   Or God may kill us."

And then he put some food upon a plate and was about to give it to his father, when his father dropped down dead from starvation.

An enquiry was held to find out how the father had come to die; and when the people had heard all they gave judgment:

"He did not give his wife and child food when they needed it. They were in their right when they gave him none when he asked for it. He died by the avenging hand of the Great Spirit."

There were two men who from their childhood had been fast friends, and never were known to have quarreled with one another. So great was their friendship that they had made their farms close to one another. They were divided one from the other, only by a native path.

Now there was a practical joker in their town, who had determined, if possible, to make these friends quarrel. This man made a coat, one side or half of which was red in color while the other was blue. And he walked past these two friends as they were busy on their farms, making enough noise to attract their attention. Each looked up to see who it was that was passing, and then went on with his work.

"Ugh, say! Did you see that man?" said one.

"Yes," answered the other.

"Did you notice the bright coat he wore?"

"Yes."

"What color should you say it was?"

"Why, blue, of course."

"Blue, man! Why, it was a kind of red!"

"Nay, friend, I am sure it was blue."

"Nonsense! I know it was red, but—"

"Well! you are a fool!"

"A fool, how now! We have been friends all our lives, and now you call me a fool! Let us fight; our friendship is at an end." And they fought.

Then their women screamed and interfered, and managed to separate them.

Then the joker walked quietly back and saw the two friends seated each in his own farm, with his elbows resting on his knees and his head between his hands.

Then they saw through the joke and they were sorry; and they ordered the joker never to come that way again.

But the women cursed the joker and hoped that he would soon die.

(BAKONGO)

73 THE TWO STRANGERS

Two strangers entered a village just as night was falling. They sought out the chief to greet him, according to custom, and to ask him for a place to spend the night. The chief replied, "Welcome, O strangers. We welcome you. There is a guesthouse in which you may sleep, and there is food for you to eat. But know that in this village there is a custom of long standing. Strangers may sleep here, but on pain of death they may not snore. Remember this well, for if you snore you will be killed as you sleep." The chief then took the strangers to the guesthouse and they composed themselves for the night's rest.

The visitors had not been asleep for long when one of them began to snore: "Vo, vo, vo." His companion awoke. He heard the snoring, "Vo, vo, vo." He heard also, "Ts, ts, ts." This was the sound the villagers made sharpening their knives. The stranger then knew that they were getting ready to kill the snorer. He thought quickly of a way that he might save his companion. As one stranger snored, "Vo, vo, vo," the other stranger composed a song:

> Vo, vo, lio, vo. Vo, vo, lio, vo.
> We walked on the road.
> We came to this town.
> We were welcomed.
> Vo, vo, lio, vo.
> Vo, vo, lio, vo.

He sang this song with a strong voice and the people could not hear the snoring above the song. They let their knives fall and began to dance. The drums were brought out and played. The people took up the song and sang. All the people, women, children, the chief and all the men, came to join the dance.

All that night one stranger snored, one stranger sang, and the townspeople danced and played.

In the morning the strangers went to bid farewell to the chief before they took to the road again. The chief wished them a good journey and pressed a good-sized purse into their hands. "I give you this present of money for your fine song. Because of you, strangers, we spent the night in dance and play. We are grateful."

The strangers went out of the village. Once again on the road, they began to argue. How should the money be shared? The snorer said, "It is to me that the larger portion should fall. If I had not snored, you would not have been moved to compose the song, and we should have received no present at all."

The singer said, "True. If you had not snored I would not have composed the song, but if I had not, you would have been killed. The people were already sharpening their knives. So I should certainly get the larger portion of the money."

Thus they argued and could not decide. Can you?

(MENDE)

74 THE LEFTOVER EYE

Pay heed to this tale. This is a tale of things that have never happened. But we will suppose these things did happen for certainly there are such things possible.

This is a tale of a man who was blind. His mother, too, was blind. His wife and his wife's mother were also blind. They dwelt together in a wretched condition; their farm

was poor and their house was badly built. They consulted
together and decided to go away. They would journey until
they came to some place where their lot would be better.

They set out and traveled along the road. As they walked,
the man stumbled over something. He picked it up and felt
it, and then knew he had come upon seven eyes. He immediately gave two eyes to his wife, and then took two for
himself. Of the three eyes remaining to him, he gave one to
his mother and another to his wife's mother. He was left
with one eye in his hand. Kai, this was a startling thing. Here
was his mother with her one eye looking at him hopefully.
There was his wife's mother with her one eye looking at him
hopefully. To whom should he give the leftover eye?

If he gives the eye to his mother he will forever be
ashamed before his wife and her mother. If he gives it to his
wife's mother, he will fear the angry and disappointed heart
of his own mother. A mother, know you, is not something
to be played with.

This is difficult indeed. Here is the sweetness of his wife.
She is good and loving. How can he hurt her? Yet his
mother, too, is a good mother and loving. Can he thus injure
her? Which would be easier, and which would be the right
way to do this thing?

If this thing would come to you, which would you choose?

(BURA)

75 THE SON-IN-LAW

An elderly man had but one daughter, Sangba, who was
very beautiful and much desired by all men. But as each
suitor came to ask for her, the father demanded that he who
would have Sangba as a wife must first bring him a live
deer. Some of the young men were discouraged immediately,

and went away. Others, though they were good hunters and
fleet of foot, tried to capture a live deer and failed. So they,
too, withdrew their suits and left.

One day two young men came from a distant village, and
they were friends. They said, "We have come to the old
man who has a daughter Sangba."

The old man came out of his house and greeted the two
visitors. "I am the father of Sangba. What is it you wish?"
Njila, one of the youths, spoke: "I have come to ask for
your daughter, whom I want to marry." And the other young
man, Sefu, said that he too had come for Sangba.

Then her father said, "There is but one Sangba. You are
two who ask for her. I have but one daughter, and you are
two. Which of you shall bring me a live deer, to him will I
give my daughter."

The two young men then prepared themselves to capture a
live deer. They went into the forest and quietly, quietly,
sought about for traces and finally they came across a deer.
They immediately gave chase, running swiftly to follow the
animal.

Sefu, not as fleet as Njila, soon dropped behind and,
overcome with fatigue, sat down beneath a tree, saying, "I
have finished. No more will I run to catch a live deer for
any woman. Why should I suffer such exhaustion and
destroy myself for Sangba? There are other women who can
be married more easily. Anyway, what sort of wooing is this,
with a live deer? I have never heard of such a thing before.
Here I will sit and wait for Njila, that we may return together." Then he slept.

When Sefu woke, he saw his friend approaching, carrying
a bound, live deer upon his back. Njila exulted: "Here is the
live deer for the old man. I have caught it because Sangba
pleases me very much. Rather than lose her I would sleep
in the forest and try again on the morrow until the deer is
captured."

They went then together to the village of the girl and presented the deer to her father. He ordered the deer killed and
cooked for the youths to eat, saying, "Keep the deer, friends.

Eat it, please. Then we will discuss this matter of my daughter's marriage."

When they had done eating, the old man called a Council of Elders to assemble. He addressed them: "You all know I have but one child, Sangba, my daughter who is dearer to me than myself, and so I need a son-in-law that is a good man, gentle of heart. These youths came to me and asked for my daughter, and I said that he who wanted her must bring me a live deer. Now, they have done this, and again together have brought the deer. But of the two, only one caught a deer. Why did the other not return with a deer? Elders of my village, I leave the matter to you. It must be as if my daughter were yours. Choose, then, a son-in-law between these two men."

The Elders questioned the youths. "You came together, but both of you asked for Sangba. Now one has brought a deer. Why has not the other?"

Njila spoke first, saying, "We went into the forest and sought out a deer. We both gave chase and followed where the deer fled. Sefu, my companion, abandoned the chase, but I was so charmed by the beauty of Sangba that I pursued the deer till I had caught it. I bound it and carried it back, joining my friend at the place where he grew tired. He has come with me now only to accompany me."

Then Sefu spoke: "I have never heard of wooing a maiden with a live deer. Nevertheless I went with my friend to seek a deer and perhaps to catch it. But there was such running through the forest that I grew weary, and thought that there was not so great a need to run as to cost my life. Women are plentiful, and most of them easier to obtain than Sangba. So I sat down to await Njila, to return with him. I saw him return with the deer, and have come here only to accompany him. I have not come to ask again for your daughter."

The Council of Elders deliberated and finally said, "You, Sefu, who abandoned the chase after the deer, you are our son-in-law. Njila caught the deer and is a man of great heart. If he wished to kill he would stop at nothing till he fulfilled his wish. He would not heed one who scolds or gives advice. If we gave him our daughter and she did wrong, he would beat her and not listen to one who pleads for her. We do not wish him for a son-in-law. But Sefu is our son-in-law because he would listen to us. If he were about to punish our daughter for any wrongdoing he would heed us when we came to pacify him. Though his anger were great, it would then cease. He is our good and gentle son-in-law."

(BURA)

76 THE HUNTER AND HIS SON

Pay heed to this tale of father and son!

A certain hunter and his son Zinnah went one day to the bush to pursue their occupation. They hunted all morning and found nothing to sustain them but a small hare. It seemed to Zinnah of no consequence, and he threw it into the bush. But they could find no other game that day, and in the afternoon they grew hungry. The father said, "Roast the hare, son, and we will at least have something to eat." When he learned that the boy had thrown the hare away he became very vexed with him. In an outburst of rage he struck Zinnah with his ax and went away, leaving his son lying on the ground.

Late in the evening, Zinnah rose up and went home. He waited until all were asleep, took up his belongings, and left the house. He took the road to Quendeh, a large town, and came there late at night. Proceeding to the center of town, he arrived at the chief's house. The chief awoke and saw him and asked, "From where do you come?"

Zinnah replied, "From such-and-such a village."

And the chief said, "Is it well with you?"

Zinnah told him, "Both I and my father went to the bush to walk and shoot. We did not find anything but one hare.

He gave it to me to carry. It was small, and I threw it into the bush. When we became hungry he asked me to cook the hare. And I said that I had not kept it. Thereupon he became vexed, and struck me with his ax. I fainted. When evening came I recovered and rose up and came here. This is how it is with me."

Now, some years before, the chief had been at war, and his only son, then a small lad, was captured and killed. And the chief said to Zinnah, "Now will you not keep a secret for me?"

The boy said, "What kind of a secret?"

The chief answered, "I have no son. When dawn comes I shall say you are my son who was captured in the war and that you have at last escaped and returned home."

Zinnah agreed, saying, "That is surely not difficult."

Then the chief entered his room and fired his gun—*Boom!*—in the middle of the night. The mother of the house awakened, came out and said, "King lion, who causes fear, what is the gun you are firing in the night?"

The chief said, "My son has returned!"

Thereupon the mother of the house raised the sound of joy, and the whole town awoke, asking, "What has happened at the chief's house, seeing that they are firing a gun at this time of night?" And the messenger from the chief's house said that the chief's son had come, he who had been captured during the war. Some of the people were joyful and some doubted and said, "Indeed?"

When dawn came, the boy bathed and dressed finely. The chief gave him gifts and he came forth into the town to be seen and welcomed. Some of the councilors said, "It is not his son!" Others said, "It is his son!" But doubt grew, and one day the headmen made a plan and said, "Wait, and we shall see if it really is his son."

The councilors summoned their own sons, dressed them in rich garments and saddled the warhorses for them. The boys mounted and their fathers said to them, "Go to the chief's house and call his son and say you are going to take the horses for exercise. When you have gone and galloped,

then pull up and dismount. Then you must slay your horses
and return home."

Each councilor gave his son a sword to sling over the
shoulder. They then set off to the chief's house.

Now, some talebearer had overheard the councilors' plan
and went to inform the chief. Thereupon the chief made
preparations and said, "If the naked man can dance, much
more can the man with the cloak." He had been warned and
thus was ready. He called Zinnah to him and told him,
"When you have gone with them, everything you see they
have done, do you also do."

Soon the boys arrived, called the son of the chief, and set
off. They galloped to a place some distance away; then they
dismounted and killed their horses with the swords. Zinnah
watched and saw what they did, and copied their actions
even to killing the valuable mount.

When they returned home, the boys told the headmen
that Zinnah had passed the test. Only the son of a chief
would display such magnificent disregard of valuable property and of life. But the councilors still did not believe, and
prepared still another test. On the next day they gave their
sons each a beautiful slave maiden and said, "Take them
into the bush and kill them."

The talebearer again informed the chief, who gave Zinnah
two female slaves and said, "Go with the others and whatever you see they have done, do you also do." Again Zinnah followed the actions of the other boys. This time the
councilors were satisfied and said, "It is his son, for only his
son would thus ignore wealth and life."

Time went on, and Zinnah lived in the chief's house as his
son. Then one day the hunter, Zinnah's father, came into
Quendeh. He was seeking his son. He questioned all the
people he encountered and when he had heard all he wished
to know, he came to the chief's house. He entered and
greeted the chief, who was sitting with Zinnah at his side.
Then the hunter said to his son, "Are you not going to get up
and come with me, so we may hunt together again?"

The boy remained silent. Then the chief said, "Hunter,

keep the secret for me and whatever you wish I will give you." But the hunter refused and continued to refuse despite all entreaties of the chief.

Then the chief ordered three horses to be saddled, and a sword to be given to Zinnah. The three, the hunter, the chief, and Zinnah, mounted and rode off. When they reached a certain place in the bush, they halted and the chief said to Zinnah, "Hear me, Zinnah. We have come unarmed, but you hold a sword. There is but one thing to do. Either you must kill me and take all these goods, and return with your father to his town and his world, or your must kill your father and you and I will go back and live as before."

The boy did not know what to do. Now if it were you, whom would you kill? Would you kill the hunter or the chief?

Off with the rat's head!

(HAUSA)

77 A TUG-OF-WAR

Tortoise considered himself a great personage. He went about calling attention to his greatness. He said to people, "We three, Elephant, Hippopotamus, and I, are the greatest, and we are equal in power and authority."

Thus he boasted, and his boasts came to the ears of Elephant and Hippopotamus. They listened and then they laughed. "Pooh, that's nothing. He is a small person of no account, and his boasting can only be ignored."

The talebearer returned to Tortoise telling him what the two great ones had said. Tortoise grew very vexed indeed. "So, they despise me, do they? Well, I will just show them my power. I am equal to them, and they will know it before long! They will yet address me as Friend." And he set off.

He found Elephant in the forest, lying down; and his trunk was eight miles long, his ears as big as a house, and his four feet large beyond measure. Tortoise approached him and boldly called out, "Friend, I have come! Rise and greet me. Your Friend is here."

Elephant looked about astonished. Then spying Tortoise he rose up and asked indignantly, "Tortoise, small person, whom do you address as Friend?"

"You. I call you Friend. And are you not, Elephant?"

"Most certainly I am not," replied the Elephant in anger. "Besides, you have been going about and saying certain things about your great power—that it is equal to mine. How do you come to talk in such a way?"

Tortoise then said, "Elephant, don't get angry. Listen to me. True, I addressed you as Friend and said we were equal. You think that because you are of such a great size, you can surpass me, just because I am small? Let us have a test. Tomorrow morning we will have a tug-of-war."

Said Elephant, "What is the use of that? I can mash you with one foot."

"Be patient. At least try the test." And when Elephant unwillingly consented, Tortoise added, "When we tug, if one pulls over the other, he shall be considered greater, and if neither overpulls, then we are equal, and will call each other Friend."

Then Tortoise cut a very long vine and brought one end to Elephant. "This end is yours. I will go off with my end to a certain spot; and we will begin to tug, and neither of us will stop to eat or sleep, until one pulls the other over, or the vine breaks." And he went off with the other end of the vine and hid it on the outskirts of the town where Hippopotamus lived.

Hippopotamus was bathing in the river and Tortoise shouted to him, "Friend, I have come! You! Come ashore! I am visiting you!"

There was a great splashing as Hippopotamus came to shore, bellowing angrily, "You are going to get it now! Whom do you call Friend?"

"Why, you, of course. There is no one else here, is there?" answered Tortoise. "But do not be so quick to fight. I do not fear your size. I say we are equals, and if you doubt me, let us have a trial. Tomorrow morning we will have a tug-of-war. He who shall overcome the other, shall be the superior. But if neither is found superior, then we are equals and will call each other Friend." Hippopotamus thought the plan was absurd, but finally he consented.

Tortoise then brought his end of the vine to Hippopotamus and said, "This end is yours. And now I go. Tomorrow when you feel a pull on the vine, know that I am ready at the other end. Then you begin to tug, and we will not eat or sleep until the test is ended."

In the morning, Tortoise went to the middle of the vine and shook it. Elephant immediately grabbed his end, Hippopotamus caught up his end, and the tugging began. Each pulled at the vine mightily and it remained taut. At times it was pulled in one direction, and then in the other, but neither was overpulling the other.

Tortoise watched the quivering vine, laughing in his heart. Then he went away to seek for food, leaving the two at their tug, and hungry. He ate his bellyful of mushrooms and then went comfortably to sleep.

Late in the afternoon he rose and said, "I will go and see whether those fools are still pulling." When he went there the vine was still stretched taut, with neither of them winning. At last, Tortoise nicked the vine with his knife. The vine parted, and at their ends Elephant and Hippopotamus, so suddenly released, fell with a great crash back onto the ground.

Tortoise started off with one end of the broken vine. He came on Elephant looking doleful and rubbing a sore leg. Elephant said, "Tortoise, I did not know you were so strong. When the vine broke I fell over and hurt my leg. Yes, we are really equals. Strength is not because the body is large. We will call each other Friend."

Most pleased with this victory over Elephant, Tortoise then went off to visit Hippopotamus, who looked sick and was rubbing his head. Hippopotamus said, "So, Tortoise, we are equal. We pulled and pulled and despite my great size I could not surpass you. When the vine broke I fell and hurt my head. Indeed, strength has no greatness of body. We will call each other Friend."

After that, whenever they three and others met in council, the three sat together on the highest seats. And always they addressed each other as Friend.

Do you think they were really equal?

(FAN)

78 THE DOG'S WISDOM

One day nine wild dogs went out to hunt. On the path they met a Lion who said that he too was on a hunt, and suggested that they join forces and hunt together. The dogs agreed, and they hunted together all day. By nightfall they had caught ten antelopes. The Lion said, "We must now go and find some person wise enough to divide this meat among us in a proper fashion."

One of the dogs said, "Why is that necessary? This does not require any special person of great wisdom. Are we not ten? We have caught ten antelopes, hence a fair division is that we each take one."

In an instant the Lion rose, and with his great hand he struck the bold dog and blinded him.

The other dogs were cowed and impressed. Then one of them ventured, "No, no, our brother was wrong. That was not the proper division of the meat. The Lion is King of the World, and if we leave nine of the antelopes to him, then they will be ten. For us, we are nine and if we take one antelope, so shall we be ten. That is the best division!"

The Lion was pleased and strutted about saying, "You

are not a fool like your brother. Such a very wise dog! How
did you come by this great wisdom?"

And the dog replied, "When you struck my brother and
blinded him, it was then I learned this wisdom, King Lion."

(BURA)

79 HOW THE SPIDER WON AND LOST
NZAMBI'S DAUGHTER

The goddess of the earth, Nzambi, had a beautiful daughter;
but she swore that no earthly being should marry her who
could not bring her the heavenly fire from Nzambi Mpungu,
who dwelt in the heavens above the blue roof. And as the
daughter was very fair to look upon, the people marveled,
saying: "How shall we secure this treasure? And who on
such a condition will ever marry her?"

Then the spider said: "I will, if you will help me."

And they all answered: "We will gladly help you, if you
will reward us."

Then the spider reached the blue roof of heaven and
dropped down again to the earth, leaving a strong silken
thread firmly hanging from the roof to the earth below.
Now, he called the tortoise, the woodpecker, the rat, and
the sandfly, and bade them climb up the thread to the roof.
And they did so. Then the woodpecker pecked a hole
through the roof, and they all entered the realm of Nzambi
Mpungu.

Nzambi Mpungu received them courteously, and asked
them what they wanted up there.

And they answered him, saying: "O Nzambi Mpungu of
the heavens above, great father of all the world, we have
come to fetch some of your terrible fire for Nzambi who
rules upon earth."

"Wait here then," said Nzambi Mpungu, "while I go to

my people and tell them of the message that you bring."

But the sandfly unseen accompanied Nzambi Mpungu and heard all that was said.

Then Nzambi Mpungu returned to them, and said: "My friend, how can I know that you have really come from the ruler of the earth, and that you are not impostors?"

"Nay," they said; "put us to some test that we may prove our sincerity to you."

"I will," said Nzambi Mpungu. "Go down to this earth of yours, and bring me a bundle of bamboos, that I may make myself a shed."

And the tortoise went down, leaving the others where they were, and soon returned with the bamboos.

Then Nzambi Mpungu said to the rat: "Get thee beneath this bundle of bamboos, and I will set fire to it. Then if thou escape I shall surely know that Nzambi sent you."

And the rat did as he was bidden. And Nzambi Mpungu set fire to the bamboos, and lo! when they were entirely consumed, the rat came from amidst the ashes unharmed.

Then he said: "You are indeed what you represent yourselves to be. I will go and consult my people again."

Then they sent the sandfly after him, bidding him to keep well out of sight, to hear all that was said, and if possible to find out where the lightning was kept. The sandfly returned and related all that he had heard and seen.

Then Nzambi Mpungu returned to them, and said: "Yes, I will give you the fire you ask for, if you can tell me where it is kept."

And the spider said: "Give me then, O Nzambi Mpungu, one of the five cases that you keep in the fowl house."

"Truly you have answered me correctly, O spider! Take therefore this case, and give it to your Nzambi."

And the tortoise carried it down to the earth; and the spider presented the fire from heaven to Nzambi; and Nzambi gave the spider her beautiful daughter in marriage.

But the woodpecker grumbled, and said: "Surely the woman is mine; for it was I who pecked the hole through the roof, without which the others never could have entered the kingdom of the Nzambi Mpungu above."

"Yes," said the rat, "but see how I risked my life among the burning bamboos; the girl, I think, should be mine."

"Nay, O Nzambi; the girl should certainly be mine; for without my help the others would never have found out where the fire was kept," said the sandfly.

Then Nzambi said: "Nay, the spider undertook to bring me the fire; and he has brought it. The girl by rights is his; but as you others will make her life miserable if I allow her to live with the spider, and I cannot give her to you all, I will give her to none, but will give you each her market value."

Nzambi then paid each of them fifty longs of cloth and one case of gin; and her daughter remained a maiden and waited upon her mother for the rest of her days.

(BAKONGO)

80 THE NATURE OF BAT

Once upon a time there was a war between the animals and birds. A serious debate took place as to which party the bat would join, and he, being a wily creature, kept his own counsel. When the birds were in the ascendant he threw in his lot with them. For forty years they kept the animals in subjection. At last the lion and the tiger, in despair of overthrowing their oppressors, advised that measures should be taken to bring about peace. This counsel was derisively rejected by the other animals, who were of opinion that fortune was, at last, about to favor them, so hostilities were resumed. A watch was now set upon the bat's movements, and it was discovered that he was holding himself aloof, at that time, from both parties. The fox was sent to arrest him and he was brought before the leaders of the animals. He was charged with playing a double game and an explanation was demanded. His defense was that he had followed the advice of his wife, who had persuaded him to hold himself in readiness to join whichever party prevailed, with the view of ultimately receiving a share of the spoils.

He was chided severely for his double-dealing and thrown into prison to await his trial at the conclusion of the war. For ten years longer the struggle continued and finally it ended in the complete defeat of the birds.

The bat was summoned before the council and, finding the case too hard for him, he engaged a clever lawyer to plead his case. The advocate contended that his client had a perfect right to side with either party, according to his inclination. He based his opinion on the anatomy of the bat. Though not a bird yet he was equipped with wings and, being able to fly, he insisted that when the bat was in the air he was not trespassing; all must admit that he was in his rightful sphere. On the other hand he was covered with fur, he had teeth and long ears, whereas the birds had none of these characteristics. All things considered there seemed no doubt that the bat possessed qualities which made it admissible for him to be termed either an animal, or a bird, or both.

81 THE FABLE OF THE STOMACH

There was once a very wonderful man. He created the different parts of the Body—the Head, Feet, Hands, Eyes and other members. When he had completed all he placed them in a beautiful garden. He gave them certain laws to observe, the chief of which were that they should be liberal in almsgiving and that they should show kindness and hospitality to all strangers.

One day the Creator decided to test the loyalty of the inmates of the garden. He disguised himself as a leper and appeared to them as one suffering from the loathsome disease in its advanced stages. He applied first to the Eyes for assistance, but they drove him away in disgust; he next appeared to the Head and received no better treatment; the Feet and the Hands also refused to succor him. Finally, he went to the Stomach who, while strongly inclined to turn his back on the unsightly object, yet remembered the commands of his Creator, and treated the poor beggar kindly before letting him go home.

The next day the Creator sent messengers to the members he had visited. To the Eyes he sent blindness; to the Head, headaches; the Feet, rheumatism; to the Hands, paralysis, and to the Stomach, pain. All were commanded to attend at his court. When charged with ungenerous and disloyal conduct, the Stomach was the only one able to plead successfully "not guilty." Hence the Creator decreed that all the other members of the body should forever be subservient to the Stomach! The Head should carry its food; the Eyes must be constantly watching the way it should take; the Hands were to procure and prepare its food; and the Feet should carry it whithersoever it chose to go!

The Stomach being very stupid, as many young children are, pleaded to be allowed to share the troubles of his brethren. The Creator acceded to his request and therefore appointed that his place should be in the forefront of all—a position which exposed him to many dangers.

A note added to the above by the man who originally narrated the legend says, "Just think of this story; it practically seems to be true—had it not been a fable."

(IBO)

82 HOW THE WIVES RESTORED
THEIR HUSBAND TO LIFE

A certain man named Nenpetro had three wives, Ndoza'ntu
the Dreamer, Songa'nzila the Guide, the Fulla Fulla the
Raiser of the Dead. Now Nenpetro was a great hunter; and
one day he killed an antelope and gave it to his three wives.
They ate it, and after a time complained of hunger. Nenpetro went out shooting again, and killed a monkey. They
ate this also, but still complained of hunger. "Oh," says
Nenpetro, "nothing but an ox will satisfy you people." So
off he went on the track of an ox. He followed the tracks
for a long way, and at last caught sight of it as it was feeding with two or three others. He stalked it carefully, and shot
it; but before he could reload, another angry ox charged him,
and killed him.

Now in town they knew nothing of all this; but his wives
grew very hungry, and cried for him to come back to them.
Still he returned not. Then Ndoza'ntu dreamt that he had
been killed by an ox, but that he had killed an ox before he
fell.

"Come along," said Songa'nzila; "I will show you the
road."

Thus they set out, and marched up hill and down dale,
through woods and across rivers, until toward nightfall they
came up to the place where their husband lay dead. And
now Fulla Fulla went into the woods and collected herbs
and plants, and set about raising him from the dead.

Then the three women began to quarrel and wonder into
whose shimbec Nenpetro would first enter.

"I dreamt that he was dead," said Ndoza'ntu.

"But I showed you where he lay dead," said Songa'nzila.

"And I have brought him back to life," said Fulla Fulla,
as the husband gradually gave signs of life.

"Well, let us each cook a pot of food, and take it to him as soon as he can eat; and let him decide out of which pot he will take his first meal."

So two killed fowls, and cooked them each in her own pot, while the third cooked some pig in hers. And Nenpetro took the pot of pig that Fulla Fulla had cooked, and said: "When you dreamt that I was dead, you did not give me food, Ndoza'ntu; for I was not yet found. And when you, Songa'nzila, had shown the others the road, I was still unfit to eat; but when Fulla Fulla gave me back my life, then was I able to eat the pig she gave me. The gift therefore of Fulla Fulla is the most to be prized."

And the majority of the people said he was right in his judgment; but the women round about said he should have put the food out of the three pots into one pot, and have eaten the food thus mixed.

(BAKONGO)

6

TALES OF HUMAN ADVENTURE

83 THE MARKET OF THE DEAD

There were two wives. The first wife gave birth to twins but herself died in childbirth. So the second wife took care of them. The elder twin was called Hwese, the other Hwevi. When the stepmother pounded grain, she took away the fine flour on top, and gave them what was not fit to eat.

One day the stepmother gave them each a small gourd and told them to go for water. They went to the stream, but on the way back Hwese slipped and broke his gourd. The other said, "If we go home now, she will beat Hwese, and let me go free. So I'll break mine, too." He threw it down and broke it.

When the stepmother saw what had happened, she got a whip and whipped them.

Hwevi said, "I am going to buy a bead." Hwese said, "Yes, let us each buy a bead for Ku. We will go there and visit the one who watches Death's door. Perhaps he will let us see our mother."

> The grave is deep,
> Deep, deep,
> Stepmother bought some gourds,
> But Hwese broke his gourd,
> And Hwevi broke his, too.
> When we told our stepmother,

> She flogged us with a whip,
> So Hwese bought a bead,
> And Hwevi bought one, too.

Good. So they went to see the guardian of Death's door. He asked them, "What do you want?"

Hwesi said, "Yesterday, when we went to get water, my brother Hwese broke his gourd. So I broke mine, too. Our stepmother beat us, and did not give us anything to eat all day. So we have come to beg you to let us enter here. We want to see our mother."

When the guardian heard this, he opened the door.

> The grave is deep,
> Deep, deep.
> Stepmother bought some gourds,
> But Hwese broke his gourd,
> And Hweve broke his, too.
> When we told our stepmother,
> She flogged us with a whip,
> So Hwese bought a bead,
> And Hwevi bought one, too.
> We gave these to the door's guardian
> And the door opened.

Inside there were two markets, the market of the living, and the market of the dead.

Good. Everybody asked them, "Where do you come from, where do you come from?" The living asked this, and the dead asked it, too. The children said, "This is what happened. Yesterday we broke the little gourds our stepmother gave us. She beat us and gave us nothing to eat. We begged the man who watches at the door to let us come in to see our mother, so she might buy two other gourds for us."

Good. Then their mother came and bought some *acasa* in the market of the living for them. Then she turned her back, and gave money to a living man to buy two gourds in the market of the living for them, and gave these to her children. Then she herself went to the market of the dead, and bought palm nuts to send to her husband's other wife. For she knew that the other liked these nuts very much. Now, once the woman ate the palm nuts, she would surely die.

Good. Then the mother said to the children, "All right. Go home now, and tell your stepmother good day. Thank her for looking after you so well."

> The grave is deep,
> Deep, deep.
> Stepmother bought some gourds,
> But Hwese broke his gourd,
> And Hwevi broke his, too.
> When we told our stepmother,
> She flogged us with a whip,
> So Hwese bought a bead,
> And Hwevi bought one, too.
> We gave these to the door's guardian
> And the door opened.
> Our mother, hearing our story,
> Bought us two gourds,
> For our stepmother.

The stepmother looked for the two boys. She looked for them everywhere, but she could not find out where they had gone. When they came back, she asked them, "Where were you?"

They said, "We went to see our mother."

But their stepmother scolded them. She said, "No, you lie. Nobody can visit the dead."

Good. The children gave her the palm nuts. They said, "Here, our mother sent these to you."

The other woman laughed at them. "So you found a dead one to send me palm nuts?"

But when the stepmother ate these palm nuts, she died.

The grave is deep,
Deep, deep.
Stepmother bought some gourds,
But Hwese broke his gourd,
And Hwevi broke his, too.
When we told our stepmother,
She flogged us with a whip,
So Hwese bought a bead,
And Hwevi bought one, too.
We gave these to the door's guardian
And the door opened.
Our mother, hearing our story,
Bought us two gourds,
For our stepmother.
At home our stepmother wanted to buy life,
But we gave her the fruit
In abundance, abundance.

In Dahomey, when a person dies, the family goes to a diviner and he makes the dead talk so that you hear his voice. So when they called the dead stepmother she said, "Tell all the other women that my death came from the orphans. Tell them also that Mawu says that when there are several wives, and one dies and leaves children, the others must care for the children of the dead woman."

This is why, if a man has two wives, and one dies leaving a child, you give that child to the second wife, and the second wife must look after the dead woman's child better than after her own children. And this is why one never mistreats orphans. For once you mistreat them, you die. You die the same day. You are not even sick. I know that myself. I am an orphan. My father never lets me go out alone at night. Whenever I ask him for something, he gives it to me.

(DAHOMEY)

84 LET THE BIG DRUM ROLL

This man was a young king. As he had gone with other
people to trade, his companions noted that he was bringing
back a large amount of goods. So they became quite jealous
and said: "Let us kill him." In fact, they fell upon him and
left him dead. After that they threw his body into the bush.

He was then changed into a little bird with pretty colors
and cowries all over its body, which went and perched on
the top of a tree in front of the criminals. He then sang:

Let the big drum roll! —*Chorus:* Let the big drum roll!
It flaps the wings,
The little bird that has come out from the deep river,
From the great river of God. Let the big drum roll!

Let the big drum roll! Let the big drum roll!
At the great river of beads and pearls
I have found fowls which pound,
Using mortars hewn from blood trees. Let the big drum
    roll!

Let the big drum roll! Let the big drum roll!
Using mortars hewn from the blood trees,
Their beaks are all white.
Here! Nemba, where are you? Let the big drum roll!

Let the big drum roll! Let the big drum roll!
Here! Nemba, where are you?
Start threading pearls,[1]
Brilliant pearls. Let the big drum roll!

Let the big drum roll! Let the big drum roll!
Start threading pearls,

[1] Pearls are worn as a token of mourning.

Brilliant pearls,
From the land I-wash-the-wrongs. Let the big drum roll!

Let the big drum roll! Let the big drum roll!
The land Where-I-wash-the-wrongs!
It is far here where you have brought me,
Me who have no feet. Let the big drum roll!

Nemba was the sister of the dead chief.

When those people heard that song, they caught the little
bird and killed it by beating it.

They had hardly resumed their march when they saw the
little bird alive once more going ahead of them, and heard
it sing:

Let the big drum roll! . . . etc.

Once more they caught it and killed it, and this time they
said: "Let us burn it to ashes." So they put it on the fire,
reduced it to a cinder, then ground it to ashes.

But it got up again, flew into the air, and went on singing
as before:

Let the big drum roll! . . .

until it flew away in the direction of their kraal.

When it reached the place, the people saw it come down
on the top of the royal house and perch there. "Come," they
said, "and see what a pretty bird." They heard it sing as
before:

Let the big drum roll! . . .

Now those people are coming to the kraal: "You have
reappeared!"

"We have reappeared."

"And the king, where have you left him?"

They answer: "On the road."

Then: "Really? On the road! Come and see a little bird which is on the roof of the royal house."

They at once said: "Let us kill it."

Meanwhile some people are digging a hole in the ground.

Then Nemba, the king's sister, says: "No, don't kill it. Let us hear the news first."

Just then the little bird started its song again: "Let the big drum roll!"

"Go into the hut, that you may explain to us exactly what the little bird sings." They went and sat down in the hut on the mat spread there, but then, *powowowo,* they tumbled down into the hole. Boiling water was brought at once and poured on top of them. That is how they died.

(BENA MUKUNI)

85 HOW AN UNBORN CHILD AVENGED ITS MOTHER'S DEATH

A man had taken a wife, and now she had the joy of being with child, but famine was acute in the land.

One day, when hunger was particularly severe, the man, accompanied by his wife, was dragging himself along in the direction of her mother's home in the hope of getting a little food there. He happened to find on the road a tree with abundant wild fruit on the top. "Wife," he said, "get up there that we may eat fruit."

The woman refused, saying, "I, who am with child, to climb up a tree!"

He said, "In that case, do not climb at all."

The husband then climbed up himself and shook and shook the branches, the woman meanwhile picking up what fell down. He said, "Do not pick up my fruit. What! Just now you refused to go up!"

And she: *"Bana!* I am only picking them up."

Thinking about his fruit, he hurried down from the top of the tree and said, "You have eaten some."

And she: "Why! Of course, I have not."

Then, assegai in hand, he stabbed his wife. And there she died on the spot.

He then gathered up his fruit with both hands. There he sat eating it, remaining where the woman was stretched out quite flat.

All of a sudden he started running. Run! Run! Run! Without stopping once, he ran until he reached the rise of a hill.

There he slept, out of sight of the place where he had left the woman.

Meanwhile the child that was in the womb rushed out of it, dragging its umbilical cord. First, it looked round for the direction which its father had taken, then it started this song:

> Father, wait for me,
> Father, wait for me,
> The little wombless.
> Who is it that has eaten my mother?
> The little wombless . . . !
> How swollen are those eyes!
> Wait till the little wombless comes.

That gave the man a shake. . . . "There," he said, "there comes the thing which is speaking." He listened, he stared in that direction. . . . "This is the child coming to follow me after all that, when I have already killed its mother. It had been left in the womb."

Then rage took his wits away, and he killed the little child! . . . There he was, making a fresh start, and going on. Here, where the little bone had been left: "Little bone, gather yourself up! . . . Little bone, gather yourself up."

Soon it was up again, and then came the song:

> Father, wait for me,

> Father, wait for me,
> The little wombless.
> Who is it that has eaten my mother?
> The little wombless . . . !
> How swollen are those eyes!
> Wait till the little wombless comes.

The father stopped. . . . "Again the child that I have killed! It has risen and is coming. Now I shall wait for him."

So he hid and waited for the child, with an assegai in his hand. The child came and made itself visible at a distance as from here to there. As soon as it came, quick with the assegai! He stabbed it! Then he looked for a hole, shoveled the little body into it, and heaped branches up at the entrance.

Then with all speed he ran! With all speed! . . .

At last he reached the kraal where the mother of his dead wife lived, the grandmother of the child.

When he came he sat down. Then his brothers and sisters-in-law come with smiling faces. . . . "Well! Well! You have put in an appearance!"

"We have," he says, "put in an appearance."

And a hut was prepared for him and his wife, who was expected.

Then the mother-in-law was heard asking from afar, "Well! And my daughter, where has she been detained?"

Said he, "I have left her at home. I have come alone to beg for a little food. Hunger is roaring."

"Sit down inside there, father."

Food was procured for him. So he began to eat. And, when he had finished, he even went to sleep.

Meanwhile, the child, on its part, had squeezed itself out of the hole wherein it had been put and, again, with its umbilical cord hanging on:

> Father, wait for me,
> Father, wait for me,
> The little wombless.

> Who is it that has eaten my mother?
> The little wombless . . . !
> How swollen are those eyes!
> Wait till the little wombless comes.

The people listened in the direction of the path. . . .
"That thing which comes speaking indistinctly, what is it?
. . . It seems to be a person. . . . What is it? . . . It
looks, man, like a child killed by you on the road. . . .
And now, when we look at your way of sitting, you seem to
be only half-seated."

"It cannot be the child, Mother; it remained at home."
The man had just got up to shake himself a little. And his
little child, too, was coming with all speed! It was already
near, with its mouth wide open:

> Father, wait for me,
> Father, wait for me,
> The little wombless.
> Who is it that has eaten my mother?
> The little wombless . . . !
> How swollen are those eyes!
> Wait till the little wombless comes!

Everyone was staring. They said, "There comes a little
red thing. It still has the umbilical cord hanging on."

Inside of the hut there, where the man stood, there was
complete silence!

Meanwhile the child was coming on feet and buttocks
with its mouth wide open, but still at a distance from its
grandmother's hut. "Straight over there!" noted everyone.
The grandmother looked toward the road and noticed that
the little thing was perspiring, and what speed! Then the
song:

> Father, wait for me,
> Father, wait for me,
> The little wombless.

> Who is it that has eaten my mother?
> The little wombless . . . !
> How swollen are those eyes!
> Wait till the little wombless comes.

Bakoo! It scarcely reached its grandmother's hut when it jumped into it . . . and up on the bed:

> Father, wait for me,
> Father, have you come?
> Yes, you have eaten my mother.
> How swollen those eyes!
> Wait till the little wombless comes.

Then the grandmother put this question to the man: "Now what sort of song is this child singing? Have you not killed our daughter?"

She had scarcely added, "Surround him!" when he was already in their hands. His very brothers-in-law tied him. And then . . . all the assegais were poised together in one direction, everyone saying, "Now today you are the man who killed our sister. . . ."

Then they just threw the body away there to the west. And the grandmother picked up her little grandchild.

(BENA MUKUNI)

86 THE CHILDREN OF THE KNEE

There was once an old man who was unmarried and lived alone in his hut. One night he went to sleep, and when he awoke in the morning, he found his knee was greatly swollen. There was nobody to attend to him, so he kept quiet as he thought he only had a boil. After remaining thus for six months, he asked himself how it was the boil did not come to a head so as to enable him to lance it. He waited two months more, and as it had not come to a head, he said to himself: "Even if it kills me, I will lance it." He therefore took his knife and lanced it; and out came two children.

He looked after the children and fed them, and when they were old enough, he told them to sit by the door of the cave while he went to look for food, and not to open to people they did not know.

On his return he sang:

> It is now soft, but not yet burst
>   My children of the knee.
> Go, my little one, let me in,
>   Open the door to me.

The children opened the door to him, and he entered and gave them their food.

One day some of the old man's enemies came to the cave and said to the children: "Open the door, children." But as the children refused, they decided to wait until the sun should set to see if the owner arrived. The old man returned in the evening and sang the usual song, whereupon the door was opened.

The enemies then elected to sleep where they were, and to go the next evening to sing the same song, and to kidnap the children. So the next evening they went to the cave and sang:

> It is now soft, but not yet burst,
>   My children of the knee.
> Go, my little one, let me in,
>   Open the door to me.

As the voice, however, did not resemble their father's, the children refused to open the door.

The men then returned to their own country and consulted a medicine man. They told him they wanted to make their voices resemble an old man's in order that they could kidnap some children they had seen in the forest. The medicine man told them to go back where the children were, and to eat nothing on the road.

But before they reached the cave they had eaten a lizard and an ant which they found, thinking that these small things would not matter. On their arrival they sang the song, but the children did not recognize their father's voice and refused to open the door. The enemies then returned to the medicine man's kraal and, on being asked what they had eaten on the road, replied: "A lizard and an ant."

They were told to go again to the cave, and to pick up nothing whatsoever on the way, not even a small ant. They did as they were told, and when they reached the cave they sang the song. The children, thinking it was their father, opened the door, whereupon the men entered and carried them off to their kraal.

In the evening the old man returned to the cave and sang, but as he received no answer, he looked for the children. When he did not find them he wept, and started off to search in the neighboring kraals.

He arrived at one kraal and sang, but received no reply. He then went on to the next one and sang again, and the children recognized his voice and wept. When their father heard them, he went outside and shouted loudly. The people told him to stop and said a spell had been put on the town. No stranger might enter without eating a certain medicine. They then put a stone in the fire, and when it was hot they told the old man to open his mouth and swallow the medicine. The old man opened his mouth, and the stone was thrown in and killed him. After this the children of the knee remained in the kraal.

(MASAI)

87 THE CITY WHERE MEN ARE MENDED

All the girls of the town had assembled and had gone to the forest to pick herbs. While they were doing this, it began to rain; from the east it came, and they ran and got inside the hollow of a baobab tree, and the devil closed it up. When the rain had ceased, the devil said that each must give him her necklace and cloth before he would release her, and all gave them to him except one girl who refused to do so. So she had to remain, but the others went off home.

Now the tree had a small hole at the top, and the girls who had returned told the girl's mother, so she started off and came to see the place where her daughter was. Then she returned home and prepared food, and in the evening she went back to the tree and said, "Daughter, daughter, stretch out your hand and take this food." So she stretched out her hand through the hole, and the girl got it and ate it, and then the mother went home again.

Now it happened a hyena had heard all this and, later on, he returned and said, "Daughter, daughter, stretch out your hand and take this food." But she replied, "That is not my mother's voice," and she would not. So the hyena went to a blacksmith and said, "Alter my voice for me, so that it will resemble that of a human being." And the other said, "If I do improve your voice for you, even before you have arrived at the foot of the tree you will have eaten whatever you have found. However," he continued, "I'll do it for you." And he did so. But as the hyena was returning, he saw a centipede, and he said, "Does one ignore what he finds in the morning?" So he took the centipede and ate it. Then he went to the tree and said, "Daughter, daughter, stretch out your hand and take this food." But she replied, "That is not my mother's voice."

So the hyena became angry, and he returned to the black-smith and was about to eat him, but the other said, "Stop, stop, stop, you must not eat me." And he continued, "Why do you want to eat me?" Then the hyena replied, "Because you did not alter my voice properly." Then the smith said, "Stop, I will do it properly." So he altered the hyena's voice and then the hyena returned to where the girl was and said, "Daughter, daughter, stretch out your hand and take this food." This time she stretched out her hand, and, when she had done so, the hyena seized it and pulled the girl out of the tree and ate her, leaving only the bones. Then he went away.

Now the girl's mother brought the food in the evening. But when she came, she saw her daughter's bones, and she burst out crying there. Then she went home and got a basket, and she returned and collected the bones and took the road to the city where men were mended.

She traveled on and on, and after a time she came to a place where food was cooking itself, and she said, "O food, show me the road to the city where men are mended." Then the food said, "Stay here and eat me," but she replied, "I have no appetite, I do not wish to eat you." So the food said, "When you have gone a certain distance, take the road on the right hand and leave that on the left."

After a time she came upon meat which was grilling itself, and she said, "O meat, show me the road to the city where men are mended." Then the meat said, "Stay here and eat me," but she replied, "I have no appetite, I do not wish to eat you." So the meat said, "When you have gone so far, take the road on the right hand and leave that on the left."

So she started again, and as she was traveling, she came upon *fura* which was mixing itself in a pot, and she said, "O *fura,* show me the road to the city where men are mended." Then the *fura* said, "Stay here and eat me," but she replied, "I have no appetite, I do not wish to eat you." So the *fura* said, "When you have gone a certain distance, take the road on the right hand and leave that on the left."

She traveled on again and, at last, there she was in the

city where men were mended. Then the people said, "What has brought you here?" And she replied, "The hyena has eaten my child." "Where are the bones?" they asked. And she put down her basket and said, "See, here they are." So they said, "Very well, tomorrow your daughter will be mended."

When morning broke, they said to her, "Go out and tend the cattle," so she unloosed the cattle and took them off to feed. Now these cattle had no food except the fruits of the *adduwa* tree, and when she had picked off the fruits above and had thrown them down, she picked out the ripe ones and gave them to the cattle, but she herself chose the green ones to eat. She fed them thus until the evening, and then they returned home, and as they reached the enclosure, the biggest bull began bellowing:

> This woman has a good heart,
> Mend her daughter well.

So the daughter was mended well, and the mother returned to her hut, for the people said to her, "Sleep here, and tomorrow you will go home." So next day the daughter was brought and restored to her mother, and they went home.

Now the mother had a rival wife, who also had a daughter, but a very ugly one, and, when the mother had returned home, the rival said that she too would kill her daughter, and go to the city where men were mended.

So she took her daughter, and put her in a mortar, and began to pound her up. Then the daughter cried out, "O Mother, are you are going to kill me?" But she went on pounding, and at last she took out the bones, and she brought a basket and put the bones into it, and then she took the road to the city where men were mended.

She traveled on and on, and after a time she came to a place where food was cooking itself, and she said, "O food, show me the road to the city where men are mended." Then the food said, "Stay here and eat me," but she replied, *"Opp,* do you need to invite me to eat you?" So she stayed and ate the food.

After a time she came upon meat which was grilling itself, and she said, "O meat, show me the road to the city where men are mended." Then the meat said, "Stay here and eat me," and she replied, *"Opp,* do you need to invite me to eat you?" So she stayed and ate up the meat.

She started again, and as she was traveling, she came upon *fura* which was mixing itself in a pot, and she said, "O *fura,* show me the road to the city where men are mended." Then the *fura* said, "Stay here and eat me," and she replied, *"Opp,* do you need to invite me to eat you?" So she stayed and ate up the *fura.*

So on she traveled again and, at last, there she was in the city where men are mended. Then the people said, "What has brought you here?" And she replied, "The hyena has eaten my child." "Where are the bones?" they asked. And she put down her basket and said, "See, here they are." So they said, "Very well, tomorrow your daughter will be mended."

When morning broke, they said to her, "Go out and tend the cattle," so she unloosed the cattle and took them off to feed. Now when she had picked off the fruits of the *adduwa* tree, and had thrown them down, she picked out the green ones, and gave them to the cattle, and she herself chose the ripe ones to eat. She fed them thus until the evening, and then they returned home, and as they reached the enclosure, the biggest bull began bellowing:

> This woman has a bad heart,
> Mend her daughter ill.

So she tied up the cattle, and went to her hut, for the people said to her, "Sleep here, and tomorrow you will go home." In the morning, the daughter was created with one leg, one buttock, one hand, the whole consisted of only one side. Half a nose was there, the other half was missing. And when the mother came and said that she was going home, the daughter was brought out to her, and they went off along the road.

When they had emerged from the forest, the mother said, "I am not your mother," and she started off at a run, and went and hid in some grass. But the daughter followed the footprints, and went on and on until she had found her, and said, "Arise, let us go on." Then the mother said, "Go away, you are not my child." But the other said, "Ah, it is you who are not my mother."

Once more the mother started off at a run and entered their own town and went into her hut and shut the door. But the daughter came to the door and called out, "O Mother, I have come." But the other remained silent. "O Mother, I have come," said the daughter again, and she opened the door, and went to her mother. So they lived together, and the rival wife had to put up with the fact that the other's daughter was beautiful while her own was hideous.

(HAUSA)

88 THE WONDER WORKER OF THE PLAINS

Once there was a man and a woman to whom were born first a boy and then a girl. When the bride price had been paid for the girl and she was married, the parents said to the son, "We have a herd for you to dispose of. It is now time for you to take a wife. We will choose you a pretty wife, one whose parents are honest people."

The son, however, firmly refused. "No," he said, "do not bother. I do not like any of the girls who are here. If I absolutely have to marry, I shall choose for myself what I want."

"Do as you will," said the parents, "but if you are unhappy later on, it will not be our fault."

Then the boy set out, left the country, and traveled far, very far, into an unknown region. Finally, he came to a village where he saw some young girls, some of them crushing corn and others cooking. Secretly he made his choice, and said to himself, "That one there is the one I like." Then he went to the men of the village and said, "Good day, fathers!"

"Good day, young man!" they answered. "What is it that you wish?"

"I want to look at your daughters, for I want to take a wife."

"Well, well," they said, "we shall show them to you, and then you can choose."

So they led all of their daughters past him and he indicated the one he wanted. She gave her consent right away.

"Your parents, we expect, will pay us a visit and bring us the bride price, is that right?" asked the young girl's parents.

"No, not at all," answered the young man. "I have my bride price with me. Take it; here it is!"

"Then," they added, "they will, we trust, come later in order to conduct your wife to you?"

"No, no, I fear they would only pain you with the hard admonitions they would give the girl. Let me, myself, take her along right away."

The parents of the young girl gave their consent to this request, but they took her aside in the hut once more to give her advice on how to conduct herself. "Be good to your parents-in-law and take diligent care of your husband!" Then they offered the young couple a younger daughter who could help with the housework. But the woman refused. Two, ten, twenty were then offered for her to choose from. All the girls were first examined before being offered to her.

"No," she insisted, "I do not want them. Give me instead the buffalo of the country, our buffalo, the Wonder Worker of the Plains. Let him serve me."

"How can you ask for him?" they said. "You know that

our life depends on him. Here he is well taken care of, but what would you do with him in a strange country? He will starve, die, and then all of us will die with him."

Before she left her parents, she took with her a pot containing a package of medicinal roots, a horn for bleeding, a little knife for making incisions, and a gourd full of fat.

Then she set out with her husband. The buffalo followed them, but he was visible to her alone. The man did not see him. He did not suspect that the Wonder Worker of the Plains was the servant accompanying his wife.

As soon as they had come to the husband's village, they were received with joyful cries: *"Hoyo, hoyo!"*

"Now look at him!" said the old ones. "So you have found a wife after all! You did not want one of those whom we suggested to you, but that makes no difference. It is well as it is. You have acted according to your own will. If, however, at some time you have enemies, you will have no right to complain."

The man then took his wife into the fields and showed her which were his and which were his mother's. The girl noted everything carefully and returned with him to the village. On the way she said, "I have lost my pearls in the field; I must return to look for them at once." In reality, however, she wanted to see the buffalo. She said to him, "Here is the boundary of the fields. Stay here! And there, too, is the forest in which you can hide."

"You are right," he replied.

Now whenever the wife wanted any water, she merely went to the cultivated fields and set the pitcher down in front of the buffalo. He ran with it to the lake, filled it, and brought the vessel back to his mistress. Whenever she wanted wood, he would go into the brush, break trees with his horns, and bring her as much as she needed.

The people in the village were surprised at all these things. "What strength she has!" they said. "She is always back from the well right away; in the twinkling of an eye she has gathered a bundle of dry wood." But no one suspected that a buffalo assisted her as a servant.

The wife did not, however, bring the buffalo anything to eat, for she had only one plate for herself and her husband. At home, of course, they had had a separate plate for the Wonder Worker and fed him carefully. Here, therefore, the buffalo was hungry. She would bring him her pitcher and send him to fetch water. This he did willingly, but he felt great pangs of hunger.

One day she showed him a corner in the brush which he was to clear. During the night the buffalo took a hoe and prepared a vast acreage. Everyone commented, "How clever she is! And how fast she has done her work!"

One evening the buffalo said to his mistress, "I am hungry and you give me nothing to eat. Soon I shall not be able to work any more!"

"Aie," said she, "what shall I do? We have only one plate at the house. The people at home were right when they said that you would have to start stealing. So, steal! Go into my field and take a bean here and there. Then, again, go farther. Do not, however, take them all from the same spot, thus the owners may not be too much aware of it and will not fall over in terror right away."

That night, accordingly, the buffalo went to the field. He devoured a bean here and a bean there, jumped from one corner to the other, and finally fled back to his hiding place. When the women came into the fields the next morning, they could not believe their eyes. "Hey, hey, what is going on here? We have never seen anything like this! A wild beast has destroyed our plants! One can even follow his spoor. Ho, the poor land!" So they ran back and told the story in the village.

In the evening the young woman said to the buffalo, "To be sure, they were very much terrified, but not too much, nevertheless. They did not fall on their backs. So keep on stealing tonight!" And so it continued. The owners of the devastated fields cried out loud and then turned to the men and asked them to summon the watchmen with their guns.

Now, the husband of the young woman was a very good marksman. He, therefore, hid in an ambush in his field and

waited. The buffalo, however, thought that someone might
be lying in wait for him where he had stolen the night before,
so he went to his mistress's beans, the place where he had
pastured the first time.

"Say," cried the man, "this is a buffalo! One has never
seen any like him here. This is a strange animal, indeed."
He fired. The bullet entered the temple of the buffalo, close
to the ear, and came out exactly opposite on the other side.
The Wonder Worker of the Plains turned one somersault
and fell dead.

"That was a good shot!" exclaimed the hunter and announced it to the village.

But the young wife began to cry out in pain and writhe.
"Oh, I have stomach-aches, oh, oh!"

"Calm yourself," she was told. She seemed sick, but in
reality she only wanted to explain why she was crying thus,
and why she was so terrified when she heard of the buffalo's
death. She was given medicine, but she poured it out when
nobody saw her.

Now everyone set out, women with baskets, and men
with weapons, in order to cut up the buffalo. The young
wife alone remained in the village. Soon, however, she followed them, holding her belly, whimpering and crying.

"What is wrong with you, that you come here," said her
husband. "If you are sick, stay at home!"

"No, I did not want to stay in the village all by myself."

Her mother-in-law scolded her, saying that she could not
understand what she was doing and that she would kill
herself by this. When they had filled the baskets with meat,
she said, "Let me carry the head!"

"But no, you are sick, it is much too heavy for you."

"No," said she, "let me do it!" So she shouldered it and
carried it.

After they had arrived at the village, however, instead of
stepping into the house, she went into the shed where the
cooking pots were kept and set down the buffalo's head.
Obstinately, she refused to move. Her husband looked for
her in order to bring her into the hut. He said she would be

much better off there, but she only replied to him harshly, "Do not disturb me!"

Then her mother-in-law came and admonished her gently. "Why do you torture yourself?"

And she replied crossly, "Will you not let me sleep even a little?"

Then they brought her some food, but she pushed it away. Night came. Her husband went to rest. He did not sleep, however, but listened.

The woman now fetched fire, cooked some water in her little pot, and poured into it the package of medicine which she had brought with her from her home. Then she took the buffalo's head and, with the knife, made incisions in front of the ear, at the temple, where the bullet had struck the animal. There she set the bleeding horn and sucked, sucked with all the force of her body, and succeeded in drawing first a few lumps of clotted blood, and then liquid blood. Thereupon she exposed the place to the steam which rose from the cooking pot, after having, however, smeared it completely with the fat that she had saved in the gourd. That soothed the spot. Then she sang as follows:

Ah, my father, Wonder Worker of the Plains,
They told me: You would go through the deep darkness;
    that in all directions you would stumble through the
    night, Wonder Worker of the Plains;
You are the young wonder tree plant, grown out of ruins,
    which dies before its time, consumed by a gnawing
    worm. . . .
You made flowers and fruit fall upon your road, Wonder
    Worker of the Plains!

When she had finished her invocation formula, the head moved, the limbs grew again, the buffalo came to life once more, shook his ears and horns, rose up, and stretched his limbs. . . .

But at this point the man, who could not sleep in the hut, stepped out and said, "Why does my wife have to cry so long? I must see why she pours out all these sighs!" He entered the shed and called for her, but in great anger she replied, "Leave me alone!" Thereupon, however, the buffalo's head fell to the ground again, dead, pierced as before.

The man returned to the hut; he had understood nothing of all this and had seen nothing. Once again the woman took the pot, cooked the medicine, made the incisions, placed the bleeding horn in the proper spot, exposed the wound to the steam, and sang as before:

Ah, my father, Wonder Worker of the Plains,
Indeed they have told me: You would go through the
    deep darkness; that in all directions you would
    stumble through the night, Wonder Worker of the
    Plains;
You are the young wonder tree plant, grown out of ruins,
    which dies before its time, consumed by a gnawing
    worm. . . .
You made flowers and fruit fall upon your road, Wonder
    Worker of the Plains!

Once again the buffalo rose up, his limbs grew together again, he felt himself coming to life, shook his ears and horns, stretched himself—but then again came the man, disquieted, in order to see what his wife was doing. Then she became very angry with him, but he settled down in the shed in order to watch what was going on. Now she took her fire, her cooking pot, and all the other things and went out. She pulled up grass to kindle the embers and began for the third time to resuscitate the buffalo.

Morning had already broken when her mother-in-law came—and once more the head fell to the ground. Day came, and the buffalo's wound began to grow worse.

Finally she said to all of them, "I would like to go bathing in the lake all alone."

They answered her, "But how will you get there since you are sick?"

She went on her way anyhow and came back and said,

"On my way I came upon someone from home. He told me that my mother is very, very sick. I told him to come here to the village but he refused and said, 'They would offer me food and that would only delay me.' He went on right away and added that I should hurry lest my mother die before my arrival. Therefore, good-bye, I am going away!"

Of course, all this was a lie. She had thought of the idea of going to the lake so that she could invent this story and have a reason for carrying the news of the buffalo's death to her people.

She went off, carrying the basket on her head and singing all along the road the end of the song about the Wonder Worker of the Plains. Whenever she passed, the people would band together behind her to accompany her into her village. Arrived there, she announced to them that the buffalo no longer lived.

Then they sent out messengers in all directions in order to gather together the inhabitants of the country. They reproached the young woman earnestly, saying, "Do you see now? We told you so. But you refused all the young girls and wanted absolutely to have the buffalo. Now you have killed all of us!"

Things had advanced thus far when the man, who had followed his wife into the village, also arrived. He rested his gun against a tree trunk and sat down. They greeted him by shouting, "Be saluted, criminal, be saluted! You have killed us all!" He did not understand this and wondered how one could call him a murderer and a criminal.

"To be sure, I have killed a buffalo," said he, "but that is all."

"Yes, but this buffalo was your wife's assistant. He drew water for her, cut wood, worked in the field."

Completely stunned, the man said, "Why did you not let me know that? I would not have killed him then."

"That is how it is," they added. "The lives of all of us depended on him."

Thereupon all of the people began to cut their own throats. First, the young woman, who, as she did it, called out: "Ah, my father, Wonder Worker of the Plains!"

Then came her parents, brothers, sisters, one after the other.

The first one said: "You shall go through darkness!"

The next: "You shall stumble through the night in all directions!"

The next: "You are the young wonder tree plant which dies before its time."

The next: "You made flowers and fruit fall upon your road!"

All cut their throats and they even slew the little children who were still being carried in skins upon the back. "Why should we let them live," they said, "since they would only lose their minds!"

The man returned home and told his people how, by shooting the buffalo, he had killed them all. His parents said to him, "Do you see now? Did we not tell you that misfortune would come to you? When we offered a fitting and wise woman for you, you wanted to act according to your own desire. Now you have lost your fortune. Who will give it back to you, since they are all dead, all of your wife's relatives, to whom you have given your money!"

This is the end.

(BARONGA)

89 THE ENCHANTED GUINEA FOWL

A certain man once upon a time set his bird line and sent his daughter, saying, "Go and look at my line while I go to dig." So his daughter went to see the line. She found a guinea fowl caught in it, and the guinea fowl sang:

> Little girl, little girl, *kirijakija*,
> What have you come to do?

Then said the girl, "I have come to look at the snare." And the guinea fowl asked her, "Whose snare is it?" And the girl said, "I have come to look at my father's snare." Thereupon the guinea fowl said to her, "Go and tell your father that I will bring a white bead and a white sheep if he will let me go."

So the girl went back and told her father, and her father abused his daughter, saying, "You are a bad child," and sent his son instead.

So his son went to look at his father's line and he too found the guinea fowl in the line. And the guinea fowl asked him, asked him in song:

> Little boy, little boy, *kirijakija*,
> What have you come to do?

Thereupon said the little boy, "I have come to look at my father's line." And the guinea fowl said, "Go and tell your father that I will bring a white chicken and a white sheep and a white bead if he will let me go."

So the boy went back and told his father in these words.

Next the man sent his wife. His wife found the guinea fowl, and the guinea fowl addressed her in the same terms he had used to the children.

Then anger overcame the man, and he went himself and found the guinea fowl in the line. The guinea fowl addressed his same song as before. But the man seized the guinea fowl firmly, and the guinea fowl said to him, "Though you seize me, seize me: here in the evening I shall seize mine."

The man then brought him home and plucked him. As he did this, the guinea fowl said to him, "Though you pluck me, pluck me: here in the evening I shall pluck mine."

The man cooked the bird, and the guinea fowl said to him, "Though you cook me, cook me: here in the evening I shall cook mine."

But he was cooked and ready to be eaten. Then the man summoned people, and the people came for food, came that they might eat the guinea fowl which had been cooked.

They all rejoiced with a careless joy and served up the guinea fowl. Suddenly the guinea fowl flew up with a quick flutter and these men were left with their joy.

Now if the man had been wise enough to take the white bead and the sheep and the white chicken, he could have eaten this guinea fowl. This was the guinea fowl of God.

(LANGO)

90 THE ADVENTURES OF MRILE

In the course of time, a man had three sons. Once, the oldest one went with his mother to dig up eddo tubers. As they were thus occupied, he saw a seed bulb. And he said, "Why, there is a seed bulb as handsome as my little brother." But his mother said to him, "How can a seed bulb be as handsome as a human child?" He, however, hid the seed bulb, and the mother tied up the eddoes to carry them home. The boy hid the seed bulb in the hollow of a tree and, using a magic formula, said *"Msura Kwivire-vire tsa kambingu ma kasanga."*

The following day he went there again. The seedling had now become a child. Whenever his mother cooked food, he carried some to it, again and again. Every day he carried food there, but he himself grew leaner and leaner. His father and mother noticed how lean he had grown and asked him, "Son, what is it that makes you so lean? Where is the food going that we always cook for you? Your younger brothers have not become so lean!" Then one of his younger brothers decided to watch the food being cooked. He saw his older brother receive his share served on a plate, and that he did not eat it but carried it away as though to save it. His brothers followed him at a distance to spy on him and saw how he put it into the hollow of a tree. Thereupon they returned home and said to their mother, "We saw how our brother put the food there into the hollow of a tree and brought it to a child living there." And she said to them, "Whose child would inhabit the hollow of a tree?" Thereupon they said to her, "Come on, we will go and direct you there, you-who-have-nursed-us!" And they led their mother there and showed her the place. And behold! there in the hollow of the tree was a little child! So his mother approached the child and killed it.

After she had killed the child, the older brother Mrile carried food there as usual but did not find the child, instead he found it slain. Thereupon he went home and wept copiously. Then his parents asked him, "Mrile, why do you cry?" And he answered, "It is because of the smoke." So they said, "Sit down here at the lower end." Yet his tears still continued unrestrained. Again they said to him, "Why do you cry all the time?" And he answered, "It is nothing but the smoke." Then they responded, "Take your father's chair along with you and go into the courtyard and sit down!" He took the chair, sat down on it in the courtyard, yet the tears continued.

Suddenly he said, "Chair, raise yourself up high like my father's rope whereby he suspends the honey barrel in the virgin forest and in the steppe." About this time his younger brothers entered the courtyard. They saw how he was traveling upward toward the sky. They informed their mother, "Mrile has traveled up toward the sky." But she said, "Why do you talk about your oldest brother traveling up toward the sky? Is there a road, pray, whereon he could ascend?" But they again spoke to her, "Come and see, you-who-have-nursed-us!" So his mother came to investigate and found that he had indeed ascended high up.

Thereupon his mother cried:

> Mrile return,
> Return, my child,
> Return!

But Mrile answered:

> I shall return no more,
> I shall return no more,
>   Mother, Ah, I,
> I shall return no more,
> I shall return no more.

Thereupon his younger brother cried:

> Mrile, return,
> Return, our brother,
> Return!
> Come home,
> Come home!

But he said:

> Oh, I,
> I shall return no more,
> I shall return no more,
>   My brothers,
> I shall return no more,
> I shall return no more.

Thereupon his father came and spoke:

> Mrile, here is your food,
>   Here is your food,
> Mrile, here it is!
> Mrile, here is your food,
>   Here is your food!

But he answered, saying:

> I want no more,
> I want no more,
>   My father, Ah, I,

I want no more,
I want no more.

Thereupon his tribal companions came and sang:

Mrile, come home!
Come home!
Mrile, come!
Come home!
Come home!
Mrile, come!

Thereupon his uncle came and sang:

Mrile, come home,
Come home!
Mrile, come!
Come home,
Come home!

But he sang in reply:

Ah, I,
I shall return no more,
I shall return no more.
Uncle, Ah, I,
I shall return no more,
I shall return no more!

And he disappeared, so that they could not see him any more.

After a while, Mrile encountered wood gatherers. He greeted them, "Wood gatherers, good day! Please show me the way to Moon King." But they answered him, "Gather some wood, then we will direct you there." So he cut some firewood for them. Then they told him, "Just go straight ahead, and you will encounter some grass cutters!"

So he went on and soon encountered some grass cutters.

"Grass cutters, good day!" They returned the greeting. "Please show me the road to Moon King." But they said to him, "Cut some grass first, then we will direct you there." So he cut some grass for them. Thereupon they told him, "Just go straight ahead, and you will encounter some tillers."

So he went on and soon encountered some tillers. "You who are tilling there, good day!" And they said to him, "Good day!" "Please show me the road to Moon King!" But they said to him, "First till for us, then we will direct you there." So he tilled for them. Thereupon they told him, "Just go straight ahead and then you will encounter some herdsmen."

He went on and soon encountered some herdsmen. "You, tending the herd there, good day!" "Good day!" "Please direct me to Moon King!" But they told him, "Watch the herd for us for a while, and we will direct you there!" So he helped them with the grazing for a while.

Then they said to him, "Just go straight ahead to the bean harvesters!" "You there, harvesting beans, good day! Please direct me to Moon King!" "Help us pick beans a little, then we will direct you there!" So he picked some beans. Thereupon they said, "Just go further along this road to the millet reapers!"

Soon he encountered some millet reapers. "You, millet reapers, greetings! Please direct me to Moon King!" "Help us first reap some millet, then we will direct you there!" "Now go further along the road to the people who seek banana stalks!"

These, in turn, he saluted: "You, banana stalk seekers, greetings! Please direct me to Moon King!" "Help us seek banana stalks first, then we will direct you there!" So he found them some banana stalks. Then they told him, "Just go straight ahead, until you come to the people who carry water!"

"You water carriers, greetings! Please show me the way to Moon King!" "Go straight ahead to the people who are just eating in their own houses!" "You house owners, greetings! Please direct me to Moon King!" "Come, first eat something, then we will direct you there."

After a while he encountered people who ate raw food. They were the people of the Moon King. And he said to them, "Why do you not cook with fire?" But they answered him thus, "What is that, fire?" He said to them, "One cooks food with it until it is done." Then they said to him, "We know nothing about fire!" And he said to them, "If I prepare you some tasty food by means of fire, what will you give me?" The Moon King said, "We shall rent you large cattle and some small stock."

And Mrile said to them, "Good, gather a lot of dry wood for me, and I will bring you the fire." So they gathered some wood, but they went behind the house where they were not seen by other people. Mrile then brought forth a fire drill and a fire board and struck fire, there, behind the house. They then lit the firewood and he placed green bananas in it for roasting. Then he said to Moon King, "Try to eat these bananas which I have roasted in the fire." Moon King ate the banana and noticed how nice it tasted. Thereupon Mrile put meat in to cook and said to him, "Now you must eat cooked meat too!" And Moon King noticed how tasty it was. Then he cooked for them all kinds of eatable things, all well done. Finally, Moon King had the people called and he said to them, "A medicine man has come from below there, from below there!"

Now Moon King spoke, "Tribute shall be paid to this man to buy his fire from him." Then they asked him, "What shall be paid you?" And he said, "Let one person bring a cow, another a goat, another something from the granary!" So they carried all these things to him. Then he distributed fire among them, whereupon they went to cook their food.

After a while he reflected: "How can I reach home again, if I cannot send a message there?" So he ordered all the various birds to come to him. They came to the place where he was staying. Then he spoke to Raven: "If I send you to my homeland as a messenger, what will you say when you get there?" Raven said, "I shall speak thus: *Coorooh, coorooh, coorooh!*" So he chased him away.

Then Rhinoceros-Bird came. "You, Rhinoceros-Bird, if I send you, how will you speak to them?" He answered, "I shall say, *Ngaa, ngaa, ngaa!*" So he chased him away, and Hawk appeared. "You, Hawk, if I send you into the homeland as a messenger, what will you say there?" Hawk answered thus: *"Chiri—i—i—o!"* So he chased him away too.

Thereupon he spoke to Buzzard: "If I send you, what will you say?" Buzzard answered, "I shall say, *Cheng, cheng, cheng!*" So he chased him away. And thus he examined in turn all the birds, every species around there, without finding a bird who understood anything. Then, finally, he called Mockingbird. "You, Mockingbird, if I send you, what message will you deliver?" Mockingbird answered:

> Mrile will come the day after tomorrow,
> The day after tomorrow;
> Mrile will come the day after tomorrow,
> The day after tomorrow,
> The day after tomorrow.
> Save some fat for him in the spoon!
> Save some fat for him in the spoon!

Thereupon Mrile said, "Well, that is good, go ahead!"

Then Mockingbird went and reached the gate to the court of Mrile's father, and he sang thus:

> Mrile wants me to tell you:
> He will come the day after tomorrow,
> The day after tomorrow,
> He will come the day after tomorrow.
> The day after tomorrow,
> Save some fat for him in the spoon!

And Mrile's father set out into the courtyard saying, "My, what is this being that shouts in the courtyard and tells me that Mrile will come the day after tomorrow? For, surely, he has perished long ago!" He drove him away and the bird disappeared.

Then Mockingbird went to Mrile and said, "I have been there." But Mrile spoke to him thus: "No, you have not been there. If you have been there—what does one find there, in my homeland?" And he said to him, "Go a second time, and when you get there, be sure to pick up my father's stick and come back therewith, so that I can be certain you have been there." So Mockingbird returned for a second time, picked up the stick and carried it to Mrile. The children in the house saw him take it, but they could not snatch it away from him.

Then Mockingbird brought it to Mrile. Thereupon Mrile was certain that Mockingbird had really been there. Now Mrile said, "Well, I shall now set out on my journey home." Moon King let him go with his cattle.

So he started out with his cattle. On the way he grew tired. Now he had a bull with him, and the bull spoke to him and said, "Since you are so tired out, if I take you upon my back, what will you do? If I take you upon my back, will you eat me when they slaughter me?" And Mrile answered him, "No, I will not eat you." So he climbed on the bull's back, and the bull supported him. Finally he arrived, singing:

> No possessions do I lack,
> The stock is mine, *hae!*
> No possessions do I lack,
> The cattle are mine, *hae!*
> No possessions do I lack,
> The small stock are mine, *hae!*
> No possessions do I lack,
> Mrile comes home, *hae!*
> No possessions do I lack.

And so Mrile came home. When he arrived at home, his father and mother smeared him with fat. Then he spoke to them thus: "This bull you shall feed until he grows old. Even when he grows old, I shall not eat his meat." But when the bull grew old, the father slaughtered him; thereupon the mother said, "Should this bull, that my son has taken so

great trouble with, be devoured without his eating there-
from?" And she hid the fat, she hid it in the honey pot.
When she knew that the meat had been used up, she ground
flour, took the fat and added it thereto. So she brought it
to her son, and Mrile tasted it. When he had tasted it with
his mouth, the meat spoke to him: "Do you dare to consume
me, me who have taken you on my back?" And it said to
him, "Therefore be consumed, as you consume me!"

Then Mrile sang:

> My mother, I told you:
> Serve me not the meat of the bull!

But when he tasted it for a second time, his foot sank into
the ground. And he sang:

> My mother, I told you:
> Serve me not the meat of the bull!

Thereupon he consumed the meal completely. Suddenly,
he was swallowed up.

And this is the end of the story.

(CHAGA)

91 THE HANDSOME OGRE-GIRL OF THE POOL

Some men once went out hunting. When they had walked
some distance, they met a girl who was decked with chains
that dangled to and fro. One of the men saluted her, and
she returned the salutation. He said to her, "Give me food!"

"Take it, here is some!"

"I do not want any!"

"What do you want, then?"

"I want to take you home as my wife to our village."

"Wait, then, and I'll fetch my mother!" She called, "Mother!"

"Wau!"

"Here is a man who wants to take me to wife!"

The man saw how the water of a pool began to surge, and it rose up and down violently. He saw a head resembling a flame of fire appearing above the surface of the water. Then the man and his friends took fright and fled, throwing away their provisions and their bows and all their clothes. They ran to their camp and said, "In this neighborhood we do not wish to sleep. We are very frightened, and tomorrow we shall go back home."

They returned home to their village and said to the people there, "We have seen a girl and her mother who live in the water. And the girl is very good-looking, but her mother, oh! oh!"

"What does she look like?"

"She is an ogre!"

"Let us go and take that girl to wife; we are not afraid of ogres," said some.

They got their equipment and set out into the wilderness. A boy who was quite small joined them. They remonstrated at length with the boy and told him to turn back, but he refused. They went on and came to the place where, on the preceding day, the other men in fright had thrown their things away. They said, "Never mind! Let us go on and bring the girl back home with us!"

They went on and found the girl. They greeted her: *"Wakra,* girl?"

"Aah!"

"Give us food!"

"There is food in the calabash."

"We do not really want food."

"What do you want, then?"

"We want to take you home with us to our village."

"Well, wait, then, and I shall fetch my mother, so that she may see you!"

"Your mother, why should you call her?"

"I summon her so that she may come and see him who wishes to take me to wife."

"Well, call her, then!"

"Mother!"

"Wau!"

"Come here that you may see the man who wants to take me to wife!"

They saw how the water began to surge, high, then higher. They saw a head looking out of the pool, and it looked like fire. They all ran away, only the small boy remained. In their flight they threw away the calabashes containing their provisions. And they repaired to the camping place from which they had started. The ogre-mother pursued the men for some distance, and then she slowly returned and became very small. Then she said to the boy, "Good day, son-in-law!"

"Aah!" said the girl.

"I understand that some man wanted to take you to wife, but this one is a child," the ogress said to her daughter.

The boy said, "So I am, Mother, but never mind that!"

"Well, sit down, then, and talk with your wife, and come tonight over there to my hut."

When evening arrived, the wife said to him, "Get up and let us go to the hut!"

"But where are we to sleep? Will that be in the water?"

"There is a hut." She took him by the arm. "Close your eyes! And open them when we are inside the hut!"

The boy shut his eyes and then opened them again, and found that he was in a hut free from water. And the woman, his mother-in-law, was sitting there weaving a bag and looking like a Kamba woman. She said to him, "You go and lie down on the bed over there and sleep!" And they went and lay down. And in the morning they went to the garden. The boy went to make a new garden for his mother-in-law. When he came back, she asked, "Do you wish to return home?"

"Yes!"

"Then take your belongings and be off!" And to her

daughter she said, "In case, when you get home, your husband should happen to die, you must give instructions that he is not to be buried, but that they must throw him outside. And when he begins to putrefy, you are to take a maggot which you shall put into a honey jar. That maggot you must smear every day with fat. You must go on smearing it with fat and, eventually, it will grow into a child. That child you must go on smearing with fat, and then it will increase in growth, and you must give it milk. And by and by you will see that it is your husband who has returned."

"I will do as you say," answered the girl. The next morning they returned to the husband's home.

When the people saw the boy arriving with the girl, they wailed and said, "Alas, alas! That beautiful girl has become the wife of a child. Has anyone ever seen the like!" And they looked about for medicine to kill the boy, but found that they were unable to kill him in that manner. Then they said, "We will show you something else."

And they took their bows and went to hunt bush buck. The boy's brother went and took up his station for the hunt in a spot out in the wilderness, and the boy placed himself opposite him. The brother shot him. Then he called for help, "Come here, all of you! I happened to shoot Syani when I aimed to kill a bush buck."

"Seeing it was you who did it, there can be no case against you, as you were his brother." They put the body of the boy down in the wilderness and returned home.

In the evening they said to the girl, "Syani is dead."

She asked, "In what way was he killed?"

"By his brother."

She wailed a great deal. Then she ceased, and asked the brother, "How did you manage to kill him?"

"I was aiming to kill a bush buck."

"Well, I do not care for other men. I am now going to live alone."

She wept for two months. After that she asked where they had put her husband in the wilderness. She went there and found a maggot. She took it, brought it home, and put it into a honey jar. She smeared it with fat and continued to do so daily. It grew into a child and could grow no further within the jar. Then she took the child out and put it underneath her bedstead. Her husband's brother lived there in the hut, but they did not sleep together.

The boy grew apace. She made food for him and brought it to him under the bed. The man asked her, "Who is it that you are feeding over there underneath the bed?"

"It is rats, it is just rats that are always hanging about there."

One day the boy went outside the hut, and then she noticed that he had grown into a big man. She gave him sword, quiver, and bow, and said to him, "It was this child that was killed when they were hunting bush buck. Tonight he will take revenge."

"Good!"

Now the brother had gone to drink beer at some villages far away. He returned in the evening, speaking with the beer. As he reached the gate of his fence, he heard someone talking with the wife within. He said, "Who is that?"

The wife answered, "Come here, and you will see him!"

He took his stick in order to beat the man. He walked in, and when he got to the door of the hut, he was shot by the brother whom he had killed and who now took his revenge. He dropped to the ground, was slashed with the sword, and died.

The next morning the husband and his wife moved away from the place. They went and settled at a place called Kavithe.

(AKAMBA)

92 UNTOMBINDE, THE TALL MAIDEN

The daughter of King Usikulumi said, "Father, I am going to the river Ilulange next year." Her father said, "Nothing goes to that place and comes back again: it goes there forever." She came again the next year and said, "Father, I am going to the Ilulange. Mother, I am going to the Ilulange." He said, "Nothing goes to that place and comes back again: it goes there forever."

Another year came round. She said, "Father, I am going to the Ilulange." She said, "Mother, I am going to the Ilulange." They said, "To the Ilulange nothing goes and returns again: it goes there forever." The father and mother at last consented to let Untombinde go.

She collected a hundred virgins on one side of the road, and a hundred on the other. So they went on their way. They met some merchants. The girls came and stood on each side of the path, on this side and that. They said, "Merchants, tell us which is the prettiest girl here; for we are two wedding companies." The merchants said, "You are beautiful, Utinkabazana; but you are not equal to Utombinde, the king's child, who is like a spread-out surface of good green grass; who is like fat for cooking; who is like a goat's gallbladder!" The marriage company of Utinkabazana killed these merchants.

They arrived at the river Ilulange. They had put on bracelets and ornaments for the breast, and collars, and petticoats ornamented with brass beads. They took them off, and placed them on the banks of the pool of the Ilulange. They went in, and both marriage companies sported in the water. When they had sported a while, a little girl went out first and found nothing there, neither the collars, nor the ornaments for the breast, nor the bracelets, nor the petticoats ornamented with brass beads. She said, "Come out; the things are no longer here." All went out.

Untombinde, the princess, said, "What can we do?" One of the girls said, "Let us petition. The things have been taken away by the Isik*q*uk*q*umadevu."[1] Another said, "You, Isik*q*uk*q*umadevu, give me my things, that I may depart. I have been brought into this trouble by Untombinde, the

[1] A bloated, bearded, squatting monster.

king's child, who said, 'Men bathe in the great pool: our first fathers bathed there.' Is it I who bring down upon you the Intontela?" The Isik*q*uk*q*umadevu gave her the petticoat.

Another girl began, and besought the Isik*q*uk*q*umadevu: she said, "You, Isik*q*uk*q*umadevu, just give me my things, that I may depart. I have been brought into this trouble by Untombinde, the king's child; she said, 'At the great pool men bathe: our first fathers used to bathe there.' Is it I who have brought down upon you Intontela?" The whole marriage company began until every one of them had done the same. There remained Untombinde, the king's child, only.

The marriage party said, "Beseech Usik*q*uk*q*umadevu, Untombinde." She refused, and said, "I will never beseech the Isik*q*uk*q*umadevu, I being the king's child." The Isik*q*uk*q*umadevu seized her, and put her into the pool.

The other girls cried, and cried, and then went home. When they arrived, they said, "Untombinde has been taken away by the Isik*q*uk*q*umadevu." Her father said, "A long time ago I told Untombinde so; I refused her, saying, 'To the Ilulange, nothing goes to that place and returns again: it goes there forever.' Behold, she goes there forever."

The king mustered the troops of young men, and said, "Go and fetch the Isik*q*uk*q*umadevu, which has killed Untombinde." The troops came to the river, and fell in with it, it having already come out of the water, and being now on the bank. It was as big as a mountain. It came and swallowed all that army; and then it went to the very village of the king; it came, and swallowed up all men and dogs; it swallowed them up, the whole country, together with the cattle. It swallowed up two children in that country; they were twins, beautiful children, and much beloved.

But the father escaped from that house; and he went, taking two clubs, saying, "It is I who will kill the Isik*q*uk*q*umadevu." And he took his large assegai and went on his way. He met with some buffalo, and said, "Whither has Isik*q*uk*q*umadevu gone? She has gone away with my children." The buffalo said, "You are seeking Unomabunge, O-gaul'-iminga. Forward! Forward! *Mametu!*"

He then met with some leopards, and said, "I am looking for Isik*q*uk*q*umadevu, who has gone off with my children." And the leopards said, "You are looking for Unomabunge, O-gaul'-iminga, O-nsiba-zimak*q*embe. Forward! Forward! *Mametu!*"

Then he met with an elephant, and said, "I inquire for Isik*q*uk*q*umadevu, who has gone away with my children." It said, "You mean Unomabunge, O-gaul'-iminga, O-nsiba-zimak*q*embe. Forward! Forward! *Mametu!*"

Then he came to Unomabunge herself: the man found her crouched down, being as big as a mountain. And he said, "I am seeking Isik*q*uk*q*umadevu, who is taking away my children." And she said, "You are seeking Unomabunge; you are seeking O-gaul'-iminga, O-nsiba-zimak*q*embe. Forward! Forward! *Mametu!*" Then the man came and stabbed the lump; and so the Isik*q*uk*q*umadevu died.

And then there came out of her cattle, and dogs, and a man, and all the men; and then Untombinde herself came out. And when she had come out, she returned to her father Usikulumi. When she arrived, she was taken by Unthlatu to be his wife.

Untombinde went to take her stand in her bridegroom's kraal. On her arrival she stood at the upper part of the kraal. They asked, "Whom have you come to marry?" She said, "Unthlatu." They said, "Where is he?" She said, "I heard said that King Usibilingwana has begotten a king." They said, "Not so: he is not here. But he did beget a son; but when he was a boy he was lost."

The mother wept, saying, "What did the damsel hear reported? I gave birth to one child; he was lost: there was no other!" The girl remained. The father, the king, said, "Why has she remained?" The people said, "Let her depart." The king again said, "Let her stay, since there are sons of mine here; she shall become their wife." The people said, "Let her stay with the mother." The mother refused, saying, "Let her have a house built for her." Untombinde therefore had a house built.

It came to pass that, when the house was built, the mother

put in it sour milk, and meat, and beer. The girl said, "Why do you put this here?" She said, "I used to place it even before you came." The girl was silent, and lay down. And in the night Unthlatu came; he took out from the sour milk, he ate the meat, and drank the beer. He stayed a long time, and then went out.

In the morning Untombinde uncovered the sour milk; she found some had been taken out; she uncovered the meat: she saw that it had been eaten; she uncovered the beer: she found that it had been drunk. She said, "Oh, Mother placed this food here. It will be said that I have stolen it." The mother came in; she uncovered the food, and said, "What has eaten it?" She said, "I do not know. I too saw that it had been eaten." She said, "Did you not hear the man?" She said, "No."

The sun set. They ate those three kinds of food. A wether was slaughtered. There was placed meat; there was placed sour milk; and there was placed beer in the house. It became dark, and Untombinde lay down. Unthlatu came in; he felt the damsel's face. She awoke.

He said, "What are you about to do here?" She said, "I come to be married." He said, "To whom?" The girl said, "To Unthlatu." He said, "Where is he?" She replied, "He was lost." He said, "But since he was thus lost, to whom do you marry?" She said, "To him only." He said, "Do you know that he will come?" He said, "Since there are the king's other sons, why do you not marry them, rather than wait for a man that is lost?" Then he said, "Eat, let us eat meat." The girl said, "I do not yet eat meat." Unthlatu said, "Not so. As regards me too, your bridegroom gives my people meat before the time of their eating it, and they eat." He said, "Drink, there is beer." She said, "I do not yet drink beer; for I have not yet had the *imvuma* slaughtered for me." He said, "Not so. Your bridegroom too gives my people beer before they have had anything killed for them."

In the morning he went away; he speaking continually, the girl not seeing him. During all this time he would not allow the girl to light a fire. He went out. The girl arose, going to feel at the wicker door, saying, "Let me feel, since I closed it, where he went out?" She found that it was still closed with her own closing; and said, "Where did the man go out?"

The mother came in the morning, and said, "My friend, with whom were you speaking?" She said, "No; I was speaking with no one." She said, "Who was eating here of the food?" She said, "I do not know." They ate that food also. There was brought out food for the third time. They cooked beer and meat, and prepared sour milk.

In the evening Unthlatu came, and felt her face, and said, "Awake." Untombinde awoke. Unthlatu said, "Begin at my foot, and feel me till you come to my head, that you may know what I am like." The girl felt him; she found that the body was slippery; it would not allow the hands to grasp it. He said, "Do you wish that I should tell you to light the fire?" She said, "Yes." He said, "Give me some snuff then." She gave him snuff. He said, "Let me take a pinch from your hand." He took a pinch, and sniffed it. He spat. The spittle said, "Hail, king! Thou black one! Thou who art as big as the mountains!" He took a pinch; he spat; the spittle said, "Hail, chief! Hail, thou who art as big as the mountains!"

He then said, "Light the fire." Untombinde lighted it, and saw a shining body. The girl was afraid, and wondered, and said, "I never saw such a body." He said, "In the morning whom will you say you have seen?" She said, "I shall say that I have seen no one." He said, "What will you say to that your mother, who gave birth to Unthlatu, because she is troubled at his disappearance? What does your mother say?" She replied, "She weeps, and says, 'I wonder by whom it has been eaten. Would that I could see the man who eats this food.'"

He said, "I am going away." The girl said, "And you, where do you live, since you were lost when a little child?" He said, "I live underground." She asked, "Why did you go away?" He said, "I went away on account of my brethren: they were saying that they would put a clod of earth into my windpipe; for they were jealous, because it was said that I was king. They said, 'Why should the king be young, while we who are old remain subjects?' "

He said to the girl, "Go and call that your mother who is afflicted." The mother came in with the girl. The mother wept, weeping a little in secret. She said, "What then did I say? I said, 'It is my child who was lost, who had the smooth body.' " He then said, "What will you say to my father?" She said, "I will say, 'Let the whole country brew beer.' "

The father said, "What is the beer to do?" The mother said, "I am going to see the people; for I used to be queen. I was deposed because I had no child." So the beer was brewed; and the people laughed, saying, "She sends for beer. What is she going to do, since she was the rejected one, and was deposed?" The beer was ready; the people came together; the soldiers went into the cattle enclosure; they had shields, and were all there. The father looked on and said, "I shall see presently what the woman is about to do."

Unthlatu came out. The eyes of the people were dazzled by the brightness of his body. They wondered, and said, "We never saw such a man, whose body does not resemble the body of men." He sat down. The father wondered. A great festival was kept. Then resounded the shields of Unthlatu, who was as great as all kings. Untombinde was given a leopard's tail; and the mother the tail of a wildcat; and the festival was kept, Unthlatu being again restored to his position as king. So that is the end of the tale.

(ZULU)

93 THE TOWN WHERE NONE MIGHT GO TO SLEEP

A certain woman had two daughters. One was married to a man who lived in a town where no one was allowed to go to sleep, the other to one in a town where no one might urinate.

One day the woman cooked a dish of sweetmeats to take to the daughter who lived in the town where no one was allowed to go to sleep. As soon as the dish was ready she started off and, when she arrived, all the household said to her, "Welcome, welcome!" Food was prepared for her, for the son-in-law said, "See, my mother-in-law has come."

But the daughter said, "O parent, no one may sleep here. Do not eat too much lest sleepiness should overcome you."

But the mother said, "I knew long before you were born that sleep was not permitted here."

"Oh, very well then," replied the daughter, "I'll say no more." And the mother ate every bit of the food that was brought to her.

That night, although she lay down, she managed to keep awake. In the morning the daughter took up her jar to go to the stream for water and said to her mother, "See here, I have put the breakfast on to boil. Please keep up the fire while I am away."

But when the daughter had gone, although her mother managed to replenish the fire for a time, drowsiness overcame her in the end, and she lay down and fell fast asleep. Just then a neighbor came to get fire and, when she saw the sleeping woman, she exclaimed, "Alas! So-and-so's mother-in-law is dead."

Then the drummers were sent for, and soon the whole town had assembled at the house and a grave had been dug. The drums were saying:

> *Birrim, birrim,* get a corpse mat,
> Death's in the son-in-law's house.

But the daughter heard from where she was, and she cried out:

> Stay, oh, stay, don't get a corpse mat,
> We are accustomed to sleep.

And when she had come to her house, she roused her mother, and said, "Wake up, wake up." Then the mother awoke with a start and the people were terrified, but they soon saw that it was nothing to be afraid of, and the whole town began to learn how to sleep.

Now the mother returned to her own home, and one day she cooked more sweetmeats and decided to visit her other daughter, the one living in the town where no one might urinate.

When she arrived, the household said, "Welcome, welcome!" And the son-in-law said, "My mother-in-law has come." So he killed a fowl and sent her a dish of rice. The daughter said to her mother, "Do not eat too much. You know that in this town no one is allowed to urinate."

The mother replied, "Thanks for the information! I knew that before ever you were born."

"Very well," said the daughter, and she took no more notice. The mother ate until she was full.

Now when night came, she wanted very much to urinate, but she did not know where she could do so without being found out. At last she went to the place where the horses were tied, and she urinated and covered the place with some of the cut grass there. But the earth was not used to this, and the part she had urinated on rose up and began to complain, saying:

> *Umm, umm*, I am not used to this,
> *Umm, umm*, I am not used to this.

Soon all the people came and said, "Who has urinated here?" Then they said, "Bring out the magic gourds, the small one and the large, and let everyone come here and step over them; and the gourd will catch hold of the one who has urinated. So all the people of the town stepped over them, but no one was seized and they were surprised. Then someone said, "See here, there is a stranger among us, let her come and step over the gourds."

Immediately when she had come and had lifted up a leg to step over, the gourds seized her, and everyone said, "It is she, it is she who has urinated!" And the gourds began singing these words:

> The things which clasp and hold on,
> The mother-in-law has got them.

She could not sit down, for they held on to her body.

Now the spider, that interfering person, met her, and said, "O mother-in-law, how lucky you are to have gourds which sing such a beautiful song. I should like to have them."

So she replied, "Very well, urinate on the ground and say that it was not you who did it."

And when he had done so, he said, "There! But it is not I who have done it, if it is I, O you magic gourds, seize me."

And immediately the gourds loosed the woman and seized him. Then they began singing:

> The things which clasp and hold on,
> The spider of spiders has got them,

and the spider felt exceedingly pleased, and began to dance.

But soon he got tired and said, "O mother-in-law, you think to be avoided, come and take your gourds." But she refused to do so.

Then the spider climbed a tree, and when he got high up he threw himself down on his buttocks so as to smash the gourds. But they moved to one side, and so the spider's back was broken and he died. Then the magic gourds returned to where they had come from, and all the townspeople began to urinate, for they saw that there was no harm in it.

(HAUSA)

94 M'WAMBIA AND THE N'JENGE

Once upon a time there was a man who married a woman, and she bore him a male child. Then he married a second wife, and she also bore him a male child. After a while the first wife died.

Now the name of the eldest son was M'wambia, and the name of the second was also M'wambia, and he was known as M'wambia the Younger, to distinguish him from his brother.

When the two boys were about twelve and ten years old, it happened that the animal known as the N'jenge* came from the wilds and ate the food in the fields. Thereupon the two brothers went into the woods, and M'wambia the Elder made a snare to catch the N'jenge, and M'wambia the Younger also made a snare at a little distance away. Now a N'jenge came into the snare of M'wambia the Younger, and he released it and killed it and ate it. And a N'jenge also came into the snare of M'wambia the Elder, but he released it and did not kill it. He let it go free into the woods, and the two boys returned to the village and said nothing to their father.

One day the mother of M'wambia the Younger went into the fields and gathered sugarcane, put it into her basket on her back, and brought it to the house. The father took a large piece and gave it to his eldest son, but to the younger he gave a small piece. Then the younger brother said, "Why have you given me a small piece and my brother a big one?"

And he said, "Because you have a mother while the mother of your brother is dead."

Then M'wambia the Younger said to his father, "Come into the woods."

Then he showed him the two snares, and told him how

* A mythical animal.

he had killed the N'jenge which he had caught, and how M'wambia the Elder had let him go. And the father was very angry and upbraided his elder son, because the N'jenge was very fat. He chose a tree, tall, with a straight stem, and made him climb up into it. Then he took spikes and stuck them into the ground around the tree with the points leaning inward toward the tree; and he made the points sharp, so that if the boy descended or fell down the points would run into him and he would die. He went away and left M'wambia the Elder in the tree.

Now M'wambia stayed in the tree for twenty days, and at the end of that time a N'jenge came and said, *"Mangi Kihuti!"*

And M'wambia said, "I am not Mangi, I am M'wambia."

And the N'jenge took one spike and carried it away, and ten N'jenge came and each took one spike and carried it away. Then the N'jenge whom M'wambia had set free came, and he said, *"Mangi."*

And the boy said, "I am M'wambia," and he told him how he had set him free. The N'jenge, when he heard this, carried away all the remaining spikes and M'wambia gradually unloosed the grip of his arms around the stem of the tree and slid to the bottom.

Next the N'jenge made a hole open in his side, and out came a big sheep. M'wambia took some fat to eat. At first he could not eat it, for he was so weak and was very sick; but afterward he ate a little, and then a little of the leg. Then the next day, he ate another piece of the leg. Thus the sheep provided him with food for four days. At the end of that time, the N'jenge opened his side again and there came out a goat, and that gave him food for four days, and then there came out two goats, and these lasted three days, for M'wambia had grown stronger and bigger. There then came an ox, and the N'jenge ate too, and M'wambia grew still bigger and stronger.

Finally, the N'jenge said, "Go among the long grass and jump." And M'wambia went among the long grass and jumped twice, and N'jenge said, "You are not yet strong enough." So they ate another ox, and then the N'jenge said, "Go and jump again." So M'wambia went and jumped four times. Finally, he said to the boy, "What would you like to possess?"

And he said, "A goat."

And the N'jenge opened his side and gave him one hundred female goats which had not borne, one hundred female goats which had borne, one hundred young goats who knew their mother, one hundred male goats, one hundred fat male goats, one hundred sheep which had not borne, one hundred sheep which had borne, one hundred young sheep who knew their mother, one hundred male sheep, one hundred fat male sheep, one hundred cows which had not borne, one hundred cows which had borne, one hundred calves, one hundred oxen, one hundred fat oxen.

And the N'jenge said to M'wambia again, "What do you want?"

And M'wambia replied, "Women."

And the N'jenge gave him two hundred goats and two hundred oxen to buy women. So M'wambia bought one hundred women. And the N'jenge said again, "What do you want?"

And he said, "I want nothing more."

Then he went to the Gura River, and he built a big village for his wives and his oxen and his goats. But no children were yet born, so M'wambia went and tended the goats, and he sat on a hillside where he could see them all, for they were many.

Now the mother of M'wambia the Younger said to her young daughter, "Take a bag and go and get vegetables." So the child went to get the vegetables but could see none; and she walked and walked, and at last she saw M'wambia sitting on the hillside herding goats, and she called out, "That is our M'wambia who was lost." But he said nothing. And then she called out again, "That is our M'wambia who was lost."

So he spoke to her and he asked, "How are they all at home, my father and my father's brother?"

She said, "They are well."

She saw his village and his wives and his cattle. Then he took a goat and killed it and cut it up and put it into her bag. She walked twelve hours and came to her home. As she came to the homestead she called out to her mother, "Bring me a cooking pot in which to cook the vegetables." And her mother brought a little one, and she said, "Bring me a big one." And she brought a bigger, and the girl said, "That is not big enough."

And the mother said, "Do you want the one in which we cook meat?" And she said, "Yes."

And her mother asked, "What kind of vegetables have you that you want so large a pot?" The mother opened the bag and saw the meat, and she said, "You have stolen a goat."

And the girl said, "I have not stolen it; it is from M'wambia."

And her mother said, "Do not tell a lie. M'wambia is lost."

And the girl said, "I have seen him, and the day after tomorrow you shall come and see him too." And she told how she had seen him and his many possessions.

So the next day they cooked the meat and ate it, and on the day after they all went together to see M'wambia. All went—his father and his father's brother, and the mother and the father's other wife, and M'wambia the Younger, and the girl, and all the family. And when they came to where M'wambia the Elder was, they saw him sitting on the hill herding goats. And there was a river between them, and M'wambia the Elder took a string and he tied a goat to the end of the string and threw it across the river. And the father took hold of it to go to him. As he was being pulled across the river he was drowned because he had been cruel to his son. But the others got across safely, and when they came to the village of M'wambia the Elder and saw his many goods, they stayed there and made their home with him.

And after a while M'wambia said, "I have many men and women to do work in my homestead." And he gave his relations work to do—one had to mind the full-grown goats, one had to mind the young goats, and one had to work in the fields. And he said, "I will go away for a while and see if they do their work well." And he went to another village and slept there for five days.

And when he came back to his homestead he saw some fat, and he said, "What is this fat on the ground?" And he looked and saw on the wall the head of N'jenge, and he knew that his friend the N'jenge had come to the village while he was away and that his relatives had killed him. And he said no word to them, but he said to himself, "My luck is gone, because the N'jenge is dead with whom I am of one heart."

And he took a stone and a knife and made his knife very sharp, and he killed all the women and all the men, and all the goats and all the cattle. Then he took the knife and plunged it into his own breast, for the N'jenge, his luck, was dead.

(AKIKUYU)

95 THE TWIN BROTHERS

Once a woman, after prolonged labor, gave birth to twins, both sons. And each one, as he was brought forth, came into this world with a valuable fetish. One the mother called Luemba, the other Mavungu. And they were almost full-grown at their birth, so that Mavungu, the firstborn, wished to start upon his travels.

Now about this time the daughter of Nzambi was ready for marriage. The tiger came and offered himself in marriage; but Nzambi told him that he must speak to her daughter himself, as she should only marry the man of her choice. Then the tiger went to the girl and asked her to marry him, but she refused him. Then the gazelle, and the pig, and all created things that had breath, one after the other, asked the daughter in marriage; but she refused them all, saying that she did not love them. And they were all very sad.

Mavungu heard of this girl, and determined to marry her. And so he called upon his charm and asked it to help him. He took some grass in his hands, and changed one blade of grass into a horse, another into a knife, another into a gun, and so on, until he was quite ready for the long journey.

Then he set out and traveled and traveled until at last hunger overcame him, when he asked his fetish whether it was true that he was going to be allowed to starve. The charm hastened to place a sumptuous feast before him, and Mavungu ate and was satisfied.

"Oh, fetish!" Mavungu said. "Are you going to leave these beautiful plates which I have used, for the use of any commoner that may come along?" The charm immediately caused all to disappear.

Then Mavungu traveled and traveled, until at length he became very tired, and had to ask his charm to arrange a place for him where he might sleep. And the charm saw to his comfort, so that he passed a peaceful night.

And after many days' weary traveling he at length arrived at Nzambi's town. And Nzambi's daughter saw Mavungu and straightway fell in love with him, and ran to her mother and father and cried, "I have seen the man I love, and I shall die if I do not marry him."

Then Mavungu sought out Nzambi, and told her that he had come to marry her daughter.

"Go and see her first," said Nzambi, "and if she will have you, you may marry her."

And when Mavungu and the daughter of Nzambi saw each other, they ran toward each other and loved one another.

They were led to a fine *shimbec;* and while all the people in town danced and sang for gladness, Mavungu and the daughter of Nzambi slept there. And in the morning, Mavungu noticed that the whole *shimbec* was crowded with mirrors, but that each mirror was covered so that the glass could not be seen. And he asked the daughter of Nzambi to uncover them, so that he might see himself in them. And she took him to one and opened it, and Mavungu immediately saw the perfect likeness of his native town. And she took him to another, and he saw another town he knew; and thus she took him to all the mirrors save one, and this one she refused to let him see.

"Why will you not let me look into that mirror?" asked Mavungu.

"Because that is the picture of the town whence no man who arrives there returns."

"Do let me see it!" urged Mavungu.

At last the daughter of Nzambi yielded, and Mavungu looked hard at the reflected image of that terrible place.

"I must go there," he said.

"Nay, you will never return. Please don't go!" pleaded the daughter of Nzambi.

"Have no fear!" answered Mavungu. "My fetish will protect me."

The daughter of Nzambi cried very much, but could not move Mavungu from his purpose. Mavungu then left his newly married wife, mounted his horse, and set off for the town from whence no man returns.

He traveled and traveled until at last he came near to the town, when, meeting an old woman, he asked her for fire to light his pipe.

"Tie up your horse first, and come and fetch it."

Mavungu descended, and having tied his horse up very securely, he went to the woman for the fire; and when he had come near to her she killed him, so that he disappeared entirely.

Now Luemba wondered at the long absence of his brother Mavungu and determined to follow him. So he took some grass, and by the aid of *his* fetish changed one blade into a horse, another into a knife, another into a gun, and so on, until he was fully prepared for his journey. Then he set out and, after some days' journeying, arrived at Nzambi's town.

Nzambi rushed out to meet him, and calling him Mavungu, embraced him.

"Nay," said Luemba, "My name is not Mavungu; I am his brother, Luemba."

"Nonsense!" answered Nzambi. "You are my son-in-law, Mavungu." And straightway a great feast was prepared. Nzambi's daughter danced for joy and would not hear of his not being Mavungu. And Luemba was sorely troubled, and did not know what to do, as he was now sure that Nzambi's daughter was Mvungu's wife. And when night came, Nzambi's daughter would sleep in Luemba's *shimbec;* but he appealed to his charm, and it enclosed Nzambi's daughter in a room, lifting her out of Luemba's room for the night and bringing her back in the early morning.

Luemba's curiosity, too, was aroused by the many closed mirrors that hung about the walls; so he asked Nzambi's daughter to let him look into them. And she showed him all excepting one. This she told him was the one that reflected the town whence no man returns. Luemba insisted upon looking into this one and when he had seen the terrible picture he knew that his brother was there.

Luemba determined to leave Nzambi's town for the town whence no man returns; and so after thanking them all for his kind reception, he set out. They all wept loudly, but were consoled by the fact that he had been there once already and returned safely, so that he could of course return a second time. Luemba traveled and traveled until he also came to where the old woman was standing, and asked her for fire.

She told him to tie up his horse and come to her to fetch it, but he tied his horse up only very lightly, and then fell upon the old woman and killed her.

Then he sought out his brother's bone and the bones of his horse, and put them together, and then touched them with his charm. And Mavunga and his horse came to life again. Then together they joined the bones of hundreds of people together and touched them with their charms, so that they all lived again. And they set off with all their followers to Nzambi's town. And Luemba told Mavungu how he had been mistaken for him by his father-in-law and wife, and how by the help of his charm he had saved his wife from dishonor. Mavungu thanked him, and said it was well.

But a quarrel broke out between the two brothers about the followers. Mavungu said they were his, because he was the elder; but Luemba said that they belonged to him, because he had given Mavungu and all of them life. Mavungu then fell upon Luemba and killed him; but his horse remained by his body. Mavungu then went on his way to Nzambi's town and was magnificently welcomed.

Now Luemba's horse took his charm and touched Luemba's body, so that he lived again. Then Luemba mounted his horse and sought out his brother Mavungu and killed him.

And when the town had heard the whole story, they all said that Luemba had done quite rightly.

(BAKONGO)

96 THE JEALOUS WIFE

Two wives busied themselves preparing *chicoanga* (bread) for their husband, who purposed going into the bush for six months to trade. Each of these women had a child; and the husband, as he left them, adjured them to be very careful with the children, and see that no harm came to them. They promised faithfully to attend to his entreaty.

When it was nearly time for the husband to return, the women said: "Let us go and fish, that we may give our husband some good food when he returns."

But as they could not leave the children alone, one had to stay with them while the other fished. The elder wife went first, and stayed in the fishing ground for two or three days to smoke what she had caught. Then the younger wife left to fish, and the elder remained to take care of the children.

Now the child of the younger wife was a much brighter and more intelligent child than that of the elder; and this made the elder wife jealous and angry. So she determined to murder the child, and get it out of the way while its mother was fishing. She sharpened a razor until it easily cut off the hairs on her arm, and then put it away until the evening when the children should be asleep. And when it was evening and they were fast asleep, she went to the place where the child was accustomed to sleep, and killed it. The other child awoke, and in its fright ran out of the house and took refuge with a neighbor.

In the morning the elder wife went to look at her evil work, thinking to put the child away before its mother should return. But when she looked again at the child she was horror-struck to find that she had killed her own child. She wept as she picked up its little body; and wrapping it up in her cloth she ran away with it into the woods, and disappeared.

The husband returned and at once missed his elder wife. He questioned the younger one; but she could only repeat to him what her child had told her, namely, that during the night the elder wife had killed her child. The husband would not believe this story, and asked his friends, the bushmen who had come with him, to help him to search for his wife. They agreed, and scoured the woods the whole day, but without success.

The next day one of the bushmen came across a woman who was nursing something; so he hid and listened to her singing. The poor woman was forever shaking the child, saying:

"Are you always going to sleep like this? Why don't you awake? Why don't you talk ? See! See! It is your mother that nurses you."

"Surely," said the bushman, "this must be my friend's wife. I will go to him and tell him that I have found her."

"Let us go," said the husband. And as they approach her

they hide themselves so that she cannot see them. And they find her still shaking the child and still singing the same sad song.

(BAKONGO)

97 THE MAIDEN WHO WAS SACRIFICED BY HER KIN

The sun was very hot and there was no rain, so the crops died, and hunger was great; and this happened one year, and again it happened a second, and yet a third year the rain failed; so the people all gathered together on the great open space on the hilltop, where they were wont to dance, and said each to the other, "Why does the rain delay in coming?" And they went to the Medicine Man, and they said to him, "Tell us why there is no rain, for our crops have died, and we shall die of hunger." And he took his gourd and poured out the lot, and this he did many times; and at last he said, "There is a maiden here who must be bought if rain is to fall, and the maiden is Wan-jí-ru. The day after tomorrow let all of you return to this place, and every one of you from the eldest to the youngest bring with him a goat for the purchase of the maiden."

So the day after the morrow, old men and young men all gathered together, and each brought in his hand a goat. Now they all stood in a circle, and the relations of Wan-jí-ru stood together, and she herself stood in the middle; and as they stood the feet of Wan-jí-ru began to sink into the ground; and she sank to her knees and cried aloud, "I am lost," and her father and mother also cried and said, "We are lost"; but those who looked on pressed close, and placed goats in the keeping of Wan-jí-ru's father and mother.

And Wan-jí-ru went lower to her waist, and she cried aloud, "I am lost, but much rain will come"; and she sank to her breast: but the rain did not come, and she said again, "Much rain will come"; then she sank to her neck, and the rain came in great drops, and her people would have rushed forward to save her, but those who stood around pressed into their hands more goats, and her relations desisted.

So she said, "My people have undone me," and sank to her eyes, and as one after another of her family stepped forward to save her, one of the crowd would give to him or her a goat, and he fell back. And Wan-jí-ru cried aloud for the last time, "I am undone, and my own people have done this thing." And she vanished from sight, and the earth closed over her, and the rain poured down, not, as you sometimes see it, in showers, but in a great deluge, and everyone hastened to his own home.

Now there was a young warrior who loved Wan-jí-ru, and he lamented continually, saying, "Wan-jí-ru is lost, and her own people have done this thing." And he said, "Where has Wan-jí-ru gone? I will go to the same place." So he took his shield, and put in his sword and spear. And he wandered over the country day and night; and at last, as the dusk fell, he came to the spot where Wan-jí-ru had vanished, and he stood where she had stood, and, as he stood, his feet began to sink as hers had sunk; and he sank lower and lower till the ground closed over him, and he went by a long road under the earth as Wan-jí-ru had gone, and at length he saw the maiden. But, indeed, he pitied her sorely, for her state was miserable, and her raiment had perished. He said to her, "You were sacrificed to bring the rain; now the rain has come, I will take you back." So he took her on his back like a child, and brought her to the road he had traversed, and they rose together to the open air, and their feet stood once more on the ground, and he said, "You shall not return to the house of your people, for they have treated you shamefully." And he bade her wait till nightfall; and when it was dark he took her to the house of his mother, and he asked his mother to leave, and said he had business, and he allowed no one to enter. But his mother said, "Why do you hide this thing from me, seeing I am your mother who bore you?" So he suffered his mother, but he said, "Tell no one that Wan-jí-ru is returned."

So she abode in the house of his mother; and then he and his mother slew goats, and Wan-jí-ru ate the fat and grew strong; and of the skins they made garments for her, so that she was attired most beautifully.

It came to pass that the next day there was a great dance, and her lover went with the throng; but his mother and the girl waited till everyone had assembled at the dance, and all the road was empty, and they came out of the house and mingled with the crowd; and the relations saw Wan-jí-ru, and said, "Surely that is Wan-jí-ru whom we had lost"; and they pressed to greet her, but her lover beat them off, for he said, "You sold Wan-jí-ru shamefully." And she returned to his mother's house. But on the fourth day her family again came, and the warrior repented, for he said, "Surely they are her father and her mother and her brothers." So he paid them the purchase price, and he wedded Wan-jí-ru who had been lost.

(AKIKUYU)

98 THE SNAKE FROM THE GREAT WATER

Two warriors went to look for wives. One was called Wa-dú-a (literally, son of the Sun) and the other Wa-m'wer'-i (son of the Moon), and as they traveled they saw a girl in the road. Now she was not beautiful, for she had lost one eye, but Wa-m'wer'-i liked her, and the girl also liked Wa-m'wer'-i; so he took her to be his wife, and proceeded no further in his search.

But Wa-dú-a said, "Why do you take a girl who has one eye missing?" And he proceeded further on his journeys. Now as he went on his way he saw a young boy, and he said

to him, "Do you know any maiden in this countryside?"
And the boy replied, "No, I know of no maiden, except,
indeed, the maiden Wa-shú-ma; but she is not to be thought
of, for she does not like young men."

And Wa-dú-a journeyed again, and he met an old man,
and he said, "Can you tell me when I can find a maiden?"
And he said, "There is no girl but Wa-shú-ma, and she will
speak to no man." Again he met an old woman, and she told
him the same tale of Wa-shú-ma, that she would not be
wooed by any man.

At last on the eighth day he met a young man, and he yet
again spoke of Wa-shú-ma in the same manner. So Wa-dú-a
inquired of him where the home of this Wa-shú-ma might
be; and he said, "On the opposite hillside, where you see the
smoke ascending." So Wa-dú-a went that day and slept that
night on the road; and after three days he came to the house
of Wa-shú-ma and tarried outside, while the girl herself was
in the *shamba*. Afterward she came in and cooked food, and
came out and went to the storehouse and got siroco and
cooked it, and came and gave it to the stranger. But he
would not take it, and she went again to the storehouse and
took beans, but he would not; and then gruel, and still he
would not; but she did not think of milk, and when she
brought milk he drank it, and she offered him more, but he
said, "It is sufficient."

Now the father of Wa-shú-ma returned, and the goats
and oxen came in for the night, and the girl took Wa-dú-a
into the homestead that he might sleep, and she said to him,
"If you should hear in the night a great noise, do not go
out." And he said, "Why?" Wa-shú-ma said, "Because a
great animal like a snake comes every night and kills and
eats the oxen." And the animal was called Mukun'ga M'búra,
and its home is in the water.

So Wa-dú-a slept in the house; but in the night, when he
heard a great noise he got up and took his spear; but Wa-
shú-ma took him by the arm and besought him not to go.
But he was too strong for her, and he went out, and he saw
the snake, and took his spear and struck it in the back of

the neck, so it died, and he came back to the house and he said nothing.

And in the morning when the birds began to chirp, the father went out to see the cattle, and he found the dead beast, and he said, "Who has done this?" And the girl told her father. And he sent out, when all the young men were gathered on the dancing green, and he set them a distance, and he said to the youths, "He who can run this distance and return, he it is who has slain the Mukun'ga M'búra." So they ran, but some fell and some panted like sheep; but when the time came for Wa-dú-a, he ran and returned and beat all the other youths. And the father said, "What shall I give you, since you have slain the beast?" And he said, "I look for a wife; give me your daughter."

But the father said, "If a man has asked for my daughter, I have said to him, 'Fetch the *ny-ó-ya*.'"* So Wa-dú-a arose and went to the big water, and Wa-shú-ma stayed on the bank and looked on; and Wa-dú-a went, and the water rose to his calf and his knees and his waist, and then to his chest and neck and eyes. Wa-shú-ma thought he would be drowned; but Wa-dú-a went right under the water and stayed there, and he did not die. Wa-shú-ma waited, and when night came she slept there; but in the morning she said, "Surely he is dead." And she turned to go. But as she went she heard a great noise in the water; and she looked round, and went back and saw Wa-dú-a and many others coming out of the water, and sheep and goats innumerable; and the water had all disappeared, and Wa-dú-a returned with the girl to her home. And he divided the sheep and goats, and he put half of them on one side and half of them on the other, for they could not be counted for multitude; and he took one half for himself, and the other half he gave to the father of Wa-shú-ma, that he might have her for his wife.

(AKIKUYU)

* Nyóya ya náge, described as "a big white and black bird, of which the young men wear the feathers."

Forty girls went to get firewood. As they came back single file along the road, they met Ilímu, who has one foot and walks with a stick, and his other foot comes out at the back of his neck, and he has two hands. And his body is like iron, so yóu cannot hurt him. And the first girl he came to said, "Do not eat me, eat the next"; but of each in turn he took a finger, and the last one he ate altogether.

Now before they went home all the girls went to have their teeth adorned, and as they came back they met a man on the road, and they asked him whose teeth were the most beautiful, and he looked at them all and he said, "Those of Wa-shí-shi and Moiré-wa-nyí-na." And these two girls were sisters by the same mother. And they met another man, and asked him the same question, and he said the same thing— and a third and fourth gave the same answer. And when they got to their homes they asked again, and the fathers and mothers still said those of Wa-shí-shi and Moiré-wa-nyí-na, so the other girls were sorely grieved.

The third day they again all went to the wood for firewood, and they made a big hole by a sacred tree, and each of the girls went in in turn and came out again, and the two sisters went last, and Moiré-wa-nyí-na came out safely; but when it came to the turn of Wa-shí-shi she went in and the others piled on firewood and earth on top of her and buried her alive.

Now her small brother kept cows near the tree, and Wa-shí-shi heard the tramping, and she cried out, "Do not bring the cows where they will tread on me."

And the boy went home and said, "There is someone crying out near the sacred tree." Now as the other girls returned they had made medicine, and they drank it, so that anyone who told at home what had happened to Wa-shí-shi would die.

The next day the boy went again, and Wa-shí-shi called out once more. Then he knew it was his sister, and said, "I have heard Wa-shí-shi." So the father and mother and all the relations went and dug out Wa-shí-shi. She was very thin, and her clothes were worn out, and they brought her home, and she rested many days.

Then she got three gourds and filled them with milk, one with the milk of wild animals, one with that of cows, and one with that of goats; and her father called all the other girls into the house, and Wa-shí-shi got the tail of a wild animal and put it into the jar of milk from wild animals and sprinkled the girls, and they went to sleep; and she sent to all the fathers of the girls and said, "Your daughters buried me in a hole because my teeth were more beautiful than theirs, and if you do not give me presents they shall die and never wake again." So they brought her many goats. Then she put the tail of a cow in the jar of cow's milk and sprinkled them with milk, and they all awoke once more.

(AKIKUYU)

100 KENKEBE

There was once a great famine in a certain country, and the people were obliged to eat wild plants to keep themselves alive. Their principal food during this time was *nongwes* which they dug out of the ground.

There was living at that place a man called Kenkebe, and one day his wife said to him, "My husband, go to my father and ask him to give us some corn."

The man said, "Yes, I will go."

So he rose up early in the morning and went on until he arrived at his father-in-law's village, where he was received

with every mark of kindness. A very large ox was killed for
his entertainment. It was so large that it was six days before
it was all eaten. His father-in-law asked of him the news.

He said, "There is no news to tell to friends. All the news is
this—that at my home there is not a grain to be eaten.
Famine is over our heads. Will you give us some corn, for
we are dying?"

His father-in-law gave him seven bags full of millet, and
his wife's sisters went with him to carry them. When they
came to a valley close by his home, he told his sisters-in-law
that they could now go back to their father.

They said, "How will you manage to carry all those bags
alone?"

He replied, "I shall be able to carry them all now, because
we are not far from my home." .

So the girls went back to their father.

Then he carried the bags, one by one, and hid them in a
cave under a great rock that was there. Afterward he took
some of the millet and ground it. When it was ground very
fine he made it into cakes just like *nongwes*. Then he dug
some real *nongwes* out of the ground and went home to his
wife.

He said to her, "There is a great famine at your father's
also. I found the people there eating themselves."

He told his wife to make a fire. Then he pretended to cut
a piece of meat out of his thigh and said, "So are they doing
at your father's village. Now, my wife, let us do the same."

His wife cut a piece from her leg and roasted it, but the
piece that Kenkebe put on the fire was some meat that he
had brought home with him.

Then Kenkebe's little boy said, "Why does my father's
meat smell nice in roasting and my mother's meat does not
smell nice?"

Kenkebe answered, "It is because it is taken from the leg
of a man."

After this he gave his wife some *nongwes* to roast. He
took for himself some of those he had made of corn.

The little boy said, "Why do my father's *nongwes* smell

nice in roasting, and my mother's do not smell nice?"

Kenkebe said, "It is because they were dug by a man."

After eating he went outside, but he had dropped one of his *nongwes* by the fire. When he went out, the boy found it. He broke it in two and gave half to his mother.

He said, "There is a difference between our *nongwes* and those of father."

His mother said, "Yes, my child, this one is made of corn."

The next morning, just at the very beginning of dawn, Kenkebe got up and went away with a pot in his hand. The boy was awake and saw his father go out. So he called to his mother and said, "Mother, Mother, awake! My father is going away with the pot in his hand!"

So she got up and they followed after Kenkebe. They saw him go to the cave where he took some corn out of one of the bags and began to grind it. Then they went on top of the rock, and rolled a big stone over.

When Kenkebe saw the stone coming he ran away, but it followed close behind him. He ran down the valley, but the stone kept running too. He jumped into a deep hole in the river. Down went the stone, too. He ran up the hill and up went the stone. He ran over the plain but, whenever he turned to look, the stone was just there behind him. So he continued all that day. At night he reached his own house and then the stone stopped. His wife had already come home and had brought with her one of the bags of corn.

Kenkebe came in crying.

His wife said to him, "Why do you cry as if you were a child?"

He said, "Because I am very tired and very hungry."

She said, "Where are your clothes and your bag?"

He replied, "I was crossing a river, and I fell down. The stream carried away my mantle, my bag, and my kerries, indeed everything that was mine."

Then his wife gave him his mantle, which she had picked up when he was running away, and she said to him, "You are foolish to do such things. There is no food for you tonight."

The next morning Kenkebe rose early and went out to hunt with his two dogs. The name of the one was Tumtumse, and the name of the other was Mbambozozele. He found an eland with a young calf which he drove to his place. He cut an ear off the calf and roasted it in the fire. It was fat, and he liked it so much that he cut the other ear off and cooked it also. Then he wished to kill the calf, but he said to himself, "If I kill this calf, I shall not be able to get milk from the eland."

So he called his two dogs and said to the one, "Tumtumse, my dog, if I kill this calf, will you imitate it and suck the eland for me?"

The dog said, "No, I shall bark like a dog."

Kenkebe said, "Get out of my sight and never come near me again, you ugly, useless animal."

He said to the other, "Mbambozozele, my dog, if I kill this calf, will you imitate it and suck the eland for me?"

The dog said, "I will do so."

Then he killed the calf and ate it. He took the skin and put it upon Mbambozozele, so that the eland thought it was her calf that sucked before Kenkebe milked her. But one day the dog was sucking too long, and Kenkebe wanted him to leave off. He tried to drink just a few drops more, when his master got angry and struck him with a stick. Thereupon the dog began to howl, and the eland saw how she had been deceived. At once she ran after Kenkebe and tried to stick him with her horns. He ran one way and the eland ran after him, then he ran another way, and still the eland chased him.

His wife came out and saw him running. She cried out to him, "Jump up quickly on the big stone." He did so, and the eland ran with such fury against the stone that it broke its head and fell down dead.

They then cut the eland up and wanted to cook it, but there was no fire. Kenkebe said to his son, "Go to the village of the cannibals that is on that hill over the valley and ask for some fire; but do not take any meat with you, lest they should smell it."

The boy went, but he hid a piece of meat and took it with him. When he got to the first house he asked for fire, but they sent him to the next. At the next they sent him farther, and so he finally had to go to the house that was farthest away. An old woman lived there. The boy gave her a little piece of meat and said, "Do not cook it until I am far away with the fire."

But as soon as the boy was gone she put it on the coals. The smell came to the noses of the cannibals and they ran to the place and swallowed the old woman, and the meat, and the fire, and even the ashes.

Then they ran after the boy. When he came near his own house, he cried out, "Hide yourselves, you that are at home!"

His father said, "My son is saying we must gather wood that will make coals."

His mother said, "No, he is saying that we must hide ourselves."

The boy cried again, "Hide yourselves!"

Then his mother hid herself in a bush. An old woman who was there covered herself with ashes, and Kenkebe climbed up into a tree, with the breast of the eland in his hand. The boy slipped into a hole which was by the side of the path.

The cannibals came to the place. First they ate the eland. Then one of them said, "Search under the ashes."

There they found the old woman, and they ate her. Then they said, "Search in the tree."

There they found Kenkebe. He cried very much, but they would not spare him. They ate him and the breast of the eland. Then the wise one said, "Look in the bush."

They looked there and found the wife of Kenkebe. They said, "We will eat her another time," and so they took her home with them. They did not look for the boy.

The woman made a plan to escape. She made beer for the cannibals and they all came to drink. They sat together in a big house, and drank very much beer. Then she said, "May I go out?"

They said, "You may go, but come back quickly."

She said, "Shall I close the entrance?"

They said, "Close it."

Then she took fire and put it on the house and all these cannibals were burned to death. So the woman escaped, and lived happily afterward with her son.

(XOSA)

101 THE LUCKY YOUNGEST SON

There was once a certain lucky Person, Ahmadu the Rich Man, who had three children, and three wives, each one having exactly one son. At last he fell ill and knew that he was about to die, so he summoned his eldest son, and said, "When I am dead, of all my riches do not take anything except my stick and my boot." But the eldest son replied, "Father, is that the kind of man you are? Of all your goods I am not to take anything except the stick and boot? Well, I shall not take only the stick and boot." Then the father said, "Very well, go and stay with your mother." So he summoned the second of them, and said, "Listen, Mohamma, when I am dead, do not take anything except the prayer jug." But Mohamma replied, "Is that the sort my father is? I shall not take the prayer jug." Then Ahmadu summoned Auto also, and said, "When I am dead, do not take anything except the stick and book." And Auta replied, "Father, I love you better than anything." And he continued, "Whatever you tell me to take, I will take only it." So Ahmadu said, "Very well, take only the boot and the stick."

Now when Auta had taken them, and had left the hut, his father died, and the women of the house mourned. When they had ceased, they applied to the king for the division of the heritage, and when it had been divided up, the eldest son was given his share, and the second was given his, but when Auta was given some of the property, he refused it, and said that the boot and stick would content him. Then his mother came up, and began to abuse Auta, but when she had finished abusing him, he still said that he would not take anything, and when he had got tired of being abused he went off into the forest.

When he had reached the main road, he met with a certain person who had collected some wood, and had lit it, and he said, "O youth, where are you going?" "What has that to do with you?" asked Auta, and he passed on. Soon he came upon a hunter, who said, "O youth, will you not give me your stick?" And Auta took the stick, and gave it to him. Then the hunter saw a bird in a tree, and he threw up the stick at it, and the stick stuck in the branches. So he took the bird, and gave it to the boy.

Then Auta went on, and came upon a certain person who had lit a fire, but had nothing to cook, and he said, "O youth, will you not give me the bird that I may cook it?" When Auta had given it to him, he cooked and ate it, and then he took some ashes and gave them to Auta, and Auta wrapped them in his coat.

So he went on, and came upon a certain woman, who was making porridge, but had no ash to put in it. So she said, "O youth, will you not give me the ash?" And he gave it to her. Then she took a broken piece of calabash with some food in it and gave it to the boy, and he went on.

Next he came upon some people digging on a farm, and they said, "O youth, will you not give us your porridge that we may eat?" And he took it and gave it to them, and they ate it, and then they took a hoe and gave it to him.

So he went on, and came upon a blacksmith who had made a great fire with his bellows, but had no iron for forging. So he said, "O youth, will you not give me that hoe that I may make knives with it?" And Auta took it and gave it to him, and the blacksmith made knives with it, and when he had made them, he gave Auta one.

When the boy had taken it, he started traveling on again in the forest, and he went on, and came upon a weaver, who had made a white cloth. Then the weaver said, "O youth, will you not give me your knife that I may cut this white cloth?" When Auta had given it to him, he cut the white cloth, and then Auta said, "Right, now pay me for my knife." So the weaver took all the white cloth and gave it to the boy.

Auta went on, and came to a place where a maiden had died. As for her people, they had no white cloth in which to take her to the grave, and they said, "O boy, will you not give us this white cloth in which to take the corpse to the grave?" So he took it and gave it to them, and they cut it up, and sewed the strips together, and wrapped it around the girl. But when they were about to take her to the grave, the boy caught hold of the corpse, and said, "Pay me for my white cloth." So they took the corpse, and gave it to him, and he lifted it on to his head.

He went on, and at last he emerged from the forest, and went on, and came near to a large city. Now there was a river at the gate of the city, and each day the king's wives would come there to get water. And when he had come with the dead girl, he dug two holes, and put her feet in them, and stretched the body upright, so that she stood up. Then he took the white cloth and wrapped it around her, right down to the ground, and after that he went back in the shade, and waited. When the king's wives came to get water at the place, he said, "For God's sake will you not give my wife some water that she may drink? I gave her some, but she refused to drink because of her pride." Then one, the chief wife of the king, got some water in her calabash, and came and said, "Here you are." Silence, she did not accept it. Then another of the king's wives bounded forward, and seized the calabash, and came, and said, "Here!" Silence. Then she hit the corpse on the forehead, and the corpse fell down. Immediately the boy ran out from the shade, and began to cry, and said that the king's wives had killed his wife at the stream. The alarm reached even to the king's palace, but the king said that it was a lie, for his wives would not quarrel. However, he said, "Go and see."

When the messengers had come, they found the corpse

lying down, so they went back, and said to the king, "Ah, it is true, your wives have done murder." Then he said, "Very well, bring the corpse here." And, when it had been lifted up and brought to the king, he said, "Here, boy, whence have you come with this woman?" But he said to the king, "What has that to do with you?" Then the judge said, "This boy may do mischief, settle with him, and let him go." So the king brought two wives of his own and gave them to him, and the boy went out of the city and entered the forest, and he went and lived in the forest, and built a house there. But when he had built the house, he drove away the two wives whom the king had given him, and said that he would live alone.

One day a frog said, "Auta, may I come to your house and live?" And he replied, "Remain certainly." Then a monkey said, "Auta, may I come to your house and live?" And he replied, "Remain certainly." Then a horse said, "Auta, may I come to your house and live?" And he replied, "Remain certainly." A camel, a donkey, stinging ants, ordinary ants, large stinging traveling ants, a mule, a large snake, a crown bird, and a white-breasted crow, all came and lived with him.

Soon all conceived, at the same time, and a bull came, and said that every one of them was to build a storehouse in the compound, there being thirty altogether. The bull came, and built thirty receptacles inside the houses, and again he came and made thirty deep holes in the compound. Then the bull filled all the storehouses with gold, that is what he gave birth to. The mule came and brought forth silver, he filled all the thirty holes. The camel filled the receptacles with cowries. The rest of the family, the small ones, brought forth slaves, they filled the house with slaves.

Now, one day, the spider came to the house to beg, and Auta took guinea corn and gave it to him, and the spider went to the king and said, "What will you give me for my news?" The king replied, "A kola nut." "How many ears have you?" asked the spider. The king replied that he had two ears. "Add two more," said the spider, "and you will hear news." And the king said that he had added them. So the spider said, "The boy here in the forest, in the whole world there is not one who is so rich." "It is a lie," exclaimed the king. Then the spider said, "Very well, send me and the councilors to go and see." So the king sent him and the councilors, and they went off, and when they had been and had seen the wealth, they knew that the riches were greater than those of the king himself. So they returned and said, "This boy is very rich."

Now the king had a white leper in his palace, and the advice of the white leper was what the king listened to, so he said, "Now white leper, what shall we do that we may take this property?" The white leper replied, "Take some soup, and put it in a bag and take grains of guinea corn, and put them in the bag." Now a great number were put inside the bag; and then black *acha* grains were taken and put in the bag; elusine was taken and put in the bag; millet was taken and put in the bag; *acha* was taken and put in the bag; rice and beans were taken and put in the bag. When the bag had been filled and tied up, it was taken to the boy's house and he was told that by daylight he must have sorted out the grains separately. The boy saw that he could not do this, and began to cry, he cried hard. But the ant came, and the stinging ant came, and they told him to be patient. So he took all his calabashes, and gave them to them, and one took a grain and put it here, one took a grain and put it there, and so by the time that day had broken, they had sorted them out separately, and when the councilors came to take them, he lifted them up, and gave them to them. Then the king again called the white leper, and said, "Well, how shall we kill that boy?"

Now there was a certain big lake which no one would enter, and there was a fan palm in the middle of the lake, so the white leper said to the king, "Tell the boy to fetch two fruits of the palm tree." So Auta was told to do so, and when he saw that he was unable to enter the water, he cried hard.

But the monkey and the frog came to the boy, and said, "Dry your tears, because of such things we asked you of old if we could come to your house and live." Then the monkey arose, and hopped to the edge of the lake, and from there he jumped, and alighted upon the fan palm. But the frog dived and did not come up until he had reached the fan palm, and he also climbed the tree. When the monkey had plucked one, he jumped straight out onto the bank, and the frog pulled off his, and fell into the river, and did not rise until he was at the bank. So they brought the two fruits of the fan palm, and the boy went and put them aside, and when the councilors came next morning to take the fruits, he took them, and gave them to them, and they brought them to the king.

Soon afterward, the king said, "Well, white leper, what shall we do to get this boy's riches?" He replied, "It is now the dry season, there is no water, so you tell him to bring a leaf of the millet about daybreak." Then the king said, "Very well," and sent to Auta to tell him. Then the boy cried hard, until the white-breasted crow and the crown bird came, and said, "O boy, what are you crying for?" "The king has said that I must bring him a millet leaf now, in the dry season," he replied. But they said, "Come, dry your tears, and be easy." Then the crow went north, the crown bird went south, and they flew along, saying *Da da da,* at least the crow did. She went on to a country where she found that the millet was high; the crown bird came to a country where the millet had begun to put out eyes. The crow found a country where the millet was ready to be threshed, so she arrested her flight and took a bundle. As for the crown bird, she found a place where the leaves were peeling off, so she also tied up a bundle. The crow carried hers, the crown bird carried hers, and they brought them to the boy, so when day broke he took them to the king.

Now the snake saw that the boy had been very near losing his life, and said, "O youth," and Auta replied, "Um." The snake said, "The king has a daughter of whom he is very fond." And it continued, "Let me enter into her stomach, and even if all the magicians in the world be assembled to attend to the girl she will not get well. But you, when you go, you will heal her. I it is who will give you medicine with which to heal her. When you go to the king," he continued, "you must say that your medicine is difficult to obtain, and the king will say, 'What can be difficult to me?' You must say, 'It will certainly be hard for you,' but he will reply, 'O youth, whatever the difficulty, I will get it.' Then you must say, 'Very well, I want a white leper's liver brought me immediately.' " The snake went on: "When you have been brought the white leper's liver, put it with some water in a pot, and give it to this girl that she may drink, and she will be healed at once." So the boy said, "Very well."

Now the girl was playing with the other girls of the city, her fellows, when the snake reached her, and it crawled inside her stomach. Then the girl said to her playmates that she had a stomach-ache, and that she was going home, so the other girls said, "Let us go, the king's daughter is not well." When she had reached her home, she lay down, and her stomach began swelling, and swelling, until it was as big as a storehouse. Then the king arose, and began crying, and crying, and crying, and falling down, and doing all kinds of things. The white leper of whom the king was fond came, and gave his advice, all the magicians in the city were summoned, every one gave her medicine. But it was no good, the girl did not get better. They went to Faki Fatatika and summoned the magicians of the town, and they came and worked their spells, but the girl got no better.

At last the rich boy came with one old rag on, he did not wear a good *tobe*, and he came to the king and said, "May your life be prolonged." Then the white leper arose, and hit him, and said, "The king's daughter is ill, have you, a wearer of rags, come to bother him?" "I have come to give her medicine," he replied. Then the white leper said, "The magicians have not been able to cure her, can you, a wearer of rags, know what medicine to prescribe?" Then the king heard, and said, "No no, leave him alone, everyone has the

gifts that God has given him." And he continued, "Go with
the white leper to where the girl is." When he had gone, and
had returned to the king, Auta said, "Now, O King, I know
an antidote, but my antidote is hard to obtain." "Tell me
what it is," replied the king; "however difficult it may be,
the medicine will be obtained and brought." Then Auta
said, "I wish you to get me the liver of a white leper at
once. Now here is a white leper with you, will one go
searching in the city to look for one?" And immediately the
councilors rained blows upon the white leper there, in the
hall, until they had killed him. Then his body was seized,
and torn open, and the liver was pulled out, and given to
the boy, who told them to get some water for him and to
put it in a pot. When water had been poured into a new pot,
it was brought to him, and he put the liver in it, and shook
it up, and then he said, "Give it to the girl to drink." Now
when it had been given to the girl, and she had drunk, she
became violently ill, and the snake came out, and went away;
no one saw it.

Then the girl arose, and asked to be given porridge to eat,
she said to give her flour and water to drink, and she was
given some, she was also given kola nuts, and she ate them.
Immediately the king took the boy aside, he brought five
horses and gave them to him, he brought five tobes and gave
them to him, he brought twenty pairs of trousers, and dark
blue tobes and gave them to him. Then he separated off
one half of the city and offered it to him, but Auto said,
"No, as far as I am concerned, I do not wish to live in the
city, I am going home."

So he took his horses and the other presents which the
king had given to him, and he went to the forest, and he
overtook the snake as he was going home. The snake said,
"O boy, the treachery is done with, there remains only mine
to you." And it continued, "Now, look here, I am going to
live in an anthill." Then Auta said, "If you live in an anthill,
how can I repay you?" The snake replied, "Every Sunday
you must give me a piece of meat." And the boy said,
"Agreed, I understand." So when Sunday came, the boy

arose from his bed, and went out, and got a piece of meat in the house, and he took it, and carried it to the anthill, and then he returned home.

Every Sunday Auta did this for him, until one day he went out of his hut in the morning, but did not see the piece of meat in the house, for as it happened, the frog had come and had taken it in the early morning. Now as he had not obtained a piece of meat, the snake arose and came to Auta and said to the boy, "Today is Sunday, but I have not seen my piece of meat." "I am now looking for it," he replied; "must you come and ask me for it?" And he continued, "Formerly I had a store of them in the house, but today when I got up I did not see any, there are no more pieces." Then the snake said, "Indeed! Is there disloyalty in your own house?" And Auta replied that he did not know. "Will you give the thieves over to me that I may come and seize them?" asked the snake. And the boy said, "Very well," for he thought that all were acting fairly toward him. "Very well," he said, "but who is the one to be punished among them?" The snake replied, "Right, I am going home, I shall know the thief when he comes." But when the snake had gone a little way, it returned and hid behind the door of Auta's house.

Now the rich boy could not rest without going and reasoning with the snake, so he went out of the door of the house, and the snake (which was by the door of the house) bit him, and when the snake had bitten him, Auta went back into the house, and lay down, for his leg was painful. Then the frog came up, and said, "What has befallen you, O rich one?" And Auta replied, "Something bit me by the door of the house." Then the frog said, "Whatever it be, I will go and see." So he went out, hopping, and came to the door of the house, and the snake bit him, so he also went and lay down. The frog died, he also, the rich boy, died.

That is the end of this. The frog brought this upon Auta. Because he took the meat, he brought disaster upon him.

(HAUSA)

102 THE KING WITH THE CANNIBAL TASTES

There was once a certain king, and, while his evening meal was being prepared a hawk, which was carrying a piece of human flesh, flew over the palace, and while she was flying the flesh slipped from her grasp and fell into the soup, and no one saw it. So when the food had been cooked, it was taken off the fire, and brought to the king, and the soup also was brought. So the piece of human flesh was put before him, and he ate it.

Now when he had eaten the food, he thought that he had never tasted anything so nice before—it was the piece of human flesh which he thought so good, but he did not know—and he asked for more. So he had a goat killed, but he did not get a flavor like that of the other, then he had a bull killed, but again he missed the delicious taste of the flesh. And though he sent and had brought to him meat of every beast of the forest, when he ate it he did not get the flavor he wanted.

At last he had a slave seized and he killed him and ate him, and then he recognized the taste, so he kept on seizing the people of his household and killing them, until they were all finished. And then the other people in the city ran away and left him alone, and so, when the longing overcame him, he would pick off a piece from his own body, and eat it. At last he was nothing but bones, and when he ran, you could hear the bones rattling and making a sound like *gwarrang, gwarrang*.

One day he went along the road to the resting place of the traders, and he lay in wait to rush upon them, and on their arrival he let them pass, and then followed one at a run to catch him and bring him back to eat. So he went and killed

him, but when he wished to carry back the corpse, he fell
down, he was too weak to carry it, and he died.

That is all.

(HAUSA)

103 THE MANY-HEADED CANNIBALS

This is a story about the *Girringas,* the Many-headed Cannibals. There was one Girringa who had two heads, and he
went to a far city to get a wife, and while they were returning, he and his wife, they met with another Girringa who
had three heads, and when he saw them he sang: "Welcome
Girringa."

And the other replied, also singing, "Um, hum, Girringa."

And then they sang again, "Welcome Girringa." "Um,
hum, Girringa."

"Where have you come from?" asked the one with three
heads.

"I come from Kano," sang the other.

"What did you go for?" asked the newcomer.

"To find a wife," replied the other.

"Where is the woman?" asked the three-headed one.

"See her behind me," was the reply.

"What is she crying for?" asked the other.

"She is crying at the sight of your heads," said the husband.

"Wait until she sees the king," replied the other.

So they parted, and the wife and her two-headed husband
went on toward the city, and lo! they met with a four-headed
being, who sang: "Welcome Girringa."

And the other replied, also singing, "Um, hum, Girringa."

And then they sang again, "Welcome Girringa." "Um,
hum, Girringa."

"Where have you come from?" asked the one with four heads.

"I come from Kano," sang the other.

"What did you go for?" asked the newcomer.

"To find a wife," replied the other.

"Where is the woman?" asked the four-headed one.

"See her behind me," was the reply.

"What is she crying for?" asked the other.

"She is crying at the sight of your heads," said the husband.

"Wait until she sees the king," replied the other.

So they parted, and the wife and her two-headed husband went on toward the city, and lo! they met with a five-headed being, who sang: "Welcome Girringa."

And the other replied, also singing, "Um, hum, Girringa."

And then they sang again, "Welcome Girringa." "Um, hum, Girringa."

"Where have you come from?" asked the one with five heads.

"I come from Kano," sang the other.

"What did you go for?" asked the newcomer.

"To find a wife," replied the other.

"Where is the woman?" asked the five-headed one.

"See her behind me," was the reply.

"What is she crying for?" asked the other.

"She is crying at the sight of your heads," said the husband.

"Wait until she sees the king," replied the other.

So they parted, and at last the wife and her two-headed husband arrived at the city, and they went to the palace, and then she saw the king of the Girringas who had ten heads! And the king sang: "Welcome Girringa."

And the other replied, also singing, "Um, hum, Girringa."

And then they sang again, "Welcome Girringa." "Um, hum, Girringa."

"Where have you come from?" asked the king.

"I come from Kano," sang the other.

"What did you go for?" asked the king.

"To find a wife," replied the other.

"Where is the woman?" asked the king.

"See her behind me," was the reply.

"What is she crying for?" asked the other.

"She is crying at the sight of your heads," said the husband.

Then she was taken to her husband's house, but she refused to go in, and cried, and cried. Then they argued and argued with her, and at last she entered the house. Goats were killed in her honor, three of them, and she hid some of the flesh to eat, and she ate her fill.

Well, she lived there for some time, and they fed her up until she had got very fat. And on the very day that they meant to kill and eat her, they gave her a pot to get water with which they were going to wash her although she did not know what it was for. So she went off to the river, but when she had got there she began to feel afraid, for they had never before allowed her to go outside the house. So she determined to escape and turned herself into a tree stump.

Now as she delayed, and did not return, one of the Girringas went and followed her tracks, but he could not find her, so he returned and told them that she had run away. Then they said "Oh well, we must put up with it," and so they went about their business. But at night she became a woman again, and she ran away to her own city.

(HAUSA)

104 THE BOY AND THE ONE-SIDED GIANTESS

There was once a certain boy, a king's son, who said that he was going out into the world. So he started off and traveled on and on in the forest. Soon he came to a big lake, and he went round and round the brink, but he could not see any footprints. Then he took out a handful of water and drank it, and he took another handful, and gave it to his dog. Then he said that he would see that very day what kind of animal used to drink water there, so he climbed a tree and his dog lay down at its foot. The width of the water was like from here to the barracks.

After a time, in the afternoon, he saw a certain woman, a giantess with one arm, one leg, and one eye, coming to the shore of the lake, and she drank up the water, *pap*, and it was finished. Then she began crying, saying that her thirst was not quenched. The water was finished really because the boy had taken a handful for himself and had given his dog one!

But she calmed herself and walked toward the house, and she went and brought out a whole barnful of corn, about two hundred bundles, and she pounded them up and made a porridge of the corn. Then she went and caught two big bulls, and came and slaughtered them and made soup with them.

Now the boy arose from where he was and came to her house, and when he arrived he saw a tree close to the door, so he climbed it and left his dog at the foot. Just then the woman brought out her soup, and she went and brought out her porridge, and then she entered her hut again to get her proper cloth to wear when eating food. While she was there, the boy pushed his spear into the porridge and drew it back, and picked off a little piece of food that had stuck to it. This he divided into two, one piece he put into his mouth, the other he threw down to his dog on the ground.

Just then the woman emerged again from her hut, and came and sat down to eat the food, and she began to eat the porridge first. When she had finished, she began to cry, and to say that something had stolen her porridge from her that day. Even until midnight she was crying, but then she calmed herself, and went inside.

Then the boy climbed down, and called his dog, and escaped at a run. He did not pause until he had reached his

own town. And when he had arrived, he said "O my father,
I have seen what is in the world."

(HAUSA)

105 WHY THE YOUNG GIANT LOST HIS STRENGTH

There was a certain youth, a giant, as high as from Jemaan
Daroro to Kano, or to Bauchi; among all the others there
was not his like. Now a magician had given him a charm,
and had said that he must never know a woman. And while
he remained single if a giant came, no matter whence or
when he arrived, then the youth killed him when they boxed.

Now there was a certain girl, a virgin, who was as tall as
Sokoto is distant from here. Men used to leave places like
Damarghera and go to see the girl because of her beauty.
Supposing the king of Damarghera said that he wanted her,
she would say that she did not like him. Supposing the king
of Zungo (Malam Yerro) came to her, she would say that
she did not like him.

But one day she heard the news of this young giant, and
she said that she would go to him. So she started off and
commenced the journey, and after two months' traveling
she came to the youth. When he saw her, he said that he
wanted to marry her, so her took her, and led her to his
house, and married her. Now for the next day a great tournament had been arranged, so the youth went out, and showed
off. And another giant came from somewhere else, and he
also showed off. Then they approached each other, and got
to close quarters, and the stranger caught the youth's hand
and he watched his armpit, and when he punched him, he
killed him.

Now, when the young giant's people saw this, they came
and said, "Girl, see, him to whom you came has been killed

in the tournament." Then the girl said, "What is the remedy for this?" They replied that there was a remedy, and when a grave had been dug, they said that if the girl came and entered this grave, and was buried inside, the youth would arise again. So she agreed, and was buried in the grave.

(HAUSA)

106 THE EGGS THAT GREW BIGGER WHILE THE MAN WAS SINGING

A certain man had eleven sons, and the youngest one was the son of his second wife. Before the man died he gave to each of the ten elder sons three head of cattle, but to the youngest he gave a small egg and told him to keep it outside, far from the kraal, and to sing to it.

The father died, and the youngest son used to go and sing to the egg, and the egg swelled and went on swelling until it was very big, bigger than a house. After a time the youngest son was afraid of it and climbed up a tree when he was singing to it. At last, one day when he was singing, the egg burst, and animals of every kraal came out, oxen, sheep, goats, in numbers. He then built his own kraal and lived happily. That is all.

(BAVENDA)

107 A WOMAN FOR A HUNDRED CATTLE

Once upon a time there were a man and a woman. They lived for many days in the land of Pata, and a son was born to them. Their fortune consisted of a hundred cattle. Beyond these they did not have a single calf; they had nothing but the cattle.

As time went by the son grew and became a big child, and when the boy was fifteen years of age, his father died. Several years later, his mother also died. So the young man had a heritage from both his parents—he inherited the hundred cattle which were left to him. He stayed in his home and observed the time of mourning for his parents. When he had finished mourning he felt an urge to look for a woman to marry.

He said to his neighbors, "I want to marry a woman, for my parents are dead and I am all alone now. I cannot stay alone. I must get married."

His neighbors said to him, "Surely, get married, for indeed you are lonely now. We shall look around for you so that you may find a suitable woman to marry."

He said, "Yes, be it so."

Later, he said, "I would like somebody to go out and look for a woman for me."

They said, "If God wills it!"

So one of the neighbors rose and went and looked for a woman whom the young man could marry, until he found one. Then he came and said to him, "I have found such a woman as you want, but she is not from this town."

He asked, "Where, then, does she live?" The neighbor said: "In a different town, pretty far away. I think it takes eight hours of traveling from here to get there."

He asked him, "Whose daughter is this girl?"

And the neighbor said to him, "She is the daughter of Abdallah, and her father is very rich. This woman owns six thousand cattle. The father has no other child, just this one daughter."

When the young man heard this, he was all full of desire to obtain this woman, and he said to his neighbor, "Would you go there tomorrow and carry my answer—which is that I am agreeable."

The neighbor said, "God willing, I will go there tomorrow." And at dawn, the matchmaker rose and traveled until he came to old Abdallah, and he carried the young man's message to him, and related all that had happened.

Finally the father answered him saying, "I have heard your words, but I desire that anyone who wants to marry my daughter should give me a hundred cattle as a bride price. If he gives such a bride price I will give him my daughter for wife."

The matchmaker said, "God willing, I shall go and carry the answer to him."

The father said to him, "Yes, do that!"

The matchmaker rose and went back, and gave the young man the answer. He told him everything that had been discussed.

The young man said, "I have heard your words, but he wants a hundred cattle as a bride price, and I have just a hundred cattle. If I give them all to him, what will my wife have to live on, if she comes to me? I have no other fortune but these hundred cattle which I have inherited from my father."

Finally his neighbor said to him, "Well now, if you do not want her, tell me so. Then I can go and carry back your reply; or if you want her, tell me so definitely."

The young man bowed his head and meditated and, when he raised his head again, he said, "It does not matter, go and say that I accept. I will go and fetch the hundred cattle and give them to him."

So the matchmaker got up and went to the father of the girl and said to him, "The young man is willing to pay the hundred cattle."

And the father said, "I am willing then that he should take my daughter." They talked over the details, and then someone was sent to bring the young man. The latter came and was amiably received, and they discussed the marriage. So the young man was wedded to the girl and paid the hundred cattle, and the wedding feast was celebrated.

Then the young man took his wife and traveled home. There they remained at first ten days; but when the provisions which they had taken along were used up, the young man had nothing for his wife to eat. Then he said to her, "Dear wife, now I have nothing left to eat. Formerly, I had my cattle. These I milked and thus I had my sustenance; but now I have given my cattle away for you and, therefore, I have nothing left. Dear wife, I will go now to my neighbors and from those who have cows I shall obtain some milk, however little it be, so that we shall have something to eat."

Then the woman said to him, "Yes, dear husband!"

So the young man went out and this now became his occupation. Every day he went out and milked other people's cows, so that he could have something to eat for himself and his wife. This he continued to do every day.

One day his wife went out and placed herself in front of her door just as a very handsome young man passed by. When he saw the woman standing by the door, he was seized with a desire to seduce her. Thereupon he sent a procurer to talk to the woman.

The woman said, "God is my witness that I have heard the message you convey to me, but you must wait a little longer, until I have made up my mind, and then I will let you know. I cannot answer yet." So the procurer rose and went home.

Three months later, the woman's father thought to himself, "I must go and pay a visit to my daughter and her husband." So he started on his journey and went his way until he came to his son-in-law's house. Arrived there, he knocked at the door. The daughter got up and answered, "Who is there?"

The old man said, "It is I, Abdallah."

The daughter rose and said to him, "Will you not come in?"

So he entered and exchanged greetings with his daughter, and she invited him into the hall, and the old man sat down there. The father asked the daughter how she was getting along, and she said, "Pretty well, my father."

Finally the daughter got up, went away from where her father was sitting and went into her room, cogitating and crying profusely, because there was not the slightest bit of food in the house that she could cook for her father. Then she left by the back door, and when she looked behind the yard, she noticed the young man who wanted to seduce her, and he called to her to come nearer. So she went over to him and said to him, "How are you getting along, sir?"

He said, "I once sent someone to you, and you said that you would come to me for a visit, but you have not come. Why are you so wavering? Since I saw you that day when you were standing by the door I have not been able to sleep any more; every day, when I lie down, I dream only of you in my sleep."

The woman answered him, saying, "God be my witness, I shall not harass you any more. If you long for me I shall come without delay. First, however, get a piece of meat for me, so that I can cook something to eat for my guest. I shall come afterward."

The young man asked her, "Who is your guest?"

The woman replied, saying, "It is my father whom I receive as a guest."

Thereupon he said, "You wait here, and I will bring you some meat right away."

So he rose and went out, and the woman remained standing there. A little later, he returned with a quarter of beef and said to her, "Here is the meat, but now do not put me off any longer."

She said, "God be my witness, I shall not put you off."

He stretched out his hand and gave her the meat, and the woman took it and went back into her house. Then he who had given her the meat paced up and down outside and waited for the fulfilment of the promise that the woman had made him.

After the woman returned, she took the meat, cut it into pieces, and put it into the pot. As soon as she had placed it in the pot, her husband came back and found his father-in-law sitting in the hall. As he saw his father-in-law sitting in the hall, his blood rose. He could not find a word to say, nor did he know what to do. He went closer until he came to where his father-in-law was sitting. He greeted him according to custom and asked him how he was getting along. After that he went to his wife and found her cooking meat and asked her, "My dear wife, what are you cooking there?"

She said, "I am cooking meat."

He asked, "Where did you get this meat from?"

She said, "I received it from the neighbors; they have given it to me." When her husband heard this he remained silent and became sad because he was so terribly poor.

Then he said to his wife, "My dear wife, what shall we do now that we have not only ourselves to feed but also a guest?"

His wife answered him, saying, "I do not know what we shall do."

Then the man said, "I will go out to the rich people where I milk the cows and tell them, 'I have a guest staying with me now, and I would like you to give me something, whatever it be, to cook for my guest.' " So he rose, went to the rich people where he worked, and appraised them of everything that had happened to him.

These rich people were sympathetic and gave him a little meat and a little milk, which he took. Then he went home.

At his house, in the meantime, his wife had finished cooking the meat that she had received from her would-be seducer. When her husband returned with the meat, the woman put out her hand, accepted it, and laid it on the floor. Then the husband rose and washed his hands and went into the hall. The woman in the kitchen withdrew the meat from the pot and placed it on the platter from which they were accustomed to eat.

Now the would-be seducer had remained where he was, walking up and down, until he saw that the time, which had been agreed upon with the woman, had passed. Then he said to his heart, "The best thing for me to do is to pass by the front door and look inside. Perhaps I shall see the woman." So he went off and passed by the door, and encountered the woman's husband and the father-in-law sitting and chatting. When the wicked man saw that, he greeted them, and the woman's husband answered the greeting, inviting him to approach. So the wicked man came up and sat down.

Then they conversed together, the woman's husband having no inkling of the stranger's plan and of what he really wanted. Thus they conversed with each other—the woman's father, and the woman's husband, and that impious creature who wanted to disturb the peace of the young man's house. The three men stayed together in the hall.

As soon as the woman inside had placed the meat on the platter, she brought it out into the hall. As soon as her husband rose to be handed the meat, the woman said, "Eat now, you three fools!"

Thereupon her father began, saying, "Well now, wherefore am I a fool?"

His daughter answered him, saying, "Please, father, eat first. Afterward I shall tell you all about your foolishness."

But the father said, "No, I shall not eat, but you shall first tell me about my foolishness. After that, I shall eat."

Thereupon the daughter rose and said, "My father, you have sold an expensive object for a cheap one."

Her father said to her, "What is it that I have sold too cheaply?"

She said, "It is I, my father, whom you have sold too cheaply."

He said, "Why so?"

She said, "Father, you have no daughter and no child except only me and you went and sold me for a hundred cattle, yet you, father, have six thousand cattle anyhow. You have regarded a hundred cattle as more valuable than me. That is why I have said, 'You have given up a valuable thing for a cheap one.'"

The father answered, "That is true, my child, I was a fool."

Then her husband rose and said, "Now, please, tell me the nature of my foolishness too."

The woman said to him, "You are even a greater fool."

He said, "Why that?"

She said, "You inherited a hundred cattle from your parents; not a single calf more did you inherit. And you took them all and wedded me in exchange for them, in exchange for all your hundred cattle; yet there were so many women in your own town whose bride price amounted to only ten or twenty cattle. But you did not look at them. Instead, you came and married me in exchange for all your cattle. And now you have nothing, not even anything to eat for me and for yourself, and you have become a servant of others. You go and milk the cows of other people to get something to eat. Had you kept half of your herd of cattle and married a woman with the other half, you would have had something to eat. Therefore, this is your foolishness, my dear husband."

Then the worthless knave asked, "And wherein does my foolishness consist? Tell me!"

Thereupon the woman rose and said, "You are even a greater fool than both the others."

And he asked, "Why is that?"

She answered him, saying, "You wanted to get with a single quarter of beef what had been bought for a hundred cattle. Are you not, therefore, a fool?"

He jumped up in a hurry and ran away as quickly as he could.

The woman's father stayed with them for two days. On the third day he made his preparation for taking leave and then went home. When he arrived at his house, he unhobbled the cattle which he had received from his son-in-law and sent them back to him. With them he sent another two hundred. Thus his daughter could live in comfort with her husband for many days.

(SWAHILI)

108 THE OLD WOMAN WHO TRIED TO FIND GOD

She was an old woman of a family with a long genealogy. Leza Shikakunamo—"The Besetting One"—had stretched out his hand against her family. He slew her mother and her father while she was yet a child; and in the course of the years all connected with her perished. She said to herself, "Surely, I shall keep those who sit on my thighs"—but no, even they, the children of her children, were taken from her. She became withered with age, and it seemed to her that she herself was at last to be taken. But no, a change came over her: she grew younger. Then came into her heart a desperate resolution to find God and ask the meaning of it all. Somewhere up there in the sky must be His dwelling: if only she could reach it!

She began to cut down trees, immense, tall trees, joining them together, and so planning a structure that would reach to heaven. It grew and grew, but as it was getting to be as she wanted it, the lowest timbers rotted and it fell. She fell with it, but without being killed or breaking a bone. She set to work again and rebuilt the structure, but once again the foundations rotted and it fell. She gave it up in despair, but not her intention of finding Leza. Somewhere on earth there must be another way to heaven!

So she began to travel, going through country after country, nation after nation, always with the thought in her mind: "I shall come to where the earth ends, and there, where the earth and sky touch, I shall find a road to God, and I shall ask him, 'What have I done to Thee that Thou afflictest me in this manner?'"

The old woman never found where the earth ends, but, though disappointed, she did not give up her search. As she passed through the different countries the people asked her, "What have you come for, old woman?"

And her answer would be, "I am seeking Leza."

"Seeking Leza! For what?"

"My brothers, you ask me! Here in the nations is there one who suffers as I have suffered?"

And they would ask again, "How have you suffered?"

"In this way. I am alone. As you see me, a solitary old woman: that is how I am!"

And they answered again, "Yes, we see. That is how you

are! Bereaved of friends and kindred. In what do you differ from others? Leza Shikakunamo sits on the back of every one of us, and we cannot shake him off!"

She never obtained her desire: she died of a broken heart.

(BAILA)

BIBLIOGRAPHY

I. SOURCES

Abrahamsson, H., *The Origin of Death*. Studies in African Mythology. Uppsala: Alquist & Wiksell, 1951. Stories 34–50.

Basden, G. T., *Among the Ibos of Nigeria*. London: Seeley Service & Co., Ltd., 1921. Stories 56, 80, 81.

Callaway, H. C., *The Religious System of the Amazulu*. Publications of the Folklore Society, XV, London, 1884. Story 13.

Dennet, R. E., *Notes on the Folklore of the Fjort*. Publications of the Folklore Society, XLI, London, 1898. Stories 10, 57, 63, 64, 72, 78, 82, 96.

Griaule, M., "Nouvelles recherches sur la notion de personne chez les Dogons (soudan français)," *Journal de Psychologie normale et pathologique*. Paris: Institut d'Ethnologie, 1947. Story 16.*

Herskovits, M. and F. S., *Dahomean Narrative; A Cross-cultural analysis*. Evanston, Illinois: Northwestern University Press, 1958. Stories 11, 12, 61, 62, 83.

Hollis, A. C., *The Masai, Their Language and Folklore*. Oxford: The Clarendon Press, 1905. Stories 14, 86.

Jablow, A., *Yes and No, the Intimate Folklore of Africa*. New York: Horizon Press, Inc., 1961. Stories 73-77.

* Stories marked by asterisk have been adapted by the editor.

Junod, H. A., *The Life of a South African Tribe*, Vol. 2. London: Macmillan & Co., Ltd., 1927. Stories 29, 58.

Pechuel-Loesche E., *Die Loango-Expedition*. Stuttgart, 1907. Story 27.

Radin, P. & Sweeney, J., *African Folktales and Sculpture*. New York: Bollingen Foundation, 1952. Stories 9, 15, 17–23, 31, 32, 51–53, 59, 65, 71, 85, 87–95, 100, 107, 108.

Rattray, R. S., *Akan-Ashanti Folktales*. Oxford: The Clarendon Press, 1930. Stories 66, 67.

———, *Ashanti Proverbs*. Oxford: The Clarendon Press, 1916. Story 8.

Routledge, K., *With a Prehistoric People, The Akikuyu of British East Africa*. London: Edward Arnold (Publishers) Ltd., 1910. Stories 97–99.

Smith, E. W., *African Ideas of God*. London: Edinburgh House Press, 1950. Stories 2,* 3,* 4,* 5,* 7.*

———, and Dale, A. M., *The Ila-speaking Peoples of Northern Rhodesia*, Vol. 2. London: Macmillan & Co., Ltd., 1920. Story 28.

Stayt, H. A., *The Bavenda*. London: Oxford University Press, under the auspices of the International African Institute, 1931. Stories 68–70, 106.

Talbot, P. A., *In the Shadow of the Bush*. London: William Heinemann Ltd., 1912. Stories 25, 60.

Torrend, J., *Specimens of Bantu Folklore from Northern Rhodesia*. London and New York: Routledge & Kegan Paul Ltd., 1921. Story 84.

Tremearne, A. J. N., *Hausa Superstitions and Customs*. London: Staples Printers Limited, 1917. Stories 54, 55, 79, 101–105.

Vedder, H., *Die Bergdama*. Abhandlungen aus dem Gebiet der Auslandskunde, Vol. 2. Hamburg: Cram de Gruyter & Co., 1923. Story 30.*

Weeks, J. H., *Among the Congo Cannibals*. Philadelphia: Lippincott, 1913. Story 26.

Werner, A., *Myths and Legends of the Bantu*. London: George C. Harrup & Company, Ltd., 1933. Stories 1,* 6,* 24.*

II. SUGGESTED READING

A. Additional Sources

Bleek, W. H. I., *Reynard the Fox in South Africa*. London, 1864.

Bleek, W. H. I., & Lloyd, L. C., *Specimens of Bushmen Folklore*. London, 1911.

Brown, J. T., *Among the Bantu Nomads*. London, 1926.

Cardinall, A. W., *Tales told in Togoland*. London, 1931.

Cendrars, B., *Anthologie Nègre*. Paris, 1947.

Chatelain, H., *Folktales of Angola*. American Folklore Society Memoirs I, Boston, 1894.

Dayrell, E., *Folk Stories from Southern Nigeria*. London 1923.

Frobenius, L., *Atlantis; Volksmärchen und Volksdichtung Afrikas,* Vol. 12. Jena, 1921–28.

Frobenius, L., *Erithräa*. Berlin, 1931.

Griaule, M., *Les Masques Dogon*. Paris, 1938.

Huffman, R., *Nuer Customs and Folklore*. London, 1931.

Jensen, A. E., *Im Lande des Goda*. Stuttgart, 1936.

Leach, M., *The Beginning*. New York, 1951.

Leiris, M., *La Langue secrète des Dogons de Sange*. Paris, 1948.

McCall, G., *Theal, Kaffir Folklore*. London, 1882.

Meinhof, C., *Afrikanische Märchen*. Jena, 1927.

Pettazzoni, R., *Miti e legende,* Vol. I. Torino, 1948.

Posselt, F. W. T., *Fables of the Veld*. London, 1929.

Roscoe, J., *The Baganda. An Account of their Native Customs and Beliefs*. London, 1911.

Tauxier, L., *Religion, moeurs et coutumes des Agnis de la Côte-d'Ivoire*. Paris, 1932.

Werner, A., *African Mythology in the Mythology of All Races*. Lit. Gray ed., Boston, 1920.

B. Studies

African Worlds. Studies in the cosmological ideas and social values of African peoples. London, New York, Toronto, 1954.

Baumann, H., *Schöpfung und Urzeit des Menschen im Mythus der Afrikanischen Volker*. Berlin, 1936.

Campbell, J., *The Masks of God: Primitive Mythology*. New York, 1959.

Campbell, J., *The Hero with a Thousand Faces*. New York, 1949.

Eliade, M., *The Myth of the Eternal Return*. New York, 1954.

Frazer, J. G., *Folklore in the Old Testament*. London, 1919.

Frazer, J. G., *Myths of the Origin of Fire*. London, 1930.

Funk & Wagnalls, *Standard Dictionary of Folklore, Mythology and Legend*. Maria Leach ed., New York, 1949.

Herskovits, M. J., *Dahomey, an Ancient West African Kingdom*. 2 vols., New York, 1938.

Herskovits, M. J., "Negro Folklore," *Encyclopaedia of Literature*. J. T. Shipley, New York, 1946.

Jung, C. G., Kereny, C., Radin, P., *The Trickster*. New York, 1956.

Krappe, A. H., *La genèse des mythes*. Paris, 1938.

Krappe, A. H., *Mythologie universelle*. Paris, 1930.

Lessa, W. A., Evon Z. Vogt, *Reader in Comparative Religion*. Evanston, 1958.

Leturmy, H., *Dieux, Héros et Mythes*. Paris, 1958.

Malinowski, B., *Myth in Primitive Psychology*. London, 1926.

Murray, H. A. ed., *Myth and Mythmaking*. New York, 1960.

Sebeok, T. A. ed., *Myth, a Symposium*. American Folklore Society Publications, 1955.

Tegnaeus, H., *Le héros civilisateur. Contribution à l'étude ethnologique de la religion et de la sociologie africaines*. Stockholm, 1950.

Thompson, S., *Motif-Index of Folk-Literature*. Rev. and enl. ed. Bloomington, 1955–58.

Thompson, S., *The Folktale*. New York, 1951.

Created in response to the interest in the new Africa which has so recently and so dramatically sprung to the world's attention.

AFRICAN INDEPENDENCE

Contains a series of original and definitive articles on the geographical, historical and administrative backgrounds of the fledgling African nations, together with a frank assessment of the dangers and difficulties—both political and economic—that lie ahead.

Countries covered include: SENEGAL • MALI • IVORY COAST • GHANA • VOLTAIC REPUBLIC • DAHOMEY • NIGER • SIERRA LEONE • LIBERIA • CAMEROON • NIGERIA • CHAD • THE CONGO • GABON • CENTRAL AFRICAN REPUBLIC

Edited by Peter Judd

A LAUREL ORIGINAL   75¢

VOLUMES IN SOCIAL SCIENCE FROM DELL

If you cannot obtain copies of these titles locally, just send the price (plus
10c per copy for handling and postage) to Dell Books, Box 2291, Grand
Central Post Office, New York, N.Y., 10017. No postage or handling charge
is required on any order of five or more books.